CIRCLES UNDER THE CLYDE

A HISTORY OF THE GLASGOW UNDERGROUND
by John Wright and Ian Maclean

Capital Transport

Foreword

by **Stephen R Lockley Director General**
Strathclyde Passenger Transport Executive

The Underground with its many unique characteristics was the third 'tube' railway following on from London and Budapest and was a reflection of confidence at that time, with the cost involved justified by the resultant ease of travel between the docks and shipbuilding areas, the City Centre and residential and recreational areas to avoid the congestion which even then was quite widespread.

The initial cable-hauled system seems quaint and uncomfortable from a modern perspective but subsequent introduction of electric power enhanced performance and by mid-century weekday patronage exceeded 100,000. Inevitably there came a time when the original stations and rolling stock no longer matched the expectations of modern society. There were fears that the high cost of modernisation might not be affordable but fortunately the correct decision was taken.

When it was modernised the highest standards were incorporated into the design. Safety is of prime importance with many measures introduced at modernisation pre-dating subsequent statutory requirements. This is matched by reliability with more than 99% of trains normally operating each year. The service the system provides is a credit to the large numbers of people who have been involved in its evolution, construction, modernisation and maintenance over many years.

The Regional Council was the Passenger Transport Authority from 1975 to 1996 and showed tremendous foresight and confidence when authorising modernisation during the late 1970s at a time when the necessity for high quality mass transit systems in our major conurbations was not as universally recognised as is now the case.

I have been Director General for the last 10 years and I am proud that during that period the Passenger Transport Executive has been able to build on further investment by the Authority in new rolling stock and equipment and a state of the art signalling system to ensure the Underground is second to none.

The Passenger Transport Authority since April 1996 has membership drawn from the twelve Councils who succeeded the former Regional Council. The contribution the Underground makes to the overall social, economic and environmental aspirations of the West of Scotland continues to be recognised.

This book is the most comprehensive and authoritative ever written about the Underground. John Wright has been employed by the Executive for more than 20 years and his close involvement in the modernisation and subsequent improvements and maintenance gives him a unique insight into the system. Ian Maclean was born at 202 Copland Road, near the station, and it would appear that he has been a Subway enthusiast ever since. Their task has been greatly helped by the assistance provided by colleagues and others and the book is a valuable and enjoyable reference document for professionals, historians, enthusiasts and those simply seeking an insight into one of the West of Scotland's most well known and valued facilities. I commend it to you.

Contents

Front cover upper Copland Road station after a fresh coat of paint, 24th May 1955, with Route 17 on the Inner Circle. *R. DeGroote*

Front cover lower A view of two trains passing in the South Turn-out Chamber. *Ian Maclean*

Back cover An 1896 map of the Glasgow Underground.

First Published 1997

ISBN 1 85414 190 2

Published by Capital Transport Publishing
38 Long Elmes, Harrow Weald, Middlesex

Printed by CS Graphics, Singapore

Preface

This book is not an official publication of Strathclyde Passenger Transport, but without the support and encouragement of the Executive and many of its staff it could not have been produced in the present form in time for the Centenary. Opinions expressed are those of the authors and not of Strathclyde Transport. The authors are particularly grateful to members of the public who took the trouble to respond to media requests for information and, in many cases, have told of their experiences of working on the system: unfortunately it has not been possible to use all of this material, but it helped to convey aspects which might otherwise have gone unrecorded. We also wish to thank SPT staff who have read drafts, made helpful suggestions and given information.

The idea for the book first occurred to John Wright shortly after he came to work for GGPTE at the Underground Car Sheds in 1974, and found several files dating back to the 1930s: here was a story waiting to be told. When serious work on the project started in 1994 many other sources of information came to light, including, somewhat unexpectedly, the Public Record Office at Kew. The Glasgow Corporation Minutes in the Strathclyde Archive, and the magazine and newspaper collections, all housed in the Mitchell Library, Glasgow, have also given up much which would probably have gone unrecorded.

In an attempt to convey the atmosphere of the periods described, dimensions are in imperial units up to the Modernisation and metric thereafter. Similarly the 24-hour clock notation has been used from about 1970. St Enoch railway station is variously described as belonging to the Glasgow & South Western Railway, the London Midland & Scottish Railway and British Railways as appropriate to the period under discussion. In the more recent period, British Rail has given way to ScotRail from 1984.

We hope the book serves as a fitting tribute to the thousands of people who have given of their insight, skill, knowledge and labour, often extending over many years or even an entire working life, in the service of the Subway and Underground. It is particularly a tribute to those employees of the Company, the Corporation and the Executive who lost their lives in the course of duty on the system: it is hoped the following list is complete:-

John Williams	Surfaceman	20th December 1902
John McMillan	Craneman	22nd September 1914
Thomas McCrae	Conductor	7th February 1921
Ernest Conner	Fitter	16th May 1941
C. Kennedy	Permanent Way burner	10th October 1954
Arthur Mooney	Shift Fitter	8th December 1957
Thomas Hamilton	Conductor	26th June 1960
Thomas Egan	Driver	5th April 1971
George Wallace	Station Master	4th January 1974

In spite of the above tragic deaths, and those of a few people who have fallen in front of trains over the years, no record has been found of a passenger in a train having been killed – a remarkable safety record to carry into its second century.

Glasgow, November 1996   *John Wright and Ian Maclean*

Chapter 1

Reason and Realisation

Setting the Scene

Glasgow's development from a mediaeval town into the centre of the most significant industrial and trading area in Scotland took vast strides during the 19th Century. Merchants had become wealthy first by importing and processing tobacco, then cotton and sugar. Thus developed an association with the sea, leading to a shipbuilding industry along both banks of the Clyde, and with design and manufacture of industrial machinery. The Clyde was the birthplace of the steamship, and, having developed the necessary skills to build ships' boilers and engines, it was a small step to lay the foundations of large and successful locomotive building and similar industries. This industrial activity attracted large numbers of immigrants from the Highlands and Lowlands of Scotland and from Ireland who were housed in tenement properties, often close to the places of employment. The more well-to-do tended to move westwards into areas such as Hillhead and south into Pollokshields from the 1870s or so. The University followed suit in 1867, moving to new premises near the River Kelvin.

The River Clyde was both an asset and a barrier – it formed Glasgow's route to large areas of the Highlands and Islands, to the Irish Sea, and of course to the Atlantic, America and the Caribbean – but it also formed a barrier between Glasgow, which was mainly on the north bank, and Govan and Kinning Park on the south bank. For many years the Jamaica Street Bridge was the one furthest down-stream, and during the 19th century a comprehensive service of 'cluthas' – steam boats – plied between various landing stages on the river, in addition to a number of pedestrian ferries.[1] The first dock (as opposed to riverside quays) to be built was the Kingston Dock, followed later by the Queens Dock complex further down river on the north bank, and later still the Princes Dock opposite it on the south bank.

The first modern land transport links were canals – the Monkland Canal partially brought into operation in 1778 bringing coal in from the Lanarkshire coalfield and iron products from the smelters at Coatbridge, and the Forth & Clyde, opened by 1790.[2] The first railway to reach Glasgow was the Garnkirk & Glasgow, in 1831, largely as a rival to the Monkland Canal which had reached capacity. This railway also ran a passenger service.[2] The Edinburgh & Glasgow Railway was completed to a terminus at Queen Street in 1842, and shortly afterwards the rail link to London was completed by what became the Caledonian Railway main line.[1]

Horse buses and, from 1871, horse-drawn street trams,[3] joined the scene during the 19th Century, and a considerable network of railways developed, including the east-west Queen Street Low Level line which included a significant length in tunnel under the city centre.

Although the city boundary was progressively extended in both the 19th and early 20th Centuries, Glasgow stayed a compact city with a high population density, and remained so until after the Second World War, when several large peripheral housing schemes were built. The rapid rise in population and boundary extensions can be seen from the following:-[4]

Year	Population	Area (acres)	Main changes
1801	77,385	1,864	
1831	202,426	2,181	
1861	395,503	5,063	Burghs of Anderston and Calton and most of Gorbals added, 1846
1891	565,714	11,861	Burgh of Hillhead
1921	1,034,174	19,183	Burgh of Kinning Park added 1906; Burghs of Govan and Partick etc added 1912

The compact nature of the city, combined with the fact that many workers lived within walking distance of their work, produced various unusual travel patterns: one which lingered on into the 1970s was the habit of many people to go home for lunch, and many city-centre offices had 1¼ hour lunch breaks to cater for this.

Unsuccessful Proposals

Towards the end of the 1880s street traffic congestion became a serious problem, and trams could only average about 5 to 6 mph.[5] No doubt encouraged by the success of the Metropolitan Railway in London, and proposals for the City & South London Railway, an ingenious scheme was proposed for Glasgow. A Bill was promoted in 1887 for an underground cable railway, 2¾ miles in length, from St Enoch Square to Byars Road (sic) with intermediate stations at Buchanan Street, Garscube Road, Kelvinbridge and Botanic Gardens: to reduce the cost of construction it was intended to have a 12 ft diameter tunnel, with interlaced tracks having the centres 3 inches apart, but separating to run on either side of an island platform at stations. The stations were to be equi-distant, and about 700 yards apart. An endless cable positioned outside the running rails was to be used to haul trains, which would have been attached to it at 1,400 yard intervals, the cables passing round a pulley at each terminus. When all trains were ready to start, the engineman would haul in 700 yards of cable and stop, by which time all trains had moved on one station.[5] A contemporary drawing shows a variation on the scheme with flank platforms at the intermediate stations, but single platforms at the termini: this gives the names of the intermediate stations as St George's (presumably at St George's Church, Buchanan Street), Cowcaddens, Garscube Road, New City Road, Kelvin Bridge and Botanic Gardens. The Bill for this £200,500 scheme was passed by the House of Lords, but rejected by the House of Commons.[5]

Another Bill was presented to Parliament in 1888, seeking authority for a twin tunnel endless loop linking the Victorian city centre to Hillhead and Partick on the north bank of the Clyde (as the 1887 scheme had done) but also Kinning Park and Govan on the south bank. This would involve passing under the Clyde twice, and crossing the Kelvin once. The route on the north side was not quite the same as the previous scheme, being by way of New City Road and Great Western Road instead of Maitland Street and North Woodside Road: after passing under Byars Road it skirted Yorkhill before passing under the Clyde to Govan Cross. Before returning under the Clyde to St Enoch Square, there was to be a station convenient to the Caledonian Railway's Bridge Street Station. This gave a length of about 6½ miles, and the estimated cost, excluding traction plant, was £677,008. This Bill was vigorously opposed by a number of interests, including the Clyde Trustees, who were concerned that the tunnels under the river, particularly at the Govan-Partick crossing, would restrict further deepening of the river by dredging. The Bill was rejected by Parliament.[5]

In 1889 a group of promoters, some of whom had probably been involved in the earlier schemes, formed the Glasgow Harbour Tunnel Company and presented a Bill to Parliament for tunnels under the Clyde at Finnieston. At this time the bridge furthest downstream was at Jamaica Street, about a mile up-stream from the proposed site of the tunnel, and the Clyde Trustees and others were keen to improve communication between the docks and quays on either side of the river. There were to be three tunnels, the outer ones straight and level, and intended for horse-drawn vehicles, reached by hydraulic lifts, and the centre one reached by long straight stairways, for pedestrians. This Bill received the Royal Assent on 12th August 1889, and nominated John Black, William Laird, James Parker Smith and William Weir as the first directors.[6] The tunnel opened in 1895, but closed again in 1897: it was re-opened in 1913 and remained in use until 1943 when the lifts were removed, but the pedestrian tunnel lingered on until 1980, by which time it had a large water main[4] running through it: subsequently the vehicle tunnels and shafts were filled in.

Third Time Lucky

Using the Harbour Tunnel Act as a precedent, the Subway promoters introduced a third Bill to Parliament in 1890, which was very similar to the 1888 Bill. The Clyde Trustees and Glasgow Corporation who had opposed the previous scheme, were evidently satisfied with the safeguards built into the Bill, so did not oppose it, while the Burghs of Govan, Partick, Kinning Park and Pollokshields and other influential bodies gave it active support. There was opposition from the Caledonian Railway, and Section 36 of the Act, running to 17 clauses, protected its interests[7] – this is probably why there was a minor change of alignment near their Bridge Street station. The route had to be changed west of Kelvinbridge, because the Glasgow Central Railway (a protégé of the Caledonian) by its Act of 1888 had powers to build a tunnel under Great Western Road between Kelvin Bridge and Botanic Gardens. Finally, the downstream river crossing was taken further west, and a station provided at Merkland Street instead of Yorkhill, though Govan Cross remained the traffic objective on the south bank. The Act nominated Henry Robert Baird, William Weir, James Parker Smith, Sir William McOnie and William Laird to act, with two others, as the first directors[7] – it will be noted that three of them were also directors of the Harbour Tunnel Company.

The Route

The route was some 11,527 yards (approximately 6½ miles or 10·4 kilometres) long, and consisted of twin single-track tunnels. The authorised route was as constructed, and as it remains today. The Subway Company was granted wayleave under streets, the line of which to a large extent it follows, but where it passed under property, the Act did not give powers to pay for wayleave, and in all cases the owners insisted that the Company purchased the properties:[7] this involved something over 90 separate transactions.[8]

The tunnels are of a nominal diameter of 11ft at distances varying between 2ft 6ins and 6ft apart. Fifteen stations were constructed all with island platforms, fourteen of which were a nominal 10ft wide, and the other (Kelvinbridge) 13ft 6ins wide. In most cases the station platform chambers were of arched concrete construction of 28ft span, but of varying heights. Several of the platform chambers had glazed roofs for at least part of their length: these were: Hillhead, Partick Cross (originally intended to be Partick East), Merkland Street (originally to be Partick West), Copland Road,[9] Cessnock, Kinning Park, West Street, Bridge Street and St Enoch. All the platforms were reached by stairs at one end of the platform, which served as both entry and exit. The platform surfaces were wooden planks.

The 1890 Act required trains be 'drawn or propelled by means of stationary engines and rope or cable haulage, or by such other means other than steam locomotives as shall be approved . . . by the Board of Trade', and that the track gauge must be the railway standard of 4ft 8½ins,[7] though the latter was amended to 'not less than 3 feet 6 inches' by the 1894 Act, of which more later. In fact the unusual gauge of 4 feet was chosen.

The Company appointed Messrs Simpson & Wilson, Civil Engineers, of Glasgow to act as their consulting engineers: and David Home Morton became the consulting mechanical engineer. Resident Engineers for the project were James Brown, who went in a similar capacity to the Central London Railway afterwards, Alex Simpson, Jun, James Andrew, Charles McFadzean and Robert Wylie.[10] Considerable differences in ground conditions occur round the route: shale and sandstone with occasional patches of clay on the north side of the river, whilst on the south side alluvial deposits such as sand and mud were mainly encountered.[5] These variations, together with statutory restrictions on opening up streets (particularly in Buchanan Street),[7] ground loadings etc and economic construction led to a number of different structural solutions round the route. (See Appendix 3 for letting of contracts).

Part of a Bartholomew map of about 1896 showing the Subway under construction and its relationship to other railways, the river and docks. *John Bartholomew and Sons*

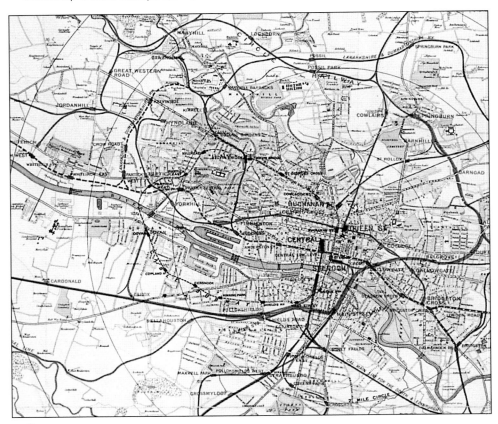

One early decision which had to be made was on the traction system to be used. At the time the system was being planned electric traction was in its infancy. It would probably be known to the promoters that the City & South London Railway intended electric traction, but it was not opened until November 1890, after the GDS Act received the Royal Assent. David Home Morton and Alexander Simpson Jun. went to the USA. to investigate electric and cable operated tramway systems, and visited New York, Philadelphia, Baltimore, Washington, Pittsburgh and Cleveland.[10] They concluded that cable haulage was more appropriate. Amongst other things this would allow steeper gradients, and mean that the stations on either side of the river crossings could be nearer the surface, thereby reducing construction costs and eliminating the need for lifts. About the same time the decision must have been taken to make use of a principle advocated some 15 years earlier for railways with short inter-station distances – namely to have rising gradients approaching stations to assist in braking and falling gradients leaving them to assist in acceleration. Other considerations rendered this impracticable at most stations except St Enoch, Merkland Street and Buchanan Street. A condition of the Act was that any steam plant used in construction should burn coke rather than coal.[7]

The first general meeting of shareholders was held on 29th October 1890, and it was resolved to pay interest to the shareholders at 3 per cent per annum out of capital. The Company Secretary, F. N. Sloane, wrote to the Board of Trade in November intimating this and stating that 'the whole share capital of the Company has been subscribed by and allocated to Shareholders legally liable for the same'. There was a total of 75,000 £10 shares held by 195 shareholders, of which 52,000 were held by the ten people (see Appendix 2), and a further 11 held 1,000 shares each.[11]

Tunnel Construction

Construction was started in the city at St Enoch Square in March 1891. The site of the station chamber was enclosed by sheet piling, and a shaft sunk to the level of the tunnels some 31ft below street level.[5, 12] Water was encountered at a depth of 15ft, and it proved very difficult to excavate below that through fine sand, and it could only be deepened by a few inches per week. It took seven months to reach the full depth and cast the concrete arch of the platform chamber. The four tunnels were then started by driving short headings and building a tunnelling shield in each, then after a further short length of tunnel had been driven, air locks were built.[11]

Cast-Iron Tunnels built under Air Pressure

Sections of cast-iron tunnel built under air pressure[5, 13] were: St Enoch to St George's Church and St Enoch to Coburg Street (about 1140 yards); the western under-river crossing working from sites at Govan and Partick (about 780 yards); the section from Hozier Street (now Beith Street) to Dumbarton Road, from the same Partick site (about 440 yards); a section from Copland Road station to Whitefield Road, Govan, (about 244 yards) which included passing under the cutting of the authorised railway to the Princes Docks; a section westwards from Shields Road station (about 170 yards) passing under the Caledonian Railway's Harbour branch; and a section of about 130 yards leaving Cowcaddens towards St George's Cross.

Each ring represented 1ft 6ins of tunnel, and consisted of eight segments and a key-piece at the top, bolted together, through holes in the inward-facing flanges. Soft wood joints secured with oak wedges were inserted between the mating faces of the segments.[12] Sixteen shields were produced for the Subway works, but some contractors decided they were more trouble than they were worth and discarded them.[12]

St Enoch to Buchanan Street

The two tunnels going north under Buchanan Street were started in April 1892, and, no doubt influenced by the ground condition and the prestigious nature of the property in the street, cast iron segments were used. The tunnel dipped steeply at a gradient of about 1 in 25 to pass under the Glasgow Central Railway (then also under construction) which ran under the centre of Argyle Street. The Subway tunnel then rose at a similar gradient for a short distance, before moderating to 1 in 75 until near St George's Place. At about this point, rock was encountered, and masonry construction was used for the final 100 yards or so to Buchanan Street station site.

St Enoch to Bridge Street

It was intended to construct the two tunnels going southwards to the Clyde in the same manner, but when they had gone some 370ft additional air locks were built in. The first (or west, later Inner Circle) tunnel reached the riverside on 20th September 1893, but before it had gone 80 feet under the river the air pressure in the workings had blown out through the river bed on ten occasions.[5, 12] The worst burst occurred on 24th February 1894, when a hole about 24 feet square and 16 feet deep was created in the river bed. One man working in the tunnel lost his cap, and sailors working on the deck of a vessel moored at Custom House Quay were showered with stones, and they ran up Dixon Street in panic. The contractor gave up his contract, and the Company took over the plant and equipment at St Enoch, then made special arrangements with Mr George Talbot, the contractor who was building the Govan to Merkland Street section, to complete the work.

The new contractor made various changes, including round-the-clock working including Saturday afternoons and Sundays, and he varied the pressure in the workings depending on the state of the tide. The east tunnel was carried right across the river (410 feet) in $3\frac{1}{2}$ months, compared with 80 feet in 5 months for the first section of the west tunnel.

One alarming incident occurred whilst this work was in progress on 14th December 1894.[12] Fifteen men were working in the longer tunnel when some timber stored in it near the air-lock caught fire, filling the workings with smoke and fumes. There was no way of extinguishing the fire or extracting the smoke, but there was a compressed air line to a grouting machine near the work face. The men took it in turns to breathe from this while the redoubtable Mr Talbot organised a rescue party to break through from the other tunnel, which was successful in releasing the men some 22 hours after the fire broke out.[12]

The maximum air pressure required at the St Enoch workings was 23 p.s.i. Coburg Street (now Bridge Street station) was used as a base from which to work towards the tunnels coming through from St Enoch, and this involved compressed air working also.

Govan to Merkland Street

Another fire occurred at Govan, but this time with fatal consequences. One Saturday night a group of miners left the work site and came out through the air lock to go to Govan for a tea break, leaving two air lock attendants, one inside and the other outside the air lock. The man inside had his meal where he was by candle-light near some stored timber, then fell asleep. Somehow the candle set fire to the wood, and after a while the man outside (who had the outer door open) smelt burning, but got no response from the man inside. He decided to fill the air lock, and opened a cock in the pipe from the main section of the tunnel, expecting the pressure in the air lock to close the outer door. Smoke came through the opened cock, so he rushed off to the surface to summon assistance without closing either the cock or the outer door. By the time he came back with four or five other men, the outer workings were full of smoke and he fell, overcome by the smoke. Two of the others tried to rescue him, but they too fell, and were rescued by the others, so they all then withdrew to a place of safety, leaving the two air-lock attendants to their fate. To extinguish the fire the air pressure in the workings was released, which caused an inrush of water and gravel. When the fire was out, air pressure was restored and the body of the man outside was found where he had fallen, and that of the man inside was found buried in gravel.[12]

Pressure in the workings from Partick, where the maximum depth of liquid mud above the tunnels was 57ft, was increased to 30 to 32 p.s.i. – thought to be the safe maximum. It is clear little was known about working at pressure in those days, and many of the men suffered considerable pain through decompressing too fast: out of an 8-hour shift men could work up to 3½ hours at pressure. There were numerous cases of partial paralysis and two men, one of them the foreman miner at Partick, died.[12]

Merkland Street to Dumbarton Road

This section was almost certainly built from the Partick end and was through clay:[12] at the point where it passed into rock, about 440 yards from Merkland Street, masonry construction took over.[13] Just after leaving the Merkland Street chamber the route passed under an embankment carrying the North British Railway Queen Street Low Level to Dumbarton line.

Cowcaddens

It had not originally been intended to use cast-iron lining in the Cowcaddens area, but difficulties were encountered whilst tunnelling eastwards in rock under New City Road when the top of the workings broke into the subsoil. The weight of traffic above forced a large quantity of sludge into the workings, and caused considerable subsidence in the street.[12] The masonry tunnel was temporarily sealed off while preparations were made to construct the last 130 yards or so from the Cowcaddens end with cast-iron segments and under air pressure.[11] This section contains the sharpest curve on the system – about 300 ft (approx. 4½ chain) radius.

Cast-Iron Tunnels built without Air Pressure

Two sections of cast-iron tunnel were built without resorting to air locks. Just under half of the distance between Bridge Street and West Street stations (at the Bridge Street end) was built in cast-iron, including the portion under Eglinton Street, and the Caledonian Railway viaducts. Compressed air working was not required here since the ground was good brick clay.[12] The problem of crossing under the river Kelvin at Kelvinbridge resulted in one of the more unusual engineering solutions in the whole project. A coffer dam was built over approximately half the width of the river, a trench dug in the river bed, the cast-iron segments forming the tunnel were then put in place, and finally a concrete cap, 2ft thick, cast on top of the completed rings, in part at least to counteract the buoyancy of the hollow tunnel. When one half had been completed the coffer dam was moved to the other half of the river, and the procedure repeated. In essence the river crossing was constructed by 'cut-and-cover'![5]

Cut-and cover tunnelling

For much of their length the tunnels ran under streets where the Company was granted free wayleave, provided they did not open up more than 100ft at any one point, and have worksites closer than 150 yards apart.[12]

The cut-and-cover method was used from Broomloan Road to Copland Road and from the end of the iron section through Cessnock to Kinning Park (mainly through sand), and under Scotland Street between Shields Road and West Street (through brick clay).[12] It is not certain how the sections under Dumbarton Road and Byres Road were built, but it is likely they were done by cut-and-cover as well.

In general two rows of piling 27ft 6ins apart, to take in both tunnels, were driven to the level of the bottom of the tunnel. If under a street these were driven from the surface, but if in vacant ground a trench 6ft deep was dug, and the piles driven from that level.

Some contractors chose to dig a trench between the rows of piles to the level of the top of the double concrete arch, and at 7ft intervals spaces 2ft square were cut through the piling. The bottom of the trench was then shaped to the double arch shape using profiles (sometimes using wooden planks laid on the ground as shuttering) then mass concrete laid, including 'nibs' in the spaces in the piling, which acted as a support for the arch in later stages of construction. The top surface of the concrete was then waterproofed, and the trench filled in. Lengths of about 15ft at a time were built in this way. The ground under the arch was then excavated, one tunnel bore at a time. Half of the mass concrete invert (tunnel base) was laid and one side wall and half of the centre wall were then built. The second bore was then built in the same way.

A similar method was used under West Scotland Street, from Cornwall Street (Kinning Park station) to the Harbour (later General Terminus Quay) branch crossing near Shields Road, and under the Joint Lines station and goods yard at Govan, but the excavation was carried out under air pressure.

Other contractors chose to dig the trench down to the full depth, put in the concrete invert, and then build the walls and 'throw' the arches on wooden frameworks known as 'centres'.

The section under Cook Street railway depot (at the West Street end of the Bridge Street to West Street section), where the ground was brick clay and the depth was not great, structurally separate brick tunnels were built.[12, 13] It was considered that in this case subsidence could be dealt with should it occur.[12]

Other tunnelling

The greater part of the tunnels through rock, shale or clay were worked from shafts sunk from streets at about $\frac{1}{4}$ mile intervals. The usual method was to blast the rock. If the rock was sufficiently stable the arch was lined with 18 inches of mass concrete and the walls with 9 inches. If the rock was soft, the arch was lined with from 2 to 4 rings of brick, and the side walls with two rings.[12] In general in masonry sections there were cross-passages 5ft high and 3ft wide every 25 yards between the tunnels, but with a few exceptions this was not the case in cast-iron sections.

One contractor, Hugh Kennedy & Sons, used the blasting method in the Kelvinbridge area, and contrary to provisions in the 1890 Act and his contract, continued blasting operations at night to the understandable annoyance of local residents, who, in March 1893, took out an interdict to stop him doing this. Apparently he took little notice, so the Police Commissioners called upon the Company to explain themselves to a Sheriff. The Company's solicitor naturally blamed the contractor, and the contractor, who did not bother to attend, blamed his sub-contractor and/or the foreman.[14]

Between Hillhead and Kelvinbridge the tunnel is at its deepest below ground level – 112 feet – but this is because the tunnels go under a hill: at the east end of the section, near the bank of the Kelvin the route ran through the site of a filled-in quarry.[12] It is likely this quarry had been filled with coal waste from disused collieries in the area, and at one stage a $\frac{1}{4}$ mile length of the workings was flooded.[10]

Possibly because of this flooding incident a 4ft diameter brick-built drain was constructed below the Inner Circle tunnel from just west of the Kelvin crossing to the point where the tunnel swings away from Byres Road, from where it makes its way under Partick Bridge Street to an outfall into the River Kelvin just upstream of Benalder Street bridge. This drain runs some 30ft below Hillhead station and has numerous connections into it from both Inner and Outer Circle tunnels.[5]

Between Kelvinbridge and St George's Cross the tunnels are between 25 and 42ft below Great Western Road.[12] Lansdowne Church had provisions put in the 1890 Act requiring the Company to take measures to protect its tall spire: in point of fact the tunnels come nearer to the spire of St Mary's Episcopal Cathedral a few hundred yards further east, and the Outer Circle tunnel takes a distinct kink towards the Inner Circle tunnel to put as much space as possible between the structures.

The section between St Buchanan Street and St George's Cross was the first tunnelling contract undertaken by Robert McAlpine & Sons,[15, 16] and was mainly through rock, though, as already stated, the method of construction was changed west of Cowcaddens station. A summary of the tunnel construction is given in Appendix 3.

The construction of Cowcaddens station presented some formidable problems to Robert McAlpine & Sons. The platform chamber had to be constructed under a busy street with tram tracks in it which could not be closed other than for a short period during the night. Another complication was the presence of a large water main and a sewer. The station was built on the cut-and-cover principle, but the tram tracks, water main and sewer had to be supported across the excavation. The depth to the top of the arch was 13 feet, and in excavating below this level rock was encountered. A mass concrete arch was formed, and the spoil was then excavated from underneath.[12] The station chamber was the longest on the system, and the arch one of the highest above platform level.

Track

The track consisted of 60 lb per yard flat-bottomed rail directly spiked to creosoted softwood sleepers of 9ft × 4½ins section set at approximately 2ft 9ins centres, and joined by fish-plates.[12] The sleepers were laid on whinstone ballast, with finer material up to the level of the tops of the sleepers. Tile drains were laid in the ballast.[12]

An added complication was the need to accommodate about 1,700 cable sheaves (pulleys) in each tunnel, set vertically at 30ft centres on straight track, reducing in pitch and incorporating increasing numbers of inclined or horizontal ones as the curvature became sharper, with a minimum of about 8ft 9ins centres on the sharpest curves.[5] The vertical and inclined sheaves were of 16ins diameter, and were set in so-called 'ballast boxes' coach-bolted to the sleepers on either side:[5, 10] horizontal sheaves were attached to base plates and secured in a similar way. The drain had to be off-set to avoid the ballast boxes. Special sheaves were used where the tunnel dipped sharply under the cutting for the General Terminus Quay branch, to prevent the cable rising too high. The cable ran centrally between the rails and 2 inches above rail head level on straight track, but the inclined sheaves were off-set slightly towards the inside of the curve to avoid contact between the upper flange of the pulley and the gripper gear of passing trains.[5] (See photograph on p. 18).

Stations

As already stated, the fifteen stations all had island platforms: these were 2ft 2ins above rail level and were approached by stairs at one end, which where necessary housed pumping plant underneath them.[5] The platform chambers varied from about 113ft long (West Street and Hillhead) to 168ft long at Cowcaddens – in many cases the stairways projected into the chamber so the effective platform length was less.

All stations had entrance halls at street level, in which were the turnstiles, pay boxes, and in some cases bookstalls.[5] In several cases, where buildings already existed, such as at Buchanan Street, St George's Cross, Kelvinbridge and Govan Cross, the ground floors were adapted. Small red brick buildings to the designs of John Gordon, formed the entrances to West Street, Partick Cross, Merkland Street and Copland Road.[5] The first-mentioned lasted without significant change until 1977.

The most imposing entrance by far was at St Enoch, where a neat building in what is said to be German Renaissance, Early 17th Century Period style was designed by James Millar. It was built by Guthrie & Co. in the middle of St Enoch Square immediately over the tunnels and just in front of St Enoch Church using red Dumfriesshire stone. The grey bulk of the Glasgow & South Western Railway St Enoch station and hotel on the east side of the Square dominated the scene, so something notable was required. Accommodation which subsequently became the Company's registered office was provided on the first floor, and the public entrance was through an arch in the north elevation of the ground floor. Stairs led to the south end of the platform. The surface building had a steeply-pitched roof, numerous turrets and dormer windows and carved detail in the stonework. Though relatively small, the colour and style made it a landmark. Later, after general blackening by the smoke-laden atmosphere, the building was disfigured first by painting slogans on the roof, and then by fitting an inappropriate canopy, but in the late 1960s the building was restored to something like its former glory.

The station platforms were lit by seven or eight pairs of 16 candle power (c. p.) lamps suspended from the roof, and stairways and corridors by single 16 c. p. lamps at intervals. In an attempt to brighten things up, the platform walls were cemented and whitewashed, and the corridors etc. were lined with white tiles:[5] one hundred years on it sounds like a Victorian public convenience! The entrance halls were lit by pairs of 16 candle power lamps.[5]

It was intended to provide lifts at three stations, Buchanan Street, St George's Cross and Kelvinbridge. Only at Kelvinbridge was this realised, but that was not until after the opening, so is dealt with in Chapter 2.[5]

Power Station and Equipment, Cables, and Electrical Installation

A site to the south of Scotland Street with rail access from the Glasgow to Paisley railway line was selected for the Power Station: other features in its favour were that the tunnels were at their shallowest, and the tunnels on either side were straight and practically level. The site was 120ft wide by 500ft long, the main features of which are shown on Figure 1.1.

The boiler house was at the southern end of the site, and contained eight Lancashire boilers fitted with mechanical stokers. Coal was delivered by rail which involved shunting by a system of ropes and pulleys.[5] (See photograph on p. 53). The boilers produced steam at 100 p.s.i. About 1904 Green's economisers were fitted which meant that only four instead of five of the eight boilers were required at any one time to supply the engines. Smoke from the boilers was led into a brick-built chimney or 'stalk', 180ft high.[12]

There was a large water tank with a capacity of 125,000 gallons which was intended as a 'buffer' should the public water supply be interrupted.[12]

The engine house was in two bays 134ft long by 50ft wide,[12] arranged side-by-side. The western bay had the machinery for the Inner Circle, and the eastern bay for the Outer Circle. Two drums to store spare cable were provided at the south end of the Engine House.[5]

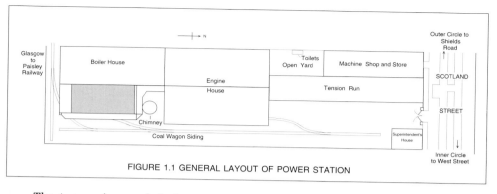

FIGURE 1.1 GENERAL LAYOUT OF POWER STATION

The two engines each had one steam jacketed horizontal cylinder, 42 inches in diameter and 6ft stroke.[5, 12] Each engine, which was of the non-condensing type, could drive its own built-up flywheel which was 25ft in diameter and 50 tons in weight, at up to 55rpm (equivalent to a cable speed of 15mph),[5] developing 1,500 horse power in the process.[5, 12]

The main drive shaft ran between the two flywheels, but incorporated couplings and clutches so that either engine could drive either or both cables, or the engines could drive one cable each. Running loose on each section of the drive shaft was a 26-groove rope drum, 13ft 9ins in diameter, power to which was transmitted by a multi-plate friction clutch, so that the cables could be started and stopped without stopping the engines.[5] The clutch-driven drum in turn drove two 25ft diameter rope drums, each of which was mounted on a separate shaft, one being 18ft in advance of the other. Of the 26 cotton driving ropes, 15 drove the first drum, and 11 drove the second: this was because the twist in the main steel drive rope created unequal forces. Each of the 25ft diameter drums was on a common shaft with a 14ft diameter cable driving drum with six grooves (see Figure 1.2). The cable entered one of these drums at (say) the top, took a series of half-wraps round the two drums and left at the bottom or vice versa. These two differential drums were held at the correct spacing by a substantial strut, because the tension in the cable would tend to pull them together. Experience in other places had shown that unequal wear could occur on the grooves, which in turn altered their effective diameter, and caused the cable either to slip or stretch. An ingenious system was incorporated whereby the power transmitted by each groove was limited to a particular level, thereby increasing the life of the cable.[5]

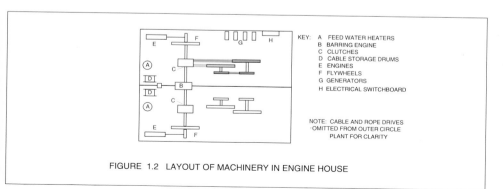

FIGURE 1.2 LAYOUT OF MACHINERY IN ENGINE HOUSE

15

Once the cables left the main engine house they entered the Tension Run, a building some 190ft long. This was the means to ensure that the cable remained at constant tension irrespective of temperature, and more significantly when it stretched with use and age. Each cable passed round a large pulley mounted on a 4-wheel bogie, before passing round another fixed pulley in the basement of the building and proceeding on its way to the tunnel via the sloping 'culvert' under the tension run. The bogie ran on rails, and at the end remote from the Engine House there was a system of levers and a weight which kept the cable under constant tension. The cables entering the Power Station did so by the same 'culvert', but did not enter the Tension Run, going straight to the bottom of the cable drums nearer the engines.

Clearly there had to be a gap between the point where the cable left the tunnel, and where it returned having been through the Power Station. Approaching the 'cross-over', as it was called, the cable dropped to below rail level, then passed on to a pulley which was nearly horizontal, and turned the cable through 90°, taking it under the south running rail, and thence into the 'culvert'. Immediately afterwards there was another similar pulley which turned the in-coming cable on to the track centre-line. The cable was then guided up to its normal position by a series of vertical pulleys: those on the Outer Circle carrying the cable over the Inner Circle cable. In case the driver forgot, the cable was automatically ejected from the grip by a trip mechanism on the track, and this was positioned before the cable started to drop.

The first batch of cables came from four different manufacturers, R. S. Newall & Son, Whitecross Company, Craddock & Co. and Thos. & Wm. Smith of Newcastle.[5] The detailed design of the cable was left to the individual manufacturers, but all were 1½ins diameter, and delivered in one length 6⅞ miles long to the Power Station,[5] so that only one splice was required. Each cable weighed about 57 tons, so there were delivery problems to be overcome, each manufacturer making his own arrangements with the railway companies.[5] T & W Smith's solution is illustrated below.

Delivery of a new cable from T & W Smith proceeds at the rear of the Subway Power Station in Scotland Street. From the pulley the cable passed along the length of the Boiler House roof and entered the rear of the Engine House. Surplus labour, Health and Safety and ash and clinker disposal were obviously next on the hatted gentleman's list. *Glasgow Museum of Transport Collection*

To install the first cable on each Circle a pull rope, some 6¾ miles long, was coiled equally on to two drums, each mounted on a wagon. Together these wagons were taken to the point in the tunnel furthest from the Power Station, the portion of the rope between the wagons was secured, and the wagons returned to the Power Station in opposite directions, reeling out the rope as they went. The rope was then used as a 'draw wire.'[12] Subsequent replacement of a cable was not particularly difficult, the old cable being used to haul in its replacement, an operation which took about 5 hours.[12]

A small steam engine, called the 'Barring Engine', was provided to move one of the main engines at low speed if it stopped on dead-centre, or for low speed movement of the cable for inspection purposes and so on.

Four 79 Kilowatt dynamos (generators) were provided, each driven by a small steam engine. A switchboard with ammeters, voltmeters, overload trips and switches to connect to the outgoing feeders was provided alongside the four dynamos. These generators supplied all the electrical needs of the Subway, including car and station lighting, the Kelvinbridge Hoist, and the lighting and other electrical needs of the Car Sheds and of the Power Station itself.

Four main feeders left the Power Station and were routed by the Inner Circle tunnel to Buchanan Street, Kelvinbridge (for the hoist), Hillhead and the Car Sheds. It would appear that the remaining stations were supplied by subsidiary cables from the Power Station, the Car Sheds, Hillhead and Buchanan Street.[5, 12]

Locomotive-type steam-driven air compressors were provided in the Power Station. Compressed air at 100 p.s.i. was piped to a storage reservoir at West Street station, where the braking system of the trains was charged and replenished.

Depot and Pit

The Car Sheds were built on land between Broomloan Road and the Glasgow & Paisley Joint Railway Govan terminus. The shed was arranged so that the tunnels ran underneath it, and access was gained to them by an opening in the floor, about 55ft long by 28ft wide, known as the 'Car Sheds Pit'. There were no sidings or ramps to the surface, the cars being lifted vertically about 20ft by a 12 ton overhead crane the travel of which extended over the pit. Having lifted a car the crane would then traverse westwards and lower the car on to one of six tracks running on a north-south axis throughout the length of the building. The crane had a swivelling hook, so could also perform the function of a turntable.[5]

The crane was steam-powered by a single cylinder horizontal engine located just south of the pit and supplied with steam from a Lancashire boiler. Power was transmitted to the crane by a system of belt drives and rotating shafts.

Apart from the lifting bay which ran east-west, and was high enough to accommodate the crane rails, there were three lower bays on either side running north-south, the westernmost two of which had three tracks each. Two of these had inspection pits over about 150ft of their length – sufficient to accommodate six cars being worked on at once. The building as first built was about 220ft long with an average width of 115ft, but an open yard was left at the north end for possible future extension, which, as will be seen in later chapters, showed useful foresight. The exterior walls were of red brick, and the interior was left as open as possible:[5] glazed roof lights were provided in all areas, as well as some arched windows high up in the brick walls. The main entrance was off Broomloan Road, but a gate was provided at the west end of the lifting bay into the Joint Railway goods yard. (See figure 5.1 on p.65.)

Maintenance of the cars and track was based at the Car Sheds.

An Inner Circle two-car train stands at the timber platform in Copland Road station, with the semaphore starting signal just visible above the tunnel mouth. Inclined sheaves were used to support the cable on curves, and were offset to the inside of the curve. *Glasgow Museum of Transport Collection*

Rolling Stock

Thirty bogie cars were ordered from the Oldbury Railway Carriage and Wagon Company[17] of Oldbury, Birmingham, twenty (Nos 1 to 20) of which were available for the first opening in 1896, the other ten (Nos 21 to 30) being delivered early in 1897, in time for the second opening.[18]

The cars were mounted on two bogies, and were 40ft 9ins long over the wooden bumpers (no buffers were provided), and 40ft 2ins long over the end body panels. Steel trussed underframes were provided, whilst the bodies were of wooden construction.[10] The cars were laid out with a vestibule at each end with a 32ft 2ins long saloon between them. The vestibules were narrower than the body, being 6ft 8ins wide against 7ft 8ins. There were pairs of half-doors in the body ends (which were lifted off their hinges when the trains were parked for the night), and collapsible trellis gates on the right hand side (in direction of travel) in each of the vestibules. The floors were level with the station platforms at 2ft 2ins above rail level, which meant that the wheels projected above the floor. The internal headroom at the centre of the passageway was 6ft 6ins.[5] The roofs were of the clerestory type to give ventilation. There were bulkheads with bi-parting sliding doors between the saloon and each vestibule, and two partially glazed bulkheads near the centre of the car, the glass of which had a painted pattern applied to it. There was a considerable 'tumblehome' at the bottom of the bodies just above which there was a substantial longitudinal moulding which acted as a rubbing strip when the car was being lifted by the crane: a similar feature was incorporated above the windows. There were 14 window spaces per side, but four of these were panelled rather than glazed. The cars weighed between 8¼ and 8½ tons empty.[10]

All the seats were longitudinal, facing inwards, and were wooden benches without arm-rests. The seats and backs were formed of alternate strips of birch and mahogany, secured to ash bearers. Nominally there were 21 seats per side – 3 of which were between the centre glazed bulkheads. The front rail of the seats was supported on turned legs, between which Wilton pile valances, with the Company initials woven in, were hung to hide the air reservoirs placed under some at least of the seats.

The outsides of the cars were painted a plum colour, except for the window frames, the 'blank' windows and the lower roofs which were cream.[13] The car number appeared twice on the platform side of the car on the panels nearest the gates, and the words GLASGOW DISTRICT SUBWAY appeared on the larger panels between in unshaded letters. All side panels and the blank 'window' panels were lined on the platform side and ends only.[19]

The saloons of the cars were electrically lit with four lamps in glass domed fittings, there was a single lamp in the leading vestibule to act as a headlight, and two in the rear vestibule which were in line with red bull's eyes, and doubled as tail lights.[5] Two oil lamps were provided as a back-up in the event of the electric lights failing.[5] The cars received their supply from a pair of trolley wheels mounted on the non-platform side of the car at about window level held by springs against a pair of continuous T shaped steel bars, one mounted above the other, known as 'T-irons': these were supported from insulators mounted on the tunnel wall, and maintained at a potential difference of 230 volts d.c. The cars were fitted with electric bells so that the driver and conductor could communicate.[5]

The grip mechanism was mounted on the forward part of the leading bogie, which was specially strengthened to transfer the traction force from the grip to the bogie and thence to the car. The 5ft wheelbase bogies were of steel with coil spring suspension between the bogie bolster and car, but no primary springing was provided, so that the grip mechanism remained at a constant height. Two lifting brackets were fitted on each side of each bogie, and it was from these eight positions that the cars were lifted by the crane. The wheels were 27ins diameter and were of the Mansell type with teak centres and steel tyres:[10] this gave some resilience to compensate for the lack of primary suspension.

There were two braking systems on the cars, a purely mechanical one, and an air system. The mechanical system, which was used most of the time, could be applied from horizontal handwheels attached to vertical shafts. These were provided in each end vestibule, on the non-platform side. Turning the handwheel wound a chain round a projection of the vertical shaft below the floor: the other end of the chain was attached to pull rods which in turn were attached to the same rigging as the air brake system, and applied a single brake block to the tread of each wheel.

The air system was the classic Westinghouse 2-pipe arrangement: an unusual, and perhaps unique,˙ feature, was that the air compressor was not carried on the vehicle. As stated above the compressed air supply came from the Power Station, and piped to a reservoir at West Street from which there were hose connections to each Circle.[5]

Each car had two main reservoirs, with a total capacity of about 10 cubic feet, and those on both cars in a train were connected by pipework (known as the Main Reservoir pipe) and railway-type flexible hoses and couplings between cars. These reservoirs were charged to 70 p.s.i. via a special fitting on the front of the cab on the platform side, on to which the hoses at West Street could be fitted.

The other pipe in the braking system was the Train Pipe, now more often known as the Brake Pipe. This pipe was charged from the main reservoir pipe through the driver's brake valve, and when charged the brakes were released: reduction in pressure caused the brakes to apply.

The brake cylinder was 6 inch diameter, with its axis fore-and-aft, but off-set from the centre-line of the car. It was estimated that there was sufficient air in the main reservoirs for 40 stops, but the normal practice was to treat the air brake as an emergency measure, and to use the manual mechanical system as the service brake.

The gripper mechanism consisted of a fixed lower die, and a moving upper die. For station stops it was usual to raise the upper die so that the cable ran freely through the bottom one. This was achieved by rotating a handwheel concentric with and immediately below the handbrake wheel in the leading driver's compartment. To move away from a station the upper die was gradually tightened down to grip the cable between it and the lower die. Approaching the Power Station cross-over it was necessary to eject the cable altogether, so, as well as lifting the upper die, a spring was brought into action which ejected the cable out of the open side of the grip mechanism. The driver had a lever to achieve this, but in case he forgot there was an automatic trip mechanism on the track approaching the cross-over. The pulleys on the track were so arranged that the cable leaving the Power Station was guided into the grip. Because the cables entered and left the Inner Circle to the right in direction of travel, and to the left on the Outer Circle the grip mechanisms were 'handed' so that the opening side was correctly oriented. This was achieved by running odd-numbered gripper cars on the Inner Circle and even numbered cars on the Outer. When stabling the trains at night it was usual to eject the cable, so before trains could enter service the cable had to be manually lifted into the open side of the grip.[20]

The gripper mechanism, showing the cable contained between the lower die, which was fixed, and the upper die, which could be raised or lowered by the driver. *Broomloan Collection*

Signalling

Signalling was installed by Saxby & Farmer[5] and was on the absolute block principle, meaning that only one train could be in a station-to-station block section at a time. Entry to a section was controlled by a lower quadrant semaphore signal mounted on the exit headwall of each station.[19] As was standard railway practice each signal had a red and green 'spectacle', but instead of being lit by the usual oil lamp, they were electrically lit.[5]

The Station Master was provided with two simple block instruments, one each for the sections ahead on the Inner and Outer Circles. These instruments showed 'Line Clear' or 'Line Blocked'. When the instrument showed 'Line Clear', and provided everything else was in order, the Station Master could lower the appropriate signal to allow a train to leave his station. Once the train had passed the signal its wheels operated an electric treadle on the track which put the block instrument in the station it had just left to 'Line Blocked' and automatically returned the signal to the horizontal 'danger' position: operation of the treadle also put the block instrument at the previous station to 'Line Clear', allowing that Station Master to lower his signal.[5]

Lowering of the signal to allow a train to start was performed by the Station Master pulling a chain.

Special signalling arrangements were in force at the Car Sheds pit,[5] but no instructions were included in the first Rule Book, or in an undated amendment to it: the April 1902 Rule Book suggests that there was a block instrument of some kind at or near the pit, and that there was at least a means of communicating with Govan and Copland Road stations. It would appear there were no signals.[21]

There was a telephone system allowing Station Masters to communicate with the Station on either side, and this was intended for use in the event of signal failure. There was also a bell system between stations and the Power Station which sounded a loud gong so that the cables could be stopped in emergency.[5]

1894 Act

The costs of construction and the time required were both under-estimated, and it became necessary to raise additional capital. A bill was promoted, seeking authority to raise a further £550,000 in capital, and giving compulsory purchase powers for some lands and property, including that for the Power Station and Car Sheds. As already mentioned, the bill also gave authority to reduce the track gauge, and extended the time limit for completion by two years to August 1897, except for the works in St Enoch Square which were only extended for one year.[22] The measure received the Royal Assent on 17th August 1894, and became the Glasgow District Subway (Further Powers) Act, 1894.

Chapter 2

Preparations for Opening, and the First Years – 1896–1914

First Inspection

The Company Secretary, F. N. Sloane wrote to the Board of Trade in August 1896 giving notice 'in terms of the Regulations of Railways Act, 1842 that this Company intends to open its Lines for Passenger Traffic.'[1]

The predictable response was that the Company had to submit the appropriate form (known as 'Second Notice'). Sloane sent off the completed form, together with other necessary documents on 16th October: the form stated the works 'will in the opinion of the Engineers of the Glasgow District Subway be sufficiently completed for safe conveyance of passengers on the First day of November 1896'.[1] On 17th October Lieutenant-Colonel H. A. Yorke, RE,[2] was appointed Inspecting Officer.

The first pages of Yorke's report, dated 17th November, are descriptive, at one point saying 'it is intended to erect lifts at two or more of the Stations', and at another 'the Carriages and Stations are lighted by electricity; but as a failure . . . might cause panic among the passengers in a train when in the tunnel . . . every train should carry . . . oil lamps for use in emergency. This is the more necessary as the white head and red tail lamps of each train are electrically lighted, and if these lights fail, the train would be without the usual protection'.[1] He made no recommendation with regard to stations, but commented adversely about 'the noise made by the cables and pulleys . . . especially in the Stations where both lines are exposed.' He stated that 'as arrangements in connection with the signals were not complete . . . it will be necessary for me to visit the subway again and see the signals and the full service of (empty) trains in operation, before I can express any final opinion on the sufficiency of the precautions'. At the time of the inspection it was not intended to issue tickets, 'but a charge of 1d will be made for entrance to the Station and for the journey irrespective of distance'. He was very concerned about 'the danger to life and limb which would result from any over-crowding the stairs and platforms', and anticipated that considerable danger would result '. . . unless very stringent and careful precautions are taken to prevent over-crowding'. He considered that:-

1: the turnstiles and barriers at the entrances to the Stations should be of sufficient height and strength to prevent all risk of their being surmounted or destroyed;

2: means of communication, either by speaking tube, telephone or dial, should be provided between the platforms and the toll collector's office whereby it will be possible for the Station Master to let the Clerk know when the platforms are full;

3: whenever necessary, extra assistance to maintain order should be given to the Clerk at the turnstile and to the Station Master on the platform.

He was satisfied 'the works, permanent way, rolling stock, mode of traction, brakes, and method of working are . . . fit for public service', but was 'unwilling to accept any responsibility as regards the Station arrangements' and was 'not prepared to recommend the Board of Trade to grant a Final Certificate as required by the Company's Act, Clause 79'. A final paragraph suggesting 'a provisional sanction only be granted for, say, six months, and that before this is confirmed a Report should be asked for from the Municipal or Police Authorities . . . as to whether any dangerous crowding has occurred at the Stations'[1] caused some debate within the Board of Trade (one viewpoint was that the Board should not attempt to pass on its responsibility for public safety to other authorities) and eventually the paragraph was omitted from the final version of the Report.[1]

A letter sent to the Company on 2nd December,[3] but not enclosing a copy of the report, said:-

Colonel Yorke reports to the Board of Trade that the construction of the stations is totally inadequate for the traffic which may be expected.

The Board of Trade have given Colonel Yorke's Report their careful consideration, and have with regret arrived at the conclusion that it is impossible for them to give a Certificate until satisfactory steps have been taken to minimise danger.[1]

At Colonel Yorke's suggestion a copy of the Report, omitting the last paragraph was sent to the Company on 8th December, with a letter requesting the Company to notify the Board of Trade when alterations to the turnstiles and barriers had been carried out so that a further inspection may be ordered.

Sloane reacted quickly to the letter of 2nd December, and in an exchange of 'wires' (telegrams) a meeting between Board of Trade officials and the Company's Engineers and Solicitors was arranged in London on Saturday 5th December, at 1pm.[1] No account of the meeting has been traced, but there is reference in the Board of Trade Glasgow Subway file to an accident (possibly in 1892) at Hampstead Heath station, North London Railway, in which eight people were killed and 14 injured, caused by a crush on a staircase when people crowded in to avoid a rain storm – so access arrangements were clearly at the forefront of officials' minds.[1] By Monday 7th December the decision had been taken to open on 14th, because on that day Jas. G. Brown (the General Manager who had previously been Station Master at Hyndland, North British Railway)[4] issued a notice from his office at 175 Scotland Street – the Power Station – that the Subway would be opened on Monday 14th December at 5am, that the service would run until 11pm with trains every six minutes, and the fare would be 1d. The Evening Citizen of Saturday 12th December carried a piece which included the gradient profile of the line, the cross-section of a cut-and-cover section, and the news that it was to open on 'Monday First', but concentrated on the methods of construction: it ended by saying that the stations at Partick (West) and Partick (East) had been renamed Partick (Merkland Street) and Partick Cross respectively.[5]

A 'Book of Rules and Regulations for Officers and Servants' had been produced for use from 1st December 1896. Later, possibly as a result of the London meeting, an undated supplement booklet was produced.[1]

Public Opening

The Glasgow District Subway opened its gates on Monday morning 14th December 1896. Despite the low-key publicity, word had evidently got round because hundreds of workmen turned up at the stations long before the first trains were due to run, keen to save time and money in getting to work, often on the other side of the Clyde. The Subway was promoted as "the first passenger-carrying underground cable-car system in the world", and by 8am the curious had joined those such as office clerks trying out the new system and almost all the stations were besieged. Many people travelled right

Passengers on opening day waiting their turns to pass through the turnstile at St Enoch station. Compare the scene with the photograph on page 134 taken some 50 years later from a neighbouring viewpoint. *The Railway Magazine, courtesy of Glasgow City Libraries*

round, or crossed over to take a train in the opposite direction, since they did not have to show tickets. During the first four hours 1,400 people had experienced travel by a non-steam train.[6]

Possibly as a result of the London meeting on 5th December it was decided to run a 3-minute service of single car trains instead of a 6-minute service of two-car trains, but this had not been known to the General Manager when he drafted the press announcement. How the additional staff were trained in time is a mystery. The intention had been to make one car smoking, the other non-smoking, but running single-car trains resulted in non-smoking trains.[6]

Things ran smoothly until just after 3pm, when, on the approach to Buchanan Street on the Outer Circle, one of the cars lost its grip on the cable, and came to a standstill. The other trains on the Circle stopped as well, and many passengers took to the tunnels to reach the nearest stations – difficult and hazardous with no tunnel lights and with the cable and its pulleys to avoid.

Many continued their new experience by transferring to the Inner Circle, sometimes with considerable waits on crowded platforms to board trains already packed. Service was further affected when employees at two stations were unable to regulate the platform crowds – similar to the problem envisaged by Colonel Yorke – and there were ugly scenes as the afternoon wore on. In the early evening Conductor John Thomson, opening a car gate at Bridge Street, was overwhelmed by people trying to board and was pushed between the car and the platform. His foot was crushed and he had to be taken to the Royal Infirmary.[6]

The day's troubles were not over: at 10.55pm, on its last run, Car 15, carrying between 50 and 60 passengers, was signalled to leave Bridge Street for St Enoch. For some reason the driver, John Ross, had to bring his train to a halt before reaching St Enoch and the following train, Car 5, was allowed to leave Bridge Street station in accordance with the vaguely written Rule 9 which said:-

> When the interlocking of any Starting Signals is defective, the working of Trains must be carried out by means of the Speaking Telephone and by Hand Signals;[7]

Although George Henderson, driver of Car 5, said he saw the other car just before the collision took place, he was unable to stop. There was considerable damage to the cars, one passenger was badly cut about the head by broken glass and some seventeen others were injured, but miraculously no-one was killed. Evidently there was some delay in stopping the cable, and stunned passengers staggered along the tunnel to Bridge Street or St Enoch.

A short entry appeared in a news summary column of the Glasgow Herald next day, saying that the Subway had opened for traffic the previous day, that there had been 'a heavy traffic; and unfortunately a breakdown in the outer circle between three and four o'clock in the afternoon. An accident occurred near St Enoch Station late last night, resulting in injury to eighteen passengers'. Next day the column announced – 'the Glasgow subway has been closed for a few days to enable further arrangements to be made in connection with the working.' In fact the 'few days' turned out to be over 5 weeks, as the second day of operation was not until Thursday 21st January 1897.

The Glasgow Herald on 21st January said 'it is understood that the . . . Subway is to be opened for traffic to-day from 8am to 8pm.'[8] Shortly afterwards the times were altered to 7·30am to 11pm on weekdays, and noon to 10pm on Sundays.[9]

The reopened system had graduated fares, no doubt to prevent people travelling round and round the system: this meant the introduction of tickets, of the punch type, printed by Williamsons of Ashton-under-Lyne.[10] The fare was 1d for 4 stations and 2d beyond 4 stations – it is not clear if there were any child fares. A ½d fare was introduced between Govan Cross and Partick Cross in June 1897, initially between 5pm and 6·30pm, but later in the month altered to all-day. The ½d fare was suspended during the 1899/1900 New Year period.[11] No doubt to counter tramway competition the fares were altered again from 23rd October 1901, with a ½d fare for all one-station journeys, the 1d fare extended to 5 stations, and the maximum becoming 1½d: these fares continued until 1916.[10] At some stage prior to March 1908, Excess Luggage and Excess Fare tickets were brought into use.[12]

Re-inspection

It is probable that the Board of Trade was not told of the difficulties on 14th December, because no reference to them has been found in the surviving Board of Trade documents, and the events largely vindicated Colonel Yorke's views. In May 1897 Sloane wrote to say Yorke's recommendations had been 'given effect to', they had had three months running 'in a perfectly satisfactory manner' and had coped with an 'International League Match at Ibrox where a crowd of 38,000 people were assembled', and requesting re-inspection and the granting of 'the necessary Certificate'.[1]

Colonel Yorke carried out this inspection, and his report is dated 13th July.[1] He said that 'the automatic signalling arrangements are now completed, and were working correctly on the occasion of (his) visit', and that telephone communication had been 'provided from every station to every other station and to the power house.' The turnstiles at all stations except St Enoch had 'been strengthened and supplemented by overhead barriers rendering it almost impossible for anyone to surmount the turnstiles when . . . locked'.[1] None of the stations, with the possible exception of St Enoch, had any architectural merit, but the visual effect of these barriers must have been unfortunate to say the least! An additional exit at the top of the stairs had been provided at Copland Road station for use in emergencies, and electric bells had been fixed in each of the booking offices, whereby the station-master or person in charge of the platform at each station could communicate with the turnstile attendant and direct him to admit no more passengers to the platform in the event of the latter being full. He was critical of the position of the 'push', that no standardised bell code had yet been set up, and that there was no means for the turnstile attendant to acknowledge the signals. Subject to the requirements he specified being met within two months and to an undertaking under the seal of the Company and signed by the Chairman and Secretary, 'that at no time shall the number of passengers waiting on any platform exceed 30' he could 'recommend the Board of Trade to issue the certificate specified in the Glasgow District Subway Act of 1890 that the subway is fit for such traffic.'[1]

The First Complaints

In 1897, as now, the last Monday in September was a public holiday in Glasgow. A partner in the firm of solicitors retained by the Company evidently used the Subway that morning on his way to St Enoch G&SWR station to 'go down the coast'. On Wednesday 29th September, back in his office, he wrote a letter of complaint to the Company Secretary asking that a number of points be raised at the Directors' meeting that afternoon. These were:-

1. On Monday 27th September, the cars stopped running at 9.30 am whereby trains to the coast were lost, and other travellers to catch their trains had to take cabs to St Enoch at an expense of 2/6d. It would be a great convenience if, when stoppages occur, the girls at the turnstiles would be supplied with information as to when the cars are likely to run again. They are generally ignorant on this point, whereby passengers are kept waiting unnecessarily and sometimes go away just before the cars restart running. This is a subject of uncomplimentary comment.

2. There are complaints now of a very bad smell of sewage in the immediate neighbourhood of Cowcaddens Station. This stench is becoming offensive, and ought to be enquired into at once.

3. The girls in the boxes are practically idle all day reading penny dreadfuls; and should be supplied with a cloth and instructed to go out occasionally and clean the iron turnstiles. They are frequently very greasy and dirty, and are only kept clean by passengers' coats, and ladies' dresses. This is also made the subject of adverse comment.[13]

It is not known what action the Directors took in these matters.

A Mr Daniel Smith wrote to the President of the Board of Trade, probably in early December 1897, complaining about over-crowding, and the Company were asked for their observations. Sloane replied, saying that 'such temporary inconvenience is the experience of all Railway Companies in populous places, and is common in the case of Glasgow Corporation Tramways, and is, on such occasions (i. e. such as Football Matches, or at certain hours on a public holiday) inevitable.' He went on to say 'my Directors are doing their best to overcome this inconvenience by putting on the line a Trail Car attached to each ordinary car. Four of these cars are already running and have given relief and the others are to be delivered weekly.'[1]

Granting of Board of Trade Certificate

Possibly reminded of the position by Mr Smith's letter, Francis Hopwood,[14] Assistant Secretary in the Railway Department of the Board of Trade, wrote on 5th January 1898 pointing out that, beyond acknowledgement, nothing had been heard from the Company in response to his letter of 24th July 1897. 'The line is consequently still being worked without a certificate from the Board of Trade, in contravention of section 79 of the Company's Act of 1890, a condition of affairs which it must be observed throws a grave responsibility upon the Company in the event of an accident. The Board will therefore be glad to learn at an early date what steps the Directors propose to take to remedy so serious a defect in the position of the Company.'[1] This letter, as might be expected, prompted swift reaction. Sloane replied on 10th January, and on the same day Messrs Simpson & Wilson (the Consulting Civil Engineers to the Company) wrote direct to Colonel Yorke, an action which he evidently considered to be incorrect.

Sloane said he would immediately submit the letter to the Directors for their instructions, but that various alterations had, during the autumn and winter months, been carried out to meet the suggestions and requirements of the Board's Inspector and that these had proved satisfactory.[1] Messrs Simpson & Wilson's letter to Colonel Yorke said 'we beg to inform you that all the requirements, as regards works, mentioned (in your Report to the Board of Trade dated 13th July 1897) were attended to immediately on receipt of the Report.' They, too, explained that 'additional cars' were being put on and expressed the view, based on 'the experience of the last few months' that the limitation to thirty people waiting on the platform was unnecessary, and begged 'the favour of your reconsideration of this matter'. They went on to remind the Colonel that he had 'expressed the desire to see the working on a busy day' and said, unconvincingly, that 'owing to its being the slack season of the year this could not be arranged'. They suggested a further re-inspection 'any Saturday afternoon', which, they felt, would satisfy him that their request was reasonable.[1]

Sloane wrote again to the Board of Trade on 13th January saying that the barrier at St Enoch had been erected, that bell communication between the telephone (i. e. platform) and turnstile boxes was in use at all stations, and that a uniform code of signals had been adopted. With regard to the limitation of people on the platforms, the directors requested that the matter be reconsidered. He stated that 57,000 people had been carried in one day and 'no difficulty was found in managing the platforms and no accident of any kind occurred', so the directors were satisfied that the number could be extended to sixty, and that they were prepared to give an undertaking on that basis.[1]

The matter was referred to Colonel Yorke and he met Messrs Simpson & Wilson, as a result of which he recommended the safe number was fifty in the changed circumstances since his second inspection. This was communicated to the Company by letter dated 19th January 1898.[1]

The directors showed defiance by sending a signed undertaking, but with a proviso limiting it to one year, which the Board of Trade rejected, though they did point out that the Company could ask for reconsideration of the matter in the future.[1] The Company capitulated, and the unconditional undertaking was signed by H. R. Baird as Chairman and F. N. Sloane as Secretary on 3rd February, with the company seal embossed on the document. On 22nd February 1898, Hopwood signed the Certificate, and sent it to the Company.[1]

'The uniform code of signalling' referred to in Sloane's letter of 13th January was as follows[15]:-

One bell	Stop Booking Inner and Outer Circles
Two bells	Resume
Three bells	Stop Booking Inner Circle
Four bells	Resume
Five bells	Stop Booking Outer Circle
Six bells	Resume

Bye Laws

Almost immediately the Certificate was issued correspondence started on the form the Bye-Laws should take, the Board of Trade being keen that wording as near as possible to the then-accepted Railway Model be adopted. Board of Trade approval was given on 14th April 1898. These Bye-Laws were short-lived, because the Board of Trade produced a revised set of Model Bye-Laws, circulated to Railway Companies in October 1905. The Company wanted to retain their Bye-Law No. 2, but the Board of Trade replied on 5th December 1905 that they were not prepared to approve such an alteration from the Model.[1]

Additional Cars

The 'additional Trail Cars' referred to in Sloane's and Simpson & Wilson's letters to the Board of Trade were a batch of 24 4-wheeled vehicles some 25 feet long ordered from the Motherwell firm of Hurst, Nelson. They were designed by David Home Morton, who supervised their construction. The underframes were steel, and the wheels, like the gripper cars, were of the Mansell type with teak centres and Bessemer steel tyres of 2ft 3in diameter. The springs were of the laminated (or plate) type bearing on the axlebox crowns, while the suspension links (at 4ft centres) were fitted with auxiliary rubber blocks. The wheelbase was 9ft 1in. The cars nominally seated 24 passengers longitudinally, 12 on each side (see photograph below). Apart from being shorter than the gripper cars with slightly shorter vestibules, they were similar in style, layout and materials, but did not have grip mechanisms, nor Westinghouse automatic continuous brakes, merely hand-brakes at each end, so in service relied on the braking of the gripper car. They were provided with four shackles, one at each corner, for attachment of the hooks and slings for lifting and lowering at the Car Sheds Pit. When running in service the front half-doors were removed as were the rear half-doors of the gripper car, and a fall plate let down to bridge the gap between the cars and accommodate relative movement. Each trailer car was fitted with two 16 candle-power incandescent lamps placed in the side roof panels in the interior and two 8 candle power lamps which served the double purpose of lighting the rear vestibule and the tail lights: the front vestibule shared the lighting of the rear vestibule of the gripper car. Current for these lamps (at 230 Volts) was obtained through a jumper cable from the gripper car, though the individual lamps were rated at 115 Volts. The empty weight of these cars was 4 tons 13 cwt. One of these cars – probably No. 39T – was put on exhibition at Earl's Court in London by Hurst, Nelson.[16] They were numbered 31T to 54T inclusive.

The trailer cars became 'smoking accommodation', the gripper cars remaining non-smoking. Lads were employed to operate the rear gate on the trailer cars, and became known as 'smoker boys'. Legend has it that a curtain was hung from the front rail of the longitudinal seats, and spittoons were carried behind these curtains, and one of the duties of the smoker boys was to empty the spittoons.

Four wheel trailer No.39T, built by Hurst, Nelson & Co Ltd of Motherwell in 1898. One of the shackles provided for lifting the car is prominent under the front of the right hand platform, and another feature of note is the canvas cover over the top of each trellis gate - obviously water leaking from the tops of the tunnels was a problem even then! *North Lanarkshire Council Library, Hurst, Nelson Collection*

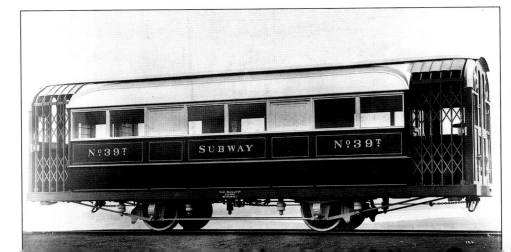

In 1901, possibly to cater for anticipated extra traffic for the International Exhibition in Kelvingrove Park, four additional gripper cars were ordered. Similar to Nos. 1 to 30, they carried the numbers 55 to 58 inclusive.

It was announced at the half-yearly meeting of shareholders in March 1903 that during the half-year to 31st January two trailer cars had been lengthened and put on bogies, making the cars approximately the same length as the gripper cars. Because the vestibules were slightly shorter, the saloons could be made slightly longer, and so seated 44 instead of 42 in the grippers. The rebuilding was regarded as a success, and was also economical (£510 being taken out of the reserve fund to cover the cost)[17] so between then and 1907 a further 12 cars were similarly treated.[18] By 1911 four of the unconverted cars had been scrapped, and the remaining six had gone by 1914.[18] The cars scrapped were Nos. 33, 40, 46 to 51, 53 and 54.

Finally in 1913 two more gripper cars were delivered, Nos. 59 and 60. Once the 10 trailer cars had gone the fleet stabilised at 50 cars and remained at this level for over 50 years.

Station Developments

As stated in Colonel Yorke's first report the Company intended to install lifts at two or more stations. Kelvinbridge was the only station where it actually happened, the electrically-powered lift being in use by the middle of 1897.[19] The Hoist Attendant, as the operator was known, also sold tickets, and these, like all others in use at the time, were of the pre-printed punch type and had as the station of origin 'Kelvinbridge High Level':[13] 'Kelvinbridge Low Level' appeared on those issued at the South Woodside Road entrance. The duties of the Hoist Attendant were detailed in the 1902 Rule Book, which, amongst other matters, instructed: 'If Attendant finds at any time that his Hoist will not work, and gets stuck in the middle of his journey, he will put his handle to "Off" position, taking his handles with him, he will descend to Motor Room, take off his switch, take off Springs on Brake, and give Armature a turn towards the right, when Hoist will go to top, he will now be able to let his passengers out, and send for Electrician.'[15] How the Attendant was to make the descent is not explained!

Changes at the Top

By 1905 Henry Robert Baird of Durris had stood down as Chairman, and Alexander Simpson of the Consulting Engineers Simpson & Wilson had taken his place, remaining until about 1920. The Rt Hon James Parker Smith of Jordanhill, MP and William Weir of Kildonan, who had both been directors in 1896, remained until about 1919 and 1913 respectively. W. S. Wilson also of the firm Simpson & Wilson was a Director by 1905 and remained until 1921, whilst Robert Simpson of the same firm became Engineer to the Company by 1905, and remained until 1914. Other directors for varying periods were James Laird, and Andrew K. McCosh, described as an ironmaster of Coatbridge.[20]

Staff Friendly Society

At their meeting on 5th March 1902 the Directors approved new Rules and Regulations to take effect from 1st April 1902. New Books were printed, and included the following passage on the last printed page:-

EMPLOYEES FRIENDLY SOCIETY

By resolution of the Directors, it is compulsory for all male Employees joining the service, after formation of the Society, to become Members of the GDSEFS, and their consent to do so is part of their engagement. Book of Rules will be obtained from the Secretary of the Society.[15]

Traffic Levels and Revenue

Passenger levels and hence revenue were never enough to make the system an economic success. It was more labour intensive than the trams, particularly after the latter were progressively electrified from 1901 onwards. The running costs as well as the capital costs were high: the stations were not particularly attractive, so were not likely to tempt people off parallel tram routes, particularly in good weather. The cross-river service between Govan and Partick did however have advantages over the ferries, largely because Merkland Street and Partick Cross stations were more conveniently sited than the ferry landing stages on the north bank .

The number of passengers carried in the first half-year – i. e. to 31st July 1897 – was 4,178,215: by the equivalent half-year in 1898 this had risen to 5,779,119,[22] and in the half-year to July 31st 1901 to 6,806,444.[23] A seasonal pattern, with diminished business in the second half of July and early August (because of the Glasgow Fair Holiday and school holidays), manifested itself from the beginning, and remains to this day.

Commenting on the accounts for the half-year to 31st July 1898 and comparing them with the previous half-year, the magazine Railway World said 'The receipts have gone up from 12.98 pence per train mile to 14.44 which, however, is still low. The average is kept down by the scarcity of passengers during the middle of the day.' It then compared the results with those of the City & South London Railway – an electrically operated Tube line, and the Liverpool Overhead Railway, which was also electrically-worked but was mainly carried on viaduct along the Liverpool dock area. The Glasgow line ran a greater train mileage per mile of track than either and carried 'nearly as many passengers per mile of track as the former and more than the latter. It is, however, handicapped by excessively low fares. If the receipts per passenger at all approached those on the other two lines the Glasgow Subway would be coining money. In proportion to the weight of train the Glasgow expenses for power are about the same as those in London and Liverpool, but . . . the former should show greater advantage as the service increases, the more especially as, up till now, the engines are working considerably under their full power.' The piece ended on an up-beat note saying 'Altogether we think the subway is going to do well, despite the keen competition of the Corporation tramways and the steam railways.'[22] This optimism was ill-founded.

Talking about the half-yearly results to 31st July 1901 the Tramway and Railway World (as it had become) remarked 'The traffic does not seem to have been benefited to any extent by the Glasgow Exhibition . . . none of the stations are in such proximity to the Exhibition gates as to enable the line to compete successfully with the municipal electric tramways which land people . . . practically at the turnstiles of the big show in Kelvingrove Park. While the tramways have all along been an active competitor on certain routes with the subway, that competition for the future will be much more keen, as horse traction has now disappeared from the Glasgow tramways.'[23]

By October 1903 the lighting in the carriages had been considerably improved and the inside walls of the stations had been whitewashed, giving a brighter appearance.[24] This, presumably, was an attempt to make the system more attractive and regain some of the passengers lost to the trams.

Traffic increased from 9·63 m passengers in 1898 to 12·45 m in 1899, levelled out at about 16·3 m between 1903 and 1907, reached a peak of 17·2 m in 1908, then dropped steadily to 14·1 m in 1914 (see Appendix 4).[25] At the Shareholders' meeting in September 1912 it was explained that 'the extension of the halfpenny fare from one stage on the Corporation Tramways and the coal strike have had an adverse affect.'[26] The directors did not think it wise to change the fares in a similar way. From the shareholders' point of view 1903 was the best year, when the ordinary shareholders received 1½% and the preference shareholders received 4%.[25]

Land and Property

As described in Chapter 1, the Company had to purchase a considerable amount of land and property over and above that needed for operational purposes, and it could not have disposed of all of it even if it had wanted to. Some was undeveloped land, but a considerable amount was housing in the form of tenement blocks and the Company found it economic to employ their own Factor to collect rents, arrange lettings, organise repairs and settle disputes over such matters as who got to use the back court wash houses on which day.

There was one complaint from the Chief Constable of Govan to the effect that there were insufficient gas jets in some of the closes.

Incidents

About the autumn of 1897 the system became partially flooded by the bursting of a municipal water main. 'The stoppage, however was not of long duration, and was much shorter than if steam or electric traction were used. The cars were run till the water was covering the car floors inside, and till it was feared the vehicles would float off the rails. If steam haulage had been in use, the water would have reached the locomotive firebox long before reaching the level of the car floors, while if electric traction with the third rail conductor had been employed, three or four inches of water would have stopped the traffic.'[27]

At about 10.35pm on 16th January 1907 a train consisting of Cars 3 and 39 was running on the Inner Circle, and after leaving Kinning Park the Conductor (Ritchie by name) heard a rattling noise from underneath the rear end of the gripper car. He went and told the driver, who decided to carry on to Shields Road and investigate there. On braking to stop at Shields Road the Driver found they had no effect, and the Conductor applied the brakes on the rear car, and by the time the train had stopped half the leading car was in the tunnel having over-run Shields Road platform. On examination the Driver found the leading wheels of the rear bogie of car 3 were de-railed. The Inner Circle was suspended from 10·38pm. The Breakdown Gang and Superinten- dent Engineer Mr Forbes were sent for, and the car was re-railed at 12·15am. On examination Mr Forbes found that the wooden wheel centre of the left hand wheel of the derailed axle was broken. There were some 20 passengers on the train at the time of the derailment, most of whom were going to Shields Road, but the rest were sent on their way on the Outer Circle, and no complaints were received.[28] It is not known how much longer the wooden centred 'Mansell' type wheels continued in use.

At about 7.45pm on the evening of 16th October 1908 there was a problem with the Outer Circle cable in the Govan area, which meant the cable had to be stopped, affecting all ten trains on the circle: in some cases passengers had to be de-trained in tunnel sections. The damaged portion of the cable had to be worked back to the Power Station for repair, an operation which rendered it unserviceable for the rest of the evening.[29]

Accidents to Staff

Three significant accidents to staff in the 1902–14 period were the subject of Assistant Inspecting Officers' Reports, details of which are:-

1. In the early hours of 20th December 1902 John Williams, a foreman surfaceman, had a 'lurry' (presumably a Permanent Way trolley in more modern parlance) loaded with a rail placed on the Outer Circle track at the Car Sheds Pit. The rail was to be taken to Merkland Street, so helped by four of his men the lurry was propelled (presumably by hand) to Govan station platform where it was stopped to be loaded with some tools.

All the service trains were examined nightly at the Car Sheds Pit, and were then run by gravity down the slight gradient to Govan station, a distance of about 150 yards, where they were stopped, ready to start service next morning. The practice was for one man to ride on each train, braking from the gripman's cab, sounding the warning gongs as they moved. In the case of the Outer Circle trains the cab was leading, but in the case of Inner Circle trains it was at the rear of the train during this manoeuvre.

Before the tool loading was complete Williams became aware of a train moving along the Outer Circle, so instructed his men to take the lurry 50 yards into the tunnel towards Merkland Street and wait there. For some unknown reason Williams then crossed the platform to the Inner Circle and was run over by a train coming down the Inner Circle simultaneously with the one he had seen on the Outer, and was killed. The General Manager accepted the recommendation of the Assistant Inspecting Officer, John P. S. Main, that a man should be stationed at the leading end of all trains when being moved.[30]

2   On 14th March 1913 Engine-room trimmer Alexander Sibbald was injured at the Power Station. At about 7.35pm he was swabbing up dirty water from the sole-plate of the east bearing of the twelve-foot return pulley of the inner circle cable, when he slipped into the pulley pit, was carried round by the spokes of the pulley then thrown on to the deck. His head was cut and his body and legs were severely bruised. The cable was forced out of the groove of the pulley.

The Company decided to fence the pulley pits and to arrange for the decks to be scrubbed as far as possible with the machinery stationary.[30]

3. On 22nd September 1914 a craneman, John McMillan, was fatally injured during shunting operations at the Car Sheds Pit. McMillan was involved in the usual nightly examination of the trains on the Inner Circle, and was carrying out the examination in the Pit itself. At about 1.45am he had just examined the third train, when the labourer controlling movement of that train pointed out to McMillan that a screw was missing from the gong treadle of the rear (presumably gripper) car. McMillan told him to stop the train whilst he attended to it, then picked up a bent screw and straightened it by tapping it against the rail with his hammer, and stepped on to the track to hand the screw and screwdriver to the labourer.

McMillan was in the habit of signalling for trains to be brought from the tunnel into the Pit area by tapping the rail with his hammer, and the labourer in control of the fourth train mistook the sound of the screw being straightened for the signal to move into the pit. The Inspector's report continues 'although a labourer was at the rear of the train, he could have seen through the open doors (i. e. the half doors at front and rear of the cars), but he was watching for the mark on the tunnel wall opposite to which he had to stop the train, and failed to notice the third train had been stopped again. McMillan was caught between the centre buffers of the two trains, and received fatal injuries.'

The Assistant Inspecting Officer, J. H. Armytage, did not consider the labourer on the fourth train entirely free from blame, but felt that the accident must be attributed to the unsatisfactory method of signalling which appeared to have been originated and adopted almost exclusively by McMillan. He recommended that definite rules for the working at the pit 'should be made and strictly enforced', and 'that no movement of any train should be allowed in the upper part of the tunnel' (i. e. on the Copland Road side of the pit) 'whilst any portion of a train is standing in the opening'. He did not seem to pick up the point made in the 1902 Report that there should be a look-out posted at the leading end of reversing trains.[30]

Unperturbed by the mass of moving machinery, two Subway Power Station employees discuss the pros and cons of Rotary Club membership. Although after Sibbald's accident, the fencing still seems sparse. *Glasgow Museum of Transport Collection*

Passenger Accidents

A strange incident occurred at about 2pm on 2nd June 1906 at Cowcaddens. A male passenger, a chef by occupation, alighted from an Inner Circle train, and had nearly reached the first landing of the stairway from the platform when he collided with a drunk man coming down. Both fell down the stairs to the platform, then on to the track, where the chef's arms became entangled in the haulage rope, and shortly afterwards a train arrived, killing the drunk and further injuring the chef, who sued the Company for £2,000. The action was heard in the Court of Session in Edinburgh the following February. The chef's case (the Pursuer in Scottish legal terminology) was found to be 'irrelevant' on the grounds that (1) there was no duty on railway companies to keep people sober; (2) the Pursuer had a duty to look ahead as he was ascending the stairs to avoid danger to himself; (3) the fact that the Station Master was reading a newspaper did not matter, because there was no general duty on the Station Master to always be on and observe the platform, and (4) there was no duty on the 'engine driver' to look out to see 'casual men lying on the rails'. Ninety years later the Court would surely take a very different view.[31]

Collisions

Two passenger train collisions led to Board of Trade Inquiries during the Company period, both conducted by J. W. Pringle.[32] who was Inspecting Officer of Railways and a Major in 1912, but had become Chief Inspecting Officer of Railways and a Colonel by 1917.

1. On 6th June 1912 an Inner Circle train consisting of Cars 29 and 34 left Buchanan Street for Cowcaddens at about 12·12pm, and about 450 yards from Buchanan Street a rod in 'the apparatus for gripping the cable' snapped, 'and the train was brought to a stand on a rising gradient of 1 in 57 by the driver applying his wheel brake'. After the first 130 yards or so the route between Buchanan Street and Cowcaddens is on rising gradients, and to comply with Rule 89 'it was necessary to let the train run back down the gradient on to the level, before assistance could be obtained'. In the meantime the following train, consisting of Cars 1 and 39 (both now in the Glasgow Museum of Transport) arrived at Buchanan Street at about 12·15pm and was allowed to leave about 12·20pm: the driver saw the reversing train, and was nearly stopped when the first train struck his at a point about 230 yards from Buchanan Street at about 12·21pm. According to Major Pringle's Report 'the collision was not a very violent one.' There was a total of about 30 people on the two trains, and although ten complained of bruises or the effects of shock, none required medical assistance.

    Major Pringle laid no blame for the accident on any of the train crew, but rather on lack of intelligence displayed by the Station Masters at Buchanan Street and Cowcaddens. When the second train was ready to start from Buchanan Street the signal could not be lowered, and the section indicator was at danger. The Station Master then telephoned his colleague at Cowcaddens to find out if the previous train had cleared the section. The Cowcaddens Station Master was unsure, and said so to his colleague at Buchanan Street. The Cowcaddens Station Master then telephoned St George's Cross and was told the train had definitely not passed there, but he was unable to contact Buchanan Street until after the second train had been despatched under 'caution order'. Major Pringle was critical about the wording of Rules 44 and 45, and also that there were 'omissions and discrepancies on the forms of order in use.' Printed copies of Major Pringle's report were sent to the Company on 24th July.[30] A new Book of Rules and Regulations was produced before the end of the year.

2. At about 8am on 26th April 1917 a collision occurred on the Inner Circle between Hillhead and Partick Cross stations. A train consisting of Cars 55 and 39 was stopped in the tunnel because the electric lighting skids broke. The following train consisting of Cars 3 and 1 was allowed to leave Hillhead and collided, though not violently, with the stationary train. 'Two passengers complained of the effect of shock and bruises'.

    Having released the cable to stop the train, and then having retracted the skids, the Driver (a lad of only 17 who had been a grip-man for two months following eleven months' service as a Conductor) found he was unable to re-engage the cable. With the assistance of his lad Conductor the Driver attempted to re-start the train by pushing it down the gradient, but this failed, so he sent his Conductor forward to Partick Cross to summon assistance. The broken skids were on the leading car, and all the electric lights had, of course, gone out. It is also suggested that the oil head light had also gone out, so to give the Conductor some means of illumination for walking along the tunnel, the driver gave him the oil tail light. Before he could apply the skids on the rear car to give protection, the following train, which had been allowed to leave Hillhead, collided with the rear of the standing train and as a consequence it rolled into Partick Cross.

When the Station Mistress at Hillhead found she could not lower the signal for the second train she correctly telephoned the Station Master at Partick Cross: the Station Master at Partick Cross said that the telephone line was bad, and that he had said that "Forsyth was the last to pass and Gibson is the next to arrive". The Station Mistress said he had said "Yes he is away". Immediately after this conversation the Conductor of the failed train arrived at Partick Cross, and the Station Master immediately telephoned Hillhead to say the train was failed in the tunnel, but the Station Mistress had already issued the driver with a line-clear ticket, and he had left.

Colonel Pringle remarked on the similarity with the 1912 collision, and again pointed out inconsistencies in the Rules, and the relative indiscipline in passing telephone messages. He was also critical of the driver removing the oil tail lamp, leaving the train with no tail-end protection. He gained the impression that the treadles frequently failed to release signals, and warned of the dangers of staff 'losing confidence in the signalling apparatus, and having too hasty recourse to the use of the telephone block, which is not a suitable method of working a high frequency service.'[30]

Costs, and the Search for Economies.

A significant running cost was the outlay on replacement cables, and the Company was keen to find a more economical product. So it was in 1899 that Messrs D. H. & G. Heggie of Sunderland, who were not one of the original suppliers, were able to claim in an advertising feature that they had manufactured the 'record rope' for the Subway. It had had a life of $14\frac{1}{4}$ months (compared with an average of about $7\frac{1}{2}$ months and a best of $10\frac{1}{2}$ months for ropes of other manufacturers), and a mileage of 85,000 (compared with an average of about 45,000, and a best of 61,000). They claimed the success was largely due to new machinery in their works.[33]

About 1905 the Company gave some thought to the possibility of electrifying the system, and appointed a firm of Consulting Engineers, Messrs Handcock & Dykes of Victoria Street, London to carry out a feasibility study. Little is known of the proposals or how far the ideas progressed, but what is known is given in Chapter 5.

In the autumn of 1907, there was some correspondence between the Secretary and Glasgow Corporation Electricity Department, and also internally between Mr Forbes, Power Station Superintendent and the General Manager, J. G. Brown, on a proposal to buy electricity from the Corporation for lighting the stations, cars etc rather than generating their own at the Power Station. The proposal was to provide individual supplies to all the premises in Glasgow, but this did not include Partick Cross and Merkland Street (which were in the burgh of Partick) and Govan Cross, Copland Road, Cessnock and Kinning Park, which were in Govan. Technically it would have been feasible to run 'branches' from Hillhead and Shields Road respectively, but the Corporation Electricity Department were not sure they had powers to supply outside their area. In the event the Company concluded that the estimated saving of £1,860 per annum in Power House costs was less than the bill they would have to pay to the Corporation, so the idea was shelved.[34]

At the half-yearly shareholders' meeting in September 1911 the subject of electrifying the system was again discussed, and the suggestion was made that the Corporation might acquire the undertaking, but it was over a decade before anything further materialised.[35]

More complaints

A lady wrote to the Secretary of the Company on 5th February 1906 drawing his attention to the rudeness of employees: she wrote 'This afternoon as I got to the foot of the stairs at Buchanan Street Station a car came in. I ran along the platform, and as I reached the door the man slammed it in my face. I asked him to allow me inside, and was informed I was too late. This I may point out was not the case, as I stood fully a minute at the door before the car moved out of the station . . . This sort of thing occurs regularly every day, especially to those who use the Subway constantly. Some of the men seem to take a huge delight in allowing passengers to get to the door, then to slam it in their faces.'[34]

William Gilchrist, Wholesale and Retail Fruiterer and Florist of Hyndland Road, wrote to the President of the Board of Trade on Saturday 28th January 1911 complaining of 'gross overcrowding of cars which is permitted on our Glasgow District Subway'. He had travelled from Hillhead to Copland Road at 2·45pm that afternoon, and had to wait while two trains which could not take any more passengers passed before being pushed into (presumably) the third. He claimed that 'close on 400 people jammed like herring in a box' were on the train and expressed concern about what would happen 'should there be a breakdown with the Cable or any accident occur in the tunnel' and trusted 'some pressure will be brought to bear on the Company and timeously avert any catastrophe.' On 3rd February the Board of Trade wrote asking for any observations.

Andrew Mitchell, who had been Company Secretary at least since March 1902 and was to remain until the end of the Company period, replied on 8th February, saying he had laid the matter before the directors at their meeting that day, the Board of Trade letter was 'the first intimation the management had received of Mr Gilchrist's complaint' and the Directors instructed him to say 'that Mr Gilchrist's statement is both exaggerated and highly coloured.' This, however, was not good enough for the Board, who asked on 14th February to be furnished with more detailed particulars showing in what respect Mr Gilchrist's complaint was inaccurate, and added a sting in the tail by enquiring whether on the date in question the number of passengers waiting on any platforms at any one time was limited to fifty in accordance with the undertaking given on 3rd February 1898.

This gave rise to a report from Inspector C. Moar to J. G. Brown, the GDS General Manager, dated 17th February, in which he stated that stations stopped booking during the time of the football match at Copland Road as follows:-

Shields Road	stopped booking for about 10 minutes
Kinning Park	" " " " 20 "
Merkland Street	" " " " 45 "
Partick Cross	" " " " 15 "

Inspector Moar's report continued 'Station Master D. Wallace, Hillhead, says that his platform was not over-crowded; at the most he might have had 30 but the average would have been about 20 passengers'. This report was sent to the Board of Trade covered by a letter dated 22nd February in which Andrew Mitchell pointed out 'it would be impossible to put anything approaching 400 passengers into a Train.' He went on 'In No. 43 of Rules and Regulations for Officers and Servants of this Company . . . the number of passengers waiting on a Station Platform must not exceed 50. There is a system of signalling from Platform to Booking Office to stop booking when this limit is reached, and the enclosed report by Inspector Moar shows how this regulation is carried out by the Staff.'

Mr David Wallace, Station Master at Hillhead
c. 1910, in his Subway Company uniform.
Mrs M. Wallace

On receipt of this explanation the Board of Trade replied to Mr Gilchrist on 2nd March, but, not to be put down, he wrote back next day suggesting one of the Board of Trade Inspectors take a journey on the subway any Saturday afternoon when a football match was to be played at Ibrox, about a quarter of an hour before kick-off.[1]

Staff Conditions

A letter appeared in The Glasgow Herald in March 1906, in support of the employees. The anonymous writer claimed Traffic staff started work at 12 noon on Sundays, worked until 10·40pm, then had to be back on duty at 4·30am on Monday morning. Further, they received no paid holidays or meal breaks. Drivers and Station Masters started at 25 shillings (s) per week, with an increment of 1s per week for each year of service up to 30s per week for Drivers and 27s per week for Station Masters. Conductors started at 21s and Lad Conductors at 9s per week, both promoted 'according to ability'.[21]

Additional Finance

Despite the additional capital raised under the provisions of the 1894 Act, the Company was still in need of capital, and a further Private Bill was put before Parliament, receiving the Royal Assent on 6th June 1899, and known as the Glasgow District Subway (Additional Capital) Act, 1899. This provided for the raising of a further £200,000 'by the issue of new ordinary shares or stock or new preference shares or stock or wholly or partially by any one or more of those modes respectively.'[36]

This photograph of gripper car No.20 and four-wheel trailer No.34T appeared in 'Tramway and Railway World' on 8th September 1898, and was titled 'Cable Train of the Glasgow District Subway'. In fact, the trailer car has been coupled in front of the gripper car, instead of behind, probably for convenience at the time. *The Railway World, courtesy of Glasgow City Libraries*

Chapter 3

The First World War Years and end of the Company, 1914–1923

Towards the end of 1913 the Directors decided further financial provisions were required, and had a Bill prepared to go before Parliament. The Government Department most involved was the Scottish Office, and apart from noting that the Bill changed the name of the Company to the Glasgow Subway Railway Company and 'deemed it to be and always to have been a railway company' the Railway Department of the Board of Trade had no comment to make: the Company had always sent in returns and statistics etc in the same way as other railway companies.[1] The main provisions of the Bill, which became the Glasgow Subway Railway Order Confirmation Act, 1914, were a further attempt to put the finances on a better footing by authorising the Company to borrow or raise further money and to extend the time for the holding and disposal of their surplus lands and properties by a further 21 years.[2]

The Board of Directors was remarkably stable – from 1905 (if not before) it had consisted of a Chairman (Alexander Simpson of Glasgow) and five Directors, Rt Hon James Parker Smith of Jordanhill who was an MP for part of the period; William Weir of Kildonan; W S Wilson, a Civil Engineer of Glasgow; James Laird, Writer (to the Signet) of Glasgow; and Andrew K McCosh, ironmaster of Coatbridge. James Laird had left the Board about 1910, and was not replaced. About 1914 William Weir also left, but in 1915 Robert Simpson, another Civil Engineer of Glasgow joined the Board. About 1917 Andrew K McCosh left, and J N Murdoch, an Accountant of Glasgow, and William Whitelaw, then of Gogar Park (near Edinburgh) joined. Steam locomotive enthusiasts will recognise the names carried by two LNER 'A4' Pacifics.[3] Parker-Smith left the Board about 1920, and about 1921 William Whitelaw became Chairman, and W W McCosh, ironmaster of Glasgow joined the board, and finally in 1922 W S Wilson left and was replaced by William James Baird of Elie, Fife.[3]

James G Brown, who had been General Manager from before the opening, left about 1915/6, and Mr R Addison became 'Engineer and Manager', and remained so until the end of the Company's ownership.[3]

The last dividend on ordinary shares had been paid in 1912, but a dividend was paid on preference shares during this period, as follows:-

1914: 2¼%, 1915: 2%, 1916: 2%, 1917: 2½% and 1918: 2½%.[3]

No dividend was paid after 1918.[3]

The First World War, whilst increasing passengers, also produced a recruitment crisis. In June 1917 the first women were employed on the Engineering side of the company. Although most of them were as car cleaners, car washers and car sweepers (whether these were distinct jobs, or merely different terms for the same job is not apparent), from October 1917 two were employed as 'Firewomen', and from the next month a 'Boilerwoman' was taken on.[4] On the Traffic side women were recruited as station mistresses (exemplified in the collision between Hillhead and Partick Cross in 1917 described in Chapter 2), and almost certainly as conductresses (as will be seen when dealing with the collision in December 1920 later in this Chapter). The extreme youth (17) of the male driver involved in the 1917 incident was also a sign of the times.

From 10th December 1916 a 1d flat fare was introduced.[5] It is possible this was done to eliminate the need for tickets, and hence to collect them, thereby reducing the train crew from three to two, but this has not been confirmed.

The Wartime traffic boom, which peaked at 20,970,950 passengers in 1918, and produced a revenue of £85,640 was short-lived,[6] and the carryings dropped to 14·8 million in 1919 and 11 million in 1920.[7] This was partly because of reduced industrial activity, but a five-week strike in early 1920 (of which more below) is probably the biggest factor for the reduction in carryings. In an attempt to maintain revenue the universal fare of 1d was increased to 1½d in March 1919 (possibly after an experimental period at 1d for two stations and 2d for greater distances).[8] It may have been in a bid to attract some traffic from the Clyde Navigation Trustees' free ferries[9] that the so-called 1d 'Ferry' tickets were issued on the Subway at a time when the universal fare was 1½d. These tickets were valid between Govan and Merkland Street or Partick Cross and vice versa, so would be reasonably competitive with the Govan Ferry.[10] Fares were again adjusted in May 1920 to 1d for one station, 1½d for two stations and 2d maximum, and on 29th August 1920 a 3 shilling weekly ticket was introduced.[11] These steps had the effect of marginally raising passenger numbers to 11.4 million in 1921 and increasing revenue.[7] Costs, however, were rising as wages and the price of coal and steel (for cables) were increasing.

Industrial Troubles

Despite a reduction in the employees' working week and wage increases in late 1918 or early 1919, labour relations deteriorated, the Traffic Staff demanding higher wages and shorter hours. All the staff worked a six-day week of 51½ hours, and in addition half the staff worked a shortened shift on alternate Sundays at double time rates: the hours worked averaged 55 per week. The Directors made an offer on 29th November 1919 of time and a half for all hours worked over 48, provided the Sunday shift (still to be paid at double time) was made the same length as the other shifts, but when this did not satisfy the staff (who wanted the basic week reduced to 48 hours without loss of earnings and a 4 shilling per week increase back-dated to 1st October 1919), the directors said their offer was all the Company could afford. They contended the offer would increase the wage bill by over 100 per cent compared with the pre-war period, and that working hours had already been reduced by over 10 per cent.[12]

After a suggestion that the dispute be submitted to arbitration had been rejected by the directors on the grounds that they did not have the money to improve their offer, an official strike was called by the Workers' Union (predecessor to the Transport & General Workers' Union) from 6·30 am on Saturday morning 17th January, and a strike committee was formed. The Union requested the Ministry of Labour to convene a Court of Inquiry, under the Industrial Courts Act, which, had it been granted promptly, might have averted the strike.[12]

Nearly all the Traffic staff joined the strike and services were completely suspended. Pickets were appointed to attend at times and places employees usually reported for work, but some, at least, of the maintenance staff remained at work, with the blessing of the Union, to keep the pumps and other plant running. The Tramways Department put every available tram on the streets to alleviate over-crowding as far as possible,[12] and the Govan to Partick ferryboats carried many more people than usual. Neil Maclean, Socialist MP for Govan, who addressed a meeting of the strikers on 22nd January, said he was pressing the Ministry of Labour to set up a Court of Inquiry: this resulted in Ministry officials in Glasgow holding exploratory interviews with both

Company and Union representatives on Friday 23rd. On the same day employees were required to return 'uniforms and other Company properties in their possession' to Copland Road station, when payment of wages due (i.e. 'lying time') would be made.[13] By this time Bailie Clymie of the Workers' Union was threatening to involve the men working the pumps.[14] Following on from the exploratory interviews, a 'conference' convened by the Ministry lasting three hours and attended by representatives of the Company and the Union was held on Tuesday 27th January. Ultimately the Company representatives agreed to submit new proposals by the workers (for a 5 shilling per week increase for all employees over 18 years old, that time and a half be paid for overtime and Sundays instead of double time on Sundays, but retaining the existing Sunday shift) to the directors on the Thursday, so the conference was adjourned till the Friday.[12] The directors could not see how they could finance these proposals, so repeated their previous offer to the resumed conference:[12] the result was that the strike continued. The Company then recruited and trained new staff to replace those deemed to have dismissed themselves, and on Monday 23rd February resumed a limited service on one circle for three hours in the morning, two hours at midday and a further three hours in the evening.[12] A slightly improved service was achieved on the Outer Circle next day.[12] This action broke the impasse, because the Union accepted the Company's terms provided there was no question of victimisation, and a full service was planned for Wednesday 25th February.[12]

Criminal proceedings were taken against two male and one female employee, who, whilst picketing, had assaulted a Subway employee. They were sentenced in Glasgow Sheriff Court, the two men to three months imprisonment, and the woman to one month. These sentences were regarded as severe, and the Scottish Trades Union Council sent a delegation to London to see the Secretary for Scotland. After the STUC had made a written submission, the Scottish Office replied that the Secretary for Scotland 'finds no sufficient reason to justify his interference with the sentences.'[15]

Traffic Congestion

About the same time Glasgow Corporation became concerned about traffic congestion on the streets, and particularly at the river crossings in the area of the Central and St Enoch railway bridges. A 'Special Sub-committee on Congestion of Traffic &c.' was set up under the Tramway Committee, and met for the first time on 17th February 1920.[16] The original remit was to report on:-

'traffic congestion in the City, and the increased facilities necessary to cope with the requirements of the public and the method of collection of fares on the tramway cars.'

At its second meeting on 1st June its remit was extended to report on five motions made at a meeting of the Corporation: these motions included:[16]-

the desirability of the Corporation obtaining powers to introduce (a) motor-buses, (b) underground railways, (c) car (i. e. tram) services on the sides of public roads and (d) other means of conveyance;

the desirability of the Corporation acquiring, by purchase, the Glasgow District Subway Company, or by contract, lease or otherwise running powers over the system of that Subway Company;

the steps necessary to be taken for such purchase, contract, lease or otherwise;

the expediency of developing and extending the underground means of transit.

In December 1920 the General Manager of the Tramways Department presented a wide-ranging report, including suggestions made by the Sub-Committee. The report mentioned that the Corporation had had powers since 1914 to build a bridge over the Clyde between Oswald Street and Commerce Street; that there was a scheme to throw a bridge across the Clyde from Dixon Street to South Portland Street and open up St Enoch Square: and that the question of cross-river communication at or near Finnieston had been before the Corporation for over 30 years. He said things had changed somewhat since 1st June, when tram fares had been increased, and patronage had dropped as a result. In discussing the Subway he recalled that it was 'many years' since a prominent shareholder of the Subway Company approached the then Lord Provost with a view to a Corporation takeover. Cost estimates had been prepared as to what work would be necessary to bring the undertaking up to an acceptable standard, but the directors did not care to meet the Corporation for discussion at that time. He thought the Subway could be made more attractive but considered a proposal from the Company was necessary. He was not keen on motor-buses to relieve congestion where tram tracks were already in existence, but saw some benefit in trolleybuses in out-lying areas to avoid the cost of tram track. The Sub-committee decided to recommend as a first step the construction of the new bridge at Oswald Street and associated street and tramway works.[16]

Operations

There were two collisions in 1920, both involving trains on the Inner Circle being sent to assist broken down trains, and colliding with them. The first occurred on August 16th between Merkland Street and Govan, and the second on 6th December between Bridge Street and St Enoch. On the first occasion a train had become disabled near the low point under the river, and the driver of the train going to assist lost control and collided with the stationary one. Three people were taken to the Western Infirmary, one of whom was detained. The second collision was more spectacular, in that a train had become disabled approaching St Enoch, and the assisting train collided with it, and both were carried through St Enoch – presumably because the assisting driver could not release the grip. Ten passengers were taken to the Royal Infirmary, one of whom was detained.[17]

There was a fatal accident on the morning of 7th February 1921 in the tunnels between the Car Sheds pit and Govan Cross platform. A conductor, Thomas McCrae, after being relieved at Govan Cross was using the tunnel as a short cut to Car Sheds during traffic hours and was hit and killed by a train. There was a Ministry of Transport Inquiry, which resulted in notices being posted at Govan Cross and the Car Sheds. One such notice, which was not an original but dated from the late 1920s, survived at Govan Cross station until its closure for modernisation in 1977.[18]

In 1921 the Company produced a new edition of its Rule Book. Apart from the change in title to Glasgow Subway Railway Company, there were minimal differences compared with the 1912 book it replaced. The original foreword dating back to 1902 was retained, but the more recent section was signed 'R. Addison, Engineer and Manager', instead of 'James G. Brown, General Manager' in the earlier Books. The main difference is that Rule 44(C) was extended to cover specific instructions for propelling trains which had lost the Cable. Rule 53 was also extended, and introduced a provision for conductors to examine tail lamps at various times during the shift. Rule 99 (b) concerning use of the brake release valve was slightly modified, presumably because the cars had been altered: both versions said:-

The Air Brakes can be released by hand when necessary, by opening the release valve.

The 1912 Book continued:-

A wire on each side of the Train is supplied for this purpose.

But the 1921 Book said:-

A hatch is fitted in the floor to enable Driver to reach Release Valve. This hatch is situated in the middle of the Car on platform side.

The 1921 Book had three passages in the Appendix, compared with one in the 1912 Book, the two new ones both concerning the February 1921 fatal accident, which may have been what prompted the new issue.

A surviving copy of the 1912 Book has the extended passage for Rule 44(c) pasted into it as an amendment slip, and a surviving copy of the 1921 Book has the times of first trains pasted on the inside of the front cover and the times of the last trains pasted inside the back cover.[19]

About 1921 the first train on the Outer Circle left Govan Cross at 6·30am, and on the Inner Circle the first train left Copland Road at 6·33am. On Sundays the times were 2pm and 2·03pm respectively. On Mondays to Saturdays the last train left Govan Cross on the Outer Circle at 11pm, and ran to Cessnock, arriving at 11·34pm, and on the Inner Circle it also left Govan at 11pm, arriving at Merkland Street at 11·36pm. Last trains on Sundays left Govan at 10pm.[20] The weekdays service was run with ten trains on each circle, and the circuit time was 42 minutes.[21]

After the First World War the duties of 'smoker boys' included collecting tickets from people leaving the rear gates of the train. One such 'smoker boy', who was employed on the system about 1920 could not understand how it was that the last Inner Circle trains were parked at the Car Sheds Pit at close of traffic, but when he came in for an early shift there were trains lined up between Govan Cross Station and the pit, and the cable had not been running during the night: his curiosity was such that he came in early one morning, and was amazed to see a train coming slowly down the Inner Circle tunnel towards Govan from the pit with a number of men and two large female car cleaners jumping up and down inside! When the train had arrived at its appointed place, they trooped back up the tunnel to repeat the process with the next train.[22] This was making use of the slight down gradient from the Pit to Govan, but as will be seen in later chapters, it sometimes led to unfortunate consequences.

The same 'smoker boy' was once taken to task by his driver after a Permanent Way man, who must have been working in the tunnels during traffic hours, and retreating into a cross-passage when trains approached, was splashed by what he thought was tea dregs being thrown out of the rear gates: in fact it was not tea – the smoker boy had been caught short![22]

Financial Crisis – the Corporation to the Rescue

At the shareholders' annual meeting in March 1921, in view of the serious financial position, the directors received the shareholders' authority to close the system temporarily at any stage they thought fit. There was no immediate prospect of steel or coal prices reducing, though one shareholder suggested cutting wages on the basis that employees might prefer this to no work: the Chairman pointed out the latter was unrealistic. It was hoped economic activity, and hence traffic levels, would experience an up-turn at some stage in the future, which might restore economic operation.[11]

On 9th February 1922 it was announced to the Corporation meeting in private session that the Glasgow Subway Railway Company directors had stated their intention to close their undertaking on 11th February, but on representations being made, they agreed to postpone the closure for another week to give the Corporation time to consider whether they should take steps to keep the Subway in operation. The Corporation decided to set up a special committee to confer with the directors and to work out the terms of an agreement for keeping the Subway running for a period not exceeding two months, and to report whether the Corporation should purchase the undertaking.[23]

By 14th February,[23] the special committee had met the directors of the Company and had arrived at the following:-

The Company would continue to run the undertaking as from and after 18th February for a period not exceeding two months with the Corporation paying the Company £200 per week towards the estimated difference between the costs of carrying on the Subway as at present and of keeping the tunnel free from water should the line be closed for public use. The Corporation reserved the right to terminate such payment at any time within the two months on giving the Company ten days' notice. In the event of the Company selling the undertaking to a syndicate or other company, the Corporation was to be repaid any sums paid by them to the Company under the foregoing arrangement.

In discussing whether the Corporation should buy the undertaking the special committee agreed to an inspection and valuation, particularly of the rented property owned by the Company. The valuation report was presented on 10th March 1922,[23] when consideration was also given to a report by the General Manager on other aspects of the Company's undertaking, including the working expenditure and revenue for 1921 (resulting in a deficit of nearly £24,000).[21] Some initial thoughts and cost estimates for electrification were included in the latter report. Members of the special committee agreed to recommend to the Corporation purchase of the undertaking for a price believed to be £300,000,[24] and to communicate this to the Chairman of the Company.

At the time of the General Manager's report, the Subway Company had a pay-roll of 287, of whom 174 were 'Traffic staff' – i. e. Inspectors, Drivers, Conductors, Ticket Collectors, Station Masters and Turnstile girls – 81 were in the Workshops, and 20 were in the Power Station. The remaining twelve were the Manager, the Secretary and their clerical staffs.[21]

The seal of the Glasgow Subway Railway Company.

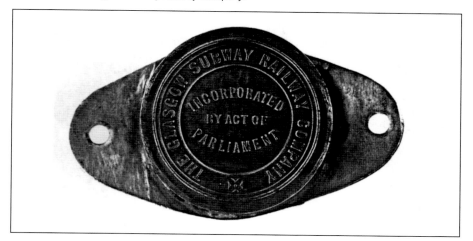

The special committee next met with the directors of the Company on 13th March. The directors submitted a price (probably £500,000)[25] below which they stated they were not prepared to sell the undertaking. The Committee recommended that the price asked, including lands and buildings, was much greater than the value to the Corporation so the purchase should not proceed. They further recommended notice be given to the Company for the termination of the arrangements reached on 14th February, as from 25th March. Arrangements were put in hand for increased ferry services between Govan and Partick, at Meadowside and Pointhouse. The above arrangements were approved by the Corporation on 16th March.[25]

A new agreement worked out by the Town-Clerk and the legal agents of the Company was signed and sealed with the City seal at the meeting of the Corporation on 21st June. The agreed price was £385,000,[26] but the amount paid on 1st August 1923 was £381,589 12s 0d[27] – the difference may have been the income from rented property which probably went straight to the Company.

At 2pm on Sunday 2nd July 1922, the Lord Provost of Glasgow, Thomas Paxton, performed the re-opening ceremony.[28] Prior to this: there had been another ceremony in the Power Station in Scotland Street, when the Lord Provost had been invited to turn on the power for the cables by Mr J N Murdoch, the senior director of the Company.[29] It was also agreed that five members of the Corporation, including the Lord Provost, should, along with the directors of the Subway Company, meet at regular intervals to perform the executive role of the undertaking, until Parliamentary formalities for the transfer had been completed, and the Subway could be fully vested in the Tramways undertaking.[30] The Managers of the Tramways Department and the Subway Company were jointly to manage the day-to-day affairs. The Corporation was keen the Subway should be worked as part of the Tramways undertaking.[25]

A meeting of the Corporation nominees with the directors took place on 3rd August 1922, at St Enoch Square, but no record of what was discussed has come to light.[30]

The Subway in the 1920s. *Dr Friedrich Grünwald*

By 9th August the General Manager had met with Messrs MacDuff & Co., the lessees of the advertising rights on the Subway stations, cars and property, and the Mechanical Trading Company Limited who had permission from the Company to place automatic weighing machines etc in the stations. Consideration was given as to whether these contracts should be continued, but no immediate decision was made.[30]

By 6th November the General Manager was able to report:-

that the work of re-painting and repairing the cars is almost completed;

that the work of cleaning the stations is being gradually overtaken; and

that the electric lift at Kelvinbridge Station had been repaired and cleaned and is ready to be put into operation shortly.[30]

At the same meeting the special committee began to sort out its policy on electrification once the undertaking was vested in the Corporation. The thinking was that new cars should be supplied under contract, and that schemes and plans for electrification be developed without delay.

At a meeting of the special committee on 8th January 1923, the matter of the contract with Messrs MacDuff, the advertising agents was discussed. The contract was not due to expire until 1st January 1928, but advertisements had been removed from both the stations and the cars in the course of cleaning and repair work, and had not been replaced. The General Manager said that as 'the stations and cars would again be in the hands of workmen for electrification so soon as the Parliamentary powers for the transfer of the undertaking to the Corporation had been obtained' that the alternative to replacement was cancellation of the contract. The special committee, however, decided to inform the Subway Company that Messrs MacDuff should be allowed to exercise their rights meantime.[31] By March 1923, however, the same committee was reconciled to the contract being cancelled.[31]

In March 1923 a letter from the Ministry of Transport indicated that the Minister of Transport could not agree to the proposal to change the status of the Subway from that of a railway to that of a tramway, and that he considered the existing provisions for the regulation of railways should continue to apply. The Sub-Committee on the Glasgow Corporation Order, 1923 resolved not to give effect to the proposal of the Minister of Transport.[31]

On 23rd May 1923, the special committee recommended acceptance of a proposal both technical and financial by the François Cementation Co. Limited of Doncaster, for the treatment of both tunnels between Kinning Park and Cessnock to reduce water inflow. This was in the nature of an experiment, partly to demonstrate the capabilities of the François process and more particularly to obtain a more definite idea of the cost of the work. They also agreed the appointment of Mr W. C. Easton, a Civil Engineer, to supervise the experiment, to report on making the Subway watertight, and on enlarging the stations and improving the entrances,[31] and he was retained from August 1923. The contract with the François Company was terminated in November 1925,[32] after the most troublesome areas had been treated.

The special committee met on 31st July when the Town-Clerk reported that the Glasgow Corporation Order, 1923, providing for the transfer of the Subway undertaking to the Corporation, had received the Royal Assent on 18th July, and that as from 1st August the undertaking would be vested in the Corporation as part of the Tramways. The special committee thereupon agreed it had completed its remit, so should be discharged, and the control and working of the Subway be transferred to the existing Committee on Tramways.[31]

Chapter 4

The Last Years of Cable Operation, 1923–1935

Improvements already started continued when the Corporation took over full control from 1st August 1923, and the system simply became the Subway Section of the Tramways Department. The staff was kept on, including the Engineer & Manager, Mr R. Addison, who probably continued to live in Broomloan Cottage, next door to the Car Sheds. The Superintendent in charge of the Power Station also lived on the premises in a house fronting on to Scotland Street which was originally the Head Office.

As seen in Chapter 3, the Tramways Acts, rather than railway legislation, applied: a strange result of this was that every train then carried the GCT Bye-Laws booklet, which included such items as speed limits for trams in Maryhill Road, but made no specific reference to the Subway. This continued until the 1960s, and the holders remained in most motor coaches until withdrawal.

The Corporation special committee formed to negotiate with the Company, then to run the undertaking jointly with the Subway Company Directors, was re-constituted as a sub-committee of the Committee on Tramways, and was known as the Sub-Committee on the Subway.[1] Its purpose was to oversee the Subway operations, and in particular the electrification, which, in 1923, was still seen as imminent. Its first meeting was on 28th August 1923.

Before electrification could be contemplated the condition of the tunnels had to be established and improved, and as seen in Chapter 3, Mr W. C. Easton was retained from August 1923, and waterproofing works were started.

By about 1927 it had become clear the electrification was not imminent, and Mr Easton's services were terminated in June of that year. The last meeting of the Sub-Committee on the Subway was about February 1928, and shortly afterwards the Municipal Transport Committee was set up to replace the Committee on Tramways, reflecting the increasing importance of buses and the absorption of the Subway.

One of the first matters the Sub-Committee on the Subway dealt with was rationalising the wage rates and hours of work of the Subway personnel. Having considered reports from the Manager in October 1923, they recommended that the standard hours of work should be 48 per week (compared with an average of about 56 under the Company), and the Corporation's standard 54 shilling per week for men over 21 be introduced. This meant that the Traffic staff had to be increased by 6 Stationmasters, 5 Drivers, 2 Conductors, 5 Turnstile Attendants and 4 Ticket Collectors, i. e from 183 to 205. On the Engineering side only 4 additional personnel were required, 2 cablemen and 2 skilled labourers, which increased that total from 113 to 117. This was estimated to increase the wages bill by some £5,718 per annum, and was partially offset by increasing the cable speed from 12 to 13 mph. This reduced the journey time from 40 to 36 minutes, the number of trains by one on each circle, and the drivers and conductors required by four of each. It would also make the service more attractive to the public. Previously the condition of the tunnels, track and rolling stock had been too poor to risk speeding up the cable, but in view of the recent work in these areas, it was now considered feasible.[2]

In February 1924 it was agreed the 'busy station' premium paid to Station Masters and Turnstile Attendants at Govan Cross, Merkland Street and Partick Cross (4 shillings and 3 shillings per week respectively) should be paid to the those working at St Enoch and Buchanan Street stations,[3] and in November 1928 a similar award was made to those at Copland Road station:[4] in both cases an increase in traffic at the stations concerned was the justification.

In January 1924 the Sub-Committee agreed that the Subway should start at the same time as the Tramways on Sundays.[3] This probably came into force on Sunday 24th February 1924, and it is likely it coincided with the speeding up of the cable: it is thought the first trains started at 10am instead of 2pm.[5] By the late 1920s, it was the practice to stop the cables at 11am on Armistice Day, 11th November for 2 minutes: conductors were instructed to stand to attention during the 2 minutes' silence, and gripmen were required to "retain a grip of the cable so as to be ready to start evenly on completion of the two minutes when the cables will resume running". The uniform staff were expected to wear naval or military medals.[6] By 1930 at least, the New Year's Day service started at 10·30am.[6] As an economy measure from 21st September 1931 the Monday to Friday service was adjusted to run to the Fair Holiday timings,[7] which involved nine trains per circle instead of ten, though the Saturday service remained at 10 trains per circle. From Sunday 17th January 1932 the Sunday service was again altered, to start at 3pm instead of 10am.[8]

For the first few months the Corporation retained the Subway Company fare structure including the 3 shilling adult and 1s 6d juvenile weekly season tickets. Season tickets were a good buy for people on a 5½ day week travelling the 2d distance and, as was very common in Glasgow, going home for lunch.

As from 30th December 1923 the fares were lowered: 1d or a ¾d Token for an adult for three stations or a juvenile for any distance and a maximum of 1½d. At the same time the weekly season tickets were discontinued.[9] Within two months the patronage had risen from about 210,000 to 360,000 per week. A Councillor queried the policy of charging a fixed 1½d on Saturday afternoons during the football season, so in September 1924 the Corporation decided to discontinue the arrangement.[3]

A proposal was made by a Councillor in March 1925 that a universal fare of 1d on the Subway, including abolition of the ¾d token fare, be adopted. The General Manager produced a report which showed that each train would need to pick up two extra passengers at every station stop for the scheme to break even. Neither the Sub-Committee on the Subway nor the Committee on Tramways was in favour of the scheme.[10] One passage from the General Manager's Report read:-

At the present time . . . we are carrying as many people at the "rush" hours as the Subway can conveniently accommodate; in fact, there are times every day when the cars are much too crowded.

We are carrying more people to-day and drawing a larger revenue than the Subway Company ever did. It would, no doubt, be contended that if the 1½d fare were reduced to 1d there would be a large increase in the number who would use the Subway . . . If this change were made we would lose ½d on every Subway traveller who presently pays 1½d, and we would lose ½d on every tramway traveller who transfers to the Subway.

From 1st July 1926 the tokens were discontinued, then from 1st July 1927 a ½d fare for a one-station journey was introduced,[11] but from 30th January 1932, it was withdrawn again except between Govan Cross and Merkland Street.[12]

There was a steady rise in annual patronage up to 1928/9, then from May 1931 to May 1934 there was a steady decline in all fare categories, no doubt as a combined effect of the Depression and decreasing reliability of the Subway. There was a slight increase in the numbers of ½d fares in the year to May 1934, however.

A 30-year-old woman was killed and her 2-year-old daughter injured when they fell on to the track at Shields Road station on Saturday evening 22nd July 1922. As they reached the platform the Station Master, the only other person there, was sitting on a stool with his back to the stairway, and hearing a scream he turned and saw the woman and child on the track of the Inner Circle. He promptly jumped on to the track to rescue them, and as he did so a train ran in: being unable to stop the train, he tried to jump back on to the platform, but the front car of the train ran over the woman and trapped the station master's legs between the train and the platform. Removal of two planks from the wooden platform released the station master. A Tramway break-down gang was called, who managed to release the child, but it them took three quarters of an hour to release the woman, and she died of her injuries.[13]

There was a flooding incident involving leakage of a water main in the Partick district on Friday 9th October 1925, involving a stoppage of the service. The General Manager rendered an account to the Water Department for loss of revenue and extra wages![10]

A memorandum from the Tramways Head Office at Bath Street to the Subway local management at Govan survived until recently in which concern and alarm was expressed at the number of derailments occurring. Apart from the fact that one of these occurred at 11·45pm on 5th June 1931 resulting in a solicitor's letter on behalf of some of the passengers involved, no details of any of these have come to light, so the nature of the problem is not known.

Some of the gripper cars were probably out of use at the time of transfer, because some new gripper bogies were ordered from Hurst, Nelson about 1924.[14] Repainting of the coaches started before the Corporation had full control, and was repeated in 1926 and 1929.[15] It is likely this was in the scarlet and cream style shown in the photographs of Car 60 immediately after conversion to electric traction, but presumably the cars were lettered 'Corporation Tramways' prior to the 1929 repaint. Improvements in the lighting of the coaches was in progress in March 1925: the number of lamps in gripper coaches was increased from 8 to 14, and in trailer cars from 8 to 15.[15] The Subway Company practice of having one window in three on the cars boarded up was discontinued from 1928, if not before.[16]

In 1925 the boilers and steam plant at the Car Sheds were replaced by electric motors – this included the drive for overhead line shafting etc.[18] Later, in October 1925, approval was obtained for more adequate office, store and workshop accommodation at an estimated cost of £1,000, and offers were received in February 1926.[17, 18] It is probable that this included building the ground floor and first floor offices at the South East corner of the building, evidently where the boiler plant had been. (See Figure 5·1 on page 65).

The Tramways Department considerably increased its land and property ownership when the Subway Company was taken over. Various organisations became interested in acquiring portions of this land, not least the Glasgow Corporation Housing Department. The Director of Land and Accommodation, H. M. Office of Works, based in Edinburgh, made enquiries in July 1923 about buying land in Broomloan Road for a telephone exchange. When ground was transferred from one Corporation Department to another, the value was assessed by the Master of Works, and the legal titles handed over as if between independent bodies. The Sub-Committee put off disposing of land, to keep as many options as possible open, until Mr Easton's reports had been received, particularly with regard to the building of siding loops or a branch to a Depot somewhere off the existing route – which are covered in the next chapter. The Sub-Committee, however, came under increasing pressure from the Corporation to agree to the Housing Department's requests. One such request for ground on the south side of Brand Street at Whitefield Road, Govan, was finally agreed to, with minor modifications, in July

1924 at a valuation of £475 4s.[3] Another larger plot of land to the north of Cessnock station valued at £1,963 7s was transferred to the Housing Department in April 1925.[3]

In April 1924 the Corporation's Master of Works reported that the tenement property formerly owned by the Subway Company at 165–169 Great George Street, Hillhead, had subsided to a considerable extent. The Tramways Manager was instructed to take such action as was necessary to secure the stability of the building.[3] Whatever steps were taken turned out to be only a temporary palliative, because the Master of Works was again in touch with the Transport Department General Manager early in 1930. By June of that year it had been decided to demolish the three closes involved, and in the September a contract was let for the demolition at a cost of £190.[19] At the time of writing (September 1996) the site is occupied by a small garden centre and a wooden shed which was formerly a snooker hall.

The Sub-Committee considered purchasing the Govan Parish Hall, adjoining the Car Sheds on Broomloan Road, when it was offered to them in 1924, but even after the asking price had been lowered it was not purchased.[20] The fact that they did not do so resulted, some 65 years later, in the extension to the Stabling Shed having a 'step' built into its east wall, because, although the Parish Hall building had been demolished a few years before, and the ground was vacant, the ownership was unclear.

Some feathers were ruffled when the Sub-Committee considered not renewing the leases after Whitsunday 1925 on some five public houses and one licensed grocer's in properties acquired from the Subway Company. Whether this was motivated, in part at least, by the temperance lobby, or whether it was strictly practical so station entrances could be improved is not now clear, but the case was taken up by the Glasgow and District Licensed Trade Defence Association, and the Corporation, at their meeting in September 1924, decided no action should be taken to dispossess the existing occupiers until such time as the Corporation actually required the properties.[3]

Consideration was also given to acquiring property at the corner of Maryhill Road and Great Western Road to enable a better entrance to St George's Cross station to be built, and also on the corner of Buchanan Street and West George Street for a new entrance to Buchanan Street station involving fewer steps. Nothing, however came of either of these projects.[10]

The Coal Strike of 1926 meant that the cost of coal for the Power Station was increased, which resulted in an increased deficit.[18] The General Strike started at midnight on Monday 3rd May 1926, and during the first week about 25% of the normal mileage was operated, and about 23% of the normal passengers travelled. During the second week over half the mileage was operated, but passengers were about 33% of normal,[21] largely because the strike was called off during the afternoon of Wednesday 12th May. A 2d flat fare was introduced for at least part of the strike period, and some 32,766 such tickets were sold at a time when the normal maximum fare was 1½d.[21] Some Subway employees joined the strike, but others worked on at some risk to their personal safety. Incentives were offered to keep employees at work – double pay was offered, students were allocated to staff to act as bodyguards, and, in the case of Subway personnel, accommodation was provided in the Govan Parish Hall, with free food sent in from the Grand Hotel at Charing Cross.[22]

The General Manager, James Dalrymple, had strong views on employees disloyal enough to join the strike, and dismissed them. There were calls for their re-instatement, and for the termination of the appointment of the General Manager. The General Manager prepared notes for the first meeting of a special sub-committee in September,[23] which indicated that 316 employees of the Tramways Department had not been reinstated, including 33 from the Subway. Of these '23 were refused reinstatement because they were inefficient', and 'had been for two years under notice of discharge as they had failed to pass the doctor, and ten were discharged because of their violent conduct during the strike'. In November the Corporation agreed the employees should be reinstated, and the next day Mr Dalrymple tendered a letter to the Town-Clerk intimating he wished to exercise his right to retire as from 31st December – he was 67 by this time and had 45 years' service.[24] One wonders how much longer he had intended to continue. The post was not advertised, and Lachlan Mackinnon, Deputy General Manager, was confirmed as General Manager in January 1927,[24] but with slightly modified terms of reference, allowing appeals to the Tramways Committee against dismissal under certain circumstances.[24]

Mr James Dalrymple   Mr Lachlan Mackinnon

As we have already seen the Corporation had set up a Sub-Committee on Traffic Congestion in 1920. It actively considered two new bridges across the river, one between Oswald Street and Commerce Street, which materialised as the George V Bridge opened in 1927, and the other from Dixon Street to South Portland Street, near the pedestrian suspension bridge. The idea was to project a tram service (short-lived as it turned out) which terminated in South Portland Street across the river to St Enoch Square, and to redevelop the Square demolishing both St Enoch Church and the Subway station. The Glasgow Corporation Order Confirmation Act of 1925 conferred powers to demolish the Subway station, and to build two underground passageways to a new sub-surface booking hall which was to be 30 feet by 36 feet. From the booking hall separate entry and exit stairs would lead up to a point in the arches under the carriageway leading up to the London Midland & Scottish Railway St Enoch station.[25] The Church was duly demolished in 1926, but nothing came of the Subway station scheme, nor of the bridge.[26] In late 1929 there was an attempt to revive the scheme as an unemployment relief measure, but still nothing happened,[4] possibly because thoughts were turning to another bridge capable of taking tram tracks, this time down-river at Finnieston. In July 1931 it was decided not to make application to further extend the time limit when it expired in 1932[27] after two previous extensions of time. Several years later the site of St Enoch Church became a Corporation bus terminus.

A new Rule Book came into effect from December 1928; the employee conduct sections were in GCT style, but the operational rules were mostly a direct copy of the 1921 GSR book, but without numbering the individual Rules. A significant difference was the omission of the former Rule 43 – the one limiting the number of people waiting on platforms to 50. A new section containing extracts from the Tramways Bye-laws was introduced.

A curious feature of the cable haulage system was that distances along the cable were measured in minutes! The following notice to 'Drivers' – presumably in error for 'Gripmen' – illustrates a number of the peculiarities of cable operation:-[6]

GLASGOW CORPORATION TRAMWAYS (SUBWAY SECTION)

NOTICE TO DRIVERS – OUTER CIRCLE.

THE PRESENT SPLICE AND PART OF CABLE EXTENDING FROM SPLICE TO BEYOND KINK 1½ MINUTES IN FRONT OF SPLICE WILL BE CUT OUT ON SATURDAY NIGHT, AND A PIECE OF USED CABLE SPLICED IN.

CONSEQUENTLY THERE WILL BE TWO NEW SPLICES ON THE CABLE ON SUNDAY, 27TH CURT. THESE SPLICES WILL BE MARKED IN THE SAME MANNER AS THE PRESENT SPLICE AND KINK ARE MARKED, THAT IS, ONE WHITE MARK FOR FIRST SPLICE, AND TWO WHITE MARKS FOR SPLICE JUST OVER 1½ MINUTES IN FRONT.

DRIVERS MUST EXERCISE CARE, AND IN ALL CASES ALLOW SPLICES TO PASS FREELY THROUGH GRIPPERS.

46, Bath Street,   BY ORDER.

25th July, 1929.

The station entrances at Bridge Street, Buchanan Street and Partick Cross were altered and improved in July 1925, 1927 and 1928 respectively.[18] Similar alterations to Govan Cross had been approved by November 1930.[18]

In July 1924 a firm called Automatic Machine Distributors was authorised to put cigarette-selling machines in all stations except West Street for a rental of £3 per annum per machine, for a period of one year, terminable at three months' notice.[3] Some, at least, of the machines lasted well beyond the year, because in June 1933 a letter from the Chairman of Glasgow and West of Scotland Branch of the National Society of Non-smokers was submitted asking that the machines be removed because young people were obtaining cigarettes from them: no action was taken.[28] Chocolate vending machines were also a feature at some stations about this time.

On the trains, the original Mansell (i. e. wooden centred) wheels were replaced with chilled iron ones but whether before or after the Corporation takeover is not certain. Between January 1930 and March 1932 some 126 old axles had new chilled iron wheels fitted by Millar & Co. of Edinburgh; meanwhile between December 1930 and April 1932 twenty pairs of wheels on new axles were delivered from the same source.[29] This type of wheel continued in use on trailer cars until the mid-1960s.

Between August 1930 and October 1932 some 1,500 creosoted timber sleepers 6ft long × 10ins wide × 4½ins thick were delivered from a variety of suppliers – slightly over half had bevelled ends to fit the cast iron sections of tunnel. Some of these sleepers were Pitch Pine, some Larch, and some American Redwood.[29]

One significant cost was that of the haulage ropes, and it is clear that no manufacturer produced one ideal for the purpose, as the products of numerous companies were tried. In 1925 five firms quoted the same price (£6,544 13s 9d) for two replacement ropes, so the Town-Clerk wrote to the Board of Trade complaining of a cartel,[10] but in the days before the Monopolies Commission there was evidently nothing that could be done. Two ropes were authorised, one from Messrs T & W Smith of Newcastle, and the other from Messrs R S Newall and Son, Ltd of Liverpool.[10] The following year offers for two more ropes were received. After the experience of the previous year, quotations were submitted by agents for a German company at £1,684 18s 9d each: the lowest bid from a British firm, J & E Wright of Birmingham, was for £2,740. This firm had last supplied a rope to the Subway Company in 1922, but it had not performed particularly well. It emerged at a meeting between the General Manager and a representative of Wright's that the wire proposed for the cable was made from acid steel, which was more expensive than basic steel (the alternative) and that the one supplied to the Subway Company had been of basic steel to reduce the cost. Wright's were prepared to guarantee their rope for 418 days in service – the average life of the last six ropes supplied by Newalls. The German ropes did not have a good reputation for this type of work, so the decision was made to buy one rope from Newalls and one from Wright's.[30] In 1928 Wright's supplied another rope for £2,711 9s 6d, but agreed to a rebate of £825 in respect of the 1927 one – so presumably it had not achieved the 418 days' service. Further new haulage ropes were authorised in June and November 1932, the first from British Ropes Ltd, and the second from W. T. Bowie & Co. of Glasgow – the latter was quoted at £3,045.[31] These ropes were delivered by rail, and the scrap ones, which usually fetched about £50-£55 in scrap value, were despatched in the same way.

Coal contracts were let on an annual basis, and were usually spread over about five agents. The majority of the originating collieries were in the Lanarkshire and Ayrshire coalfields. Samples from each source were sent for test of calorific value, ash content etc to Pinkston, the Corporation Tramways power station. Coal consumption in the early 1930s was about 150 tons per week,[32] delivered, of course, by rail. (See photograph opposite.)

The labour-intensive anachronistic methods of operation largely persisted. It is significant that some wage rates reduced between 1924 and 1933 and that there was a differential between Station Masters and Station Mistresses. There was a gradual decline in numbers of employees from just over 400 in May 1924 to about 366 in May 1933 when the build up in the Repairs & Maintenance totals from 102 in 1933 to 245 in 1935, followed by a reduction to 235 in 1936 reflected the work load on the direct labour force in carrying out the electrification.

At its meeting on 28th January 1925 the Sub-Committee on Works and Stores opened offers for an electric locomotive for the Subway.[10] About May the same year correspondence took place with British Electric Vehicles of Southport and their agents Wingrove & Rogers of Liverpool, with a view to their supplying a battery electric locomotive

A view of the rear of the Boiler House in the Power Station complex probably taken about 1935, showing the elevated water storage tank and the railway sidings. Just beyond the chimney is the Engine House, and to its right is the back of the Superintendent's house. Facing the house is the line of the Scotland Street tenements. In the Coal Store under the water tank an additional large drum had been installed to store worn cables prior to disposal, and an independent steam engine was provided to drive the drum. As it was seldom used in that capacity, alternative employment for the engine was found in driving a rope haulage system which moved coal and ash wagons up and down the sidings. Below the right hand end of the leading wagon is a vertical pulley used in this system, and the rope itself, with regularly spaced horizontal pulleys, can just be made out alongside each of the two tracks. The vertical iron ladder is an improvement over the previous access to the roof - see Photo on page 16. *Glasgow Museum of Transport Collection*

capable of 'hauling 10 tons up a gradient of 1 in 16 at 3 mph'. They indicated a budget price of £1,500. As a result, in May 1927 a four wheeled battery locomotive was delivered. This machine had its wheels outside the frames and two longitudinally mounted motors just inside the buffer beams driving a central gear box via cardan shafts. This gear box had an internal chain drive to a cross-shaft, which passed through the frames to external cranks which then drove the wheels through external connecting and coupling rods.[33] The locomotive had a central cab, but as will be seen later it was extensively rebuilt in 1937 or so. The only brake was a hand brake.

The locomotive saved time in the running of the main engines and reduced the amount of overtime for Power Station employees.[15]

Cable trains in Glasgow Corporation Transport service at Kinning Park. The train on this page appears to be fitted with a battery tail light. *The late John Thomas (Glasgow Museum of Transport Collection)*

In the early 1930s thought was given to the exterior headlights on the cars. A firm called Thomas Bishop supplied paraffin headlight cases fitted with new reflectors and cisterns. Six batches of 4 lamps each had been received by October 1930, some of which (probably the first 4) had new burners: further lamps and accessories were received in January 1931.[29] Consideration was given to battery electric lamps about the same time which the manufacturers considered would work for 2 or 3 days between being re-charged. Electric handlamps were provided for the Driver's equipment boxes from late September 1930 in substitution for oil lamps used up to that time. From early October battery tail lamps were provided: in both cases these were re-charged by the Car Sheds Switchboard Attendant to whom they were returned each night. Drivers were issued with their handlamps and Conductors with tail lamps each morning.

The financial performance did not improve under Corporation management, because the increased patronage failed to meet the cost of the improved staff conditions, and the continued high cost of replacement cables etc. In a report in November 1930 the General Manager stated that consideration was being given to replacing the boilers and main engines at the Power Station by 1,700/2,000HP electric motors driving the

existing main shaft:[15] nothing, however, came of this idea. The situation throughout the Transport Department was reviewed for which the General Manager produced a report in December 1931: on the Subway he pointed out that there had been a deficit every year since the Corporation took over, and that the cumulative figure now stood at £184,424 11s 6d. Various options had been considered to reduce the loss: one of those rejected was to operate the system during the peaks only. It was thought this would confuse the public, was unlikely to make matters better, and that it would be better to close the system entirely. Another suggestion was to operate the same number of cars per circle (20), but to form them into six 3-car trains and one 2-car train. A trial had not given promising results, and it was concluded the expense of strengthening the grip gear, the unknown long-term detrimental effect on the cable, and the need to provide repeater signals in the tunnels would render the scheme uneconomic, despite saving twelve traffic staff.[15]

In the same report the General Manager gave details of the service reductions of September 1931 and those eventually implemented in January 1932[8, 15]

These measures, however, had little effect, and the deficits increased by another £176,821 over the next four years.

As a further economy, West Street station was closed on Sundays from 14th February 1932. A public notice advised passengers that 1d tickets issued from Buchanan Street were only valid to Bridge Street and those issued at Cessnock were only valid to Shields Road. A notice to station staffs and conductors included the phrase " . . . and Turnstile Attendants at Cessnock and Buchanan Street must without fail notify the passengers purchasing 1d tickets from these stations that they cannot travel to West Street." A separate notice to gripmen stated:-

> When it is necessary to stop at West Street for the purpose of taking "air", passengers must not be permitted to alight. Gripmen will keep inside sliding doors snibbed and conductors will remain on their own platforms.[6]

The slight down gradient from the Car Sheds pit to Govan Cross station was an occasional source of trouble over the years, and one such incident must have occurred in early June 1932, because a notice to Gripmen was issued from Bath Street on 3rd June as follows:-[6]

NOTICE TO GRIPMEN

INNER CIRCLE

WHEN A DISABLED TRAIN HAS TO BE PROPELLED TO THE CARSHEDS BY THE TRAIN FOLLOWING, THE TWO TRAINS MUST NOT BE UNCOUPLED UNTIL THE DISABLED CAR HAS BEEN PLACED UNDER THE LIFTING SLINGS.

THE PROPELLING TRAIN WILL REMAIN IN THE TUNNEL UNTIL INSTRUCTIONS HAVE BEEN GIVEN TO PROCEED, AND MUST ON NO ACCOUNT BE ALLOWED TO RUN BACK BY GRAVITY TO GOVAN CROSS STATION.

46, BATH STREET,   BY ORDER.
GLASGOW, C. 2.

3RD JUNE, 1932

As will be seen in the next Chapter, cable operations ended on the Inner Circle on 28th March 1935, and on the Outer Circle on Saturday 30th November 1935.

In 1932–34 Hall Telephone Accessories (1928) Ltd supplied seven coin-in-the-slot ticket machines. The first on 5th July 1932, was said to be in an oak case and set up to issue 1d tickets. On 9th July a 1d machine and a 1½d machine were received together with 150,000 1d tickets and 100,000 1½d tickets. In each of August and September a further 1½d machine was received. On 11th June 1934 two further machines (mechanisms only) were received, and on 19th June enamelled plates reading '1½d.' and '1d.' (one of each) and two small plates reading 'PENNIES OR HALFPENNIES' arrived, presumably for the latest two machines. Finally on 5th March 1938 an electric machine was delivered, but the ticket value is not recorded. The fact that the last machine is recorded as "electric" may not exclude the others being electric too.[29] No record has been found as to where these machines were used or the type of ticket they issued.

In January 1933 Automaticket Ltd delivered four 'Autoslot' machines, two for 1d tickets and two for 1½d tickets.[29] Nothing else is known about these either.

In November 1934 it was decided to experiment – probably at Hillhead – with two coin-in-the-slot ticket machines. These were supplied by the Westinghouse Ticket Machine Co, and were delivered on 19th February 1935, complete with enough paper for 180,000 tickets. Further paper was supplied in June 1935 and January 1936. In March 1936 a third machine, and in April a fourth, were delivered, but it is not clear where these were put to work.

Of all these machines, some were installed at Shields Road because on 8th November 1935 the Secretary of the Kingston Ward Committee forwarded a petition by Subway travellers asking 'that the automatic ticket selling machines installed at Shields Road Subway Station be removed and the booking office . . . be re-opened.' The Transport Committee at first turned down the request,[34] but after a further letter and petition it was agreed in September 1936 that the machines '. . . be transferred to Byres Road station (sic) where similar machines are on trial.'[34]

Photographic reproductions, for proof reading purposes, of 1d and 1½d pre-printed tickets have been found. The proofs are for Bridge Street and Cessnock, and are headed "G. C. T. Underground", but no date is evident. This may suggest some of the machines were used at those two stations. (In both cases the 1½d ticket had unlimited travel on one Circle, but the Bridge Street 1d ticket was valid to Kinning Park or Cowcaddens, and the Cessnock one to Merkland Street and West Street). The tickets are about 44mm by 32mm and are not serial numbered.

The Engine House at the Power Station, looking north west. This is one of a series of photographs commissioned by Glasgow Corporation Transport in 1935 to record features of the building before its closure. Just beyond the railed pit is the barring engine, and on either side of it are the clutch drums, one for each Circle. Only the Outer Circle machinery is available for use; the Inner Circle has been converted to electric traction and so the cable has been removed from its drum and pulleys, on the left. *Glasgow Museum of Transport Collection*

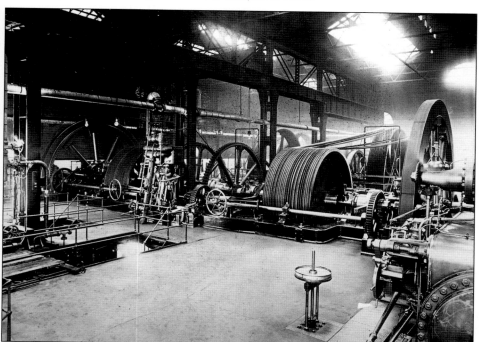

Chapter 5

Electrification, 1932–1940

Whilst employed by the British Thomson Houston Company on the installation of generating plant at the Corporation Tramways' Pinkston Power Station about 1901, Gustavus Frederick Moller had been asked to report to BTH on the possibility of electrifying the Subway. About the same time British Westinghouse (later Metropolitan Vickers) and Bruce Peebles were considering the same thing. Because no motors small enough to fit under the floor of the coaches were available, electric locomotives (presumably similar to the City & South London Railway ones) were being considered. The cost, however, was prohibitive.[1]

The idea was not abandoned: in December 1905 a London firm of Consulting Engineers, Handcock & Dykes, wrote to the Board of Trade on the Company's behalf asking whether, since the Company's 1890 Act said that electricity could be adopted with the sanction of the Board of Trade, it was necessary to apply under the Railways (Electrical Power) Act of 1903. The letter stated that for the scheme being considered it would not be necessary to acquire any more land, and finally asked if it would make any difference 'if the Company purchased its electrical energy instead of generating . . . on its own premises.'[2] The reply was to the effect that the provisions of the 1890 Act were adequate, but that the Board of Trade would need to be 'satisfied as to the details' for the securing of public safety.[2] The Board's main concern was that, although there was a requirement in the 1890 Act for the protection of the Postmaster General and the National Telephone Co., and gas and tramway undertakings, there was no specific mention of electrolytic effects on pipes, cables etc, as covered in the 1903 Act.[2]

In April 1906 it was rumoured that negotiations were in progress between a group of London financiers and electrical engineering experts and the Company for a transference of ownership of the Subway to the financiers with a view to electrification.[3] Nothing came of this.

The Corporation started investigations as to how the system could be electrified before the formalities of takeover of the Subway had been completed in 1923. This was influenced by the Tramways Department's heavy commitment to electric traction, including its own generating station and network of rectifier sub-stations throughout the City, the labour-intensive nature of the Subway operation, and the expansions in progress or planned on the London 'Tube' network.

In a report prepared in February 1922 into the condition and operation of the Subway, James Dalrymple, Tramways Department General Manager, reviewed the options for electrification, should the Corporation decide to purchase the system. Four ideas for rolling stock were suggested:-

Coupling powerful motor bogies ahead of the existing gripper coaches

Using separate locomotives as on the City & South London

Lengthening the gripper coaches by adding a power bogie and equipment compartment at the driving end

Building new power coaches[4]

As described in Chapter 3, W. C. Easton, a consulting Civil Engineer, was appointed to report on future actions, including electrification. He was keen to install standard gauge track, and concluded it would be possible to electrify the system on the 'Central London Railway principle' with centre third rail, involving relatively minor alterations to the tunnels. This would have required new rolling stock. To avoid running the same number of trains all day, he proposed siding loops to both circles near the Car Sheds. These would have had inspection pits, and from there the cars would have been lifted into the sheds. No site could be found for a depot with ramped access which, it was recognised, would have been preferable. The conversion would have meant closure of at least one tunnel at a time for several months. It was estimated the scheme would cost £600,000,[5] later revised to £1,000,000 to cover purchase of property and legal costs etc,[5] but since Government money evidently was not available, the Corporation did not progress to seeking Parliamentary powers.

As mentioned in Chapter 4, replacing the steam engines in the Power Station with electric motors was briefly considered in the early 1930s.

On the retirement of Mr Addison and with effect from 23rd October 1931 Mr W. R. Bruce was appointed Superintendent to oversee the operation of the Subway at a salary of £400 per annum.[7] Mr Bruce had come to the Glasgow Tramways in 1923 when the Paisley District Tramways Company was absorbed. He concluded it might be practicable to convert the existing rolling stock, retain the existing track gauge and fit an outside third rail – a far less grandiose and cheaper scheme than the 1924 proposals.

In November 1931 a sub-committee of the Transport Committee was set up to 'consider and report on the question of underground facilities and as to the expediency of improving the present system . . . and the suggestion by the Manager that the Transport Department be relieved of the constant financial burden imposed on the undertaking by continual operation of the Subway'. This was because the cumulative deficit since 1923 had reached £156,138[6] by 31st May 1930, and £184,424 a year later.[8] This sub-committee recommended in September 1932 'that the suggestion by the Manager to electrify the Subway between Merkland Street and Copland Road stations in the inner circle tunnel as an experiment, at a cost of £1,200, be approved,' – and so it was.[7] The proposal (no doubt originating from Mr Bruce) was to convert one coach to electric traction which would allow detailed designs to be worked out, performance checked, and cost estimates for conversion of the rest of the system to be established.

Electrification Trials

Car 60, the newest in the fleet, was selected for conversion to electric traction: judging by the speed with which the project proceeded the formal approval may have been anticipated. A gripper car was probably selected because the larger end platforms gave more space in the cab for the master controller and for an electrical cubicle on the conductor's rear platform.

Material for the conversion was received between September 1932 and January 1933.[9] Upholstered seats came from G. D. Peters & Co. as did air engine fittings for the gates. Traction equipment and main resistance frames were supplied by Metropolitan-Vickers, but no record has been found of the delivery of wheels, axles, gears or traction motors. GCT was no doubt keen to use standard tram motors for two reasons:-

1. The tried and tested railway traction motors of the day, even for London Tube stock, were too bulky, and were not used with wheels of less than about 36 inch diameter, so something smaller was required.

2. Standardisation with at least part of the tram fleet was desirable.

Prototype and production power bogies: The upper photograph shows the collector shoe side of one of the Car Sheds-built prototype bogies for Car 60. In the lower picture the tripcock and raised track-mounted trainstop arm are shown on the opposite side of a Hurst, Nelson production bogie. The differences in profile of the centres of the side frames are noticeable. The inner end of each bogie is on the left. The live rail insulator stands in the upper photograph are different from the brackets subsequently adopted. *SPT Broomloan Collection*

The existing 5ft wheelbase bogies could not be adapted to take traction motors, so a pair of prototypes with 5ft 6ins wheelbase was built at the Subway Car Sheds.[10] (See photograph above.) These were designed to take two 60 h.p. motors each, but the 27 ins wheel diameter was retained. Unlike the original bogies which had no primary suspension, leaf springs were fitted over the axleboxes: the bogie bolster was supported on nests of coil springs, similar to the arrangement on the original bogies. Likewise, the adaptation of the original underframe was almost certainly done at the Subway Car Sheds. The first recorded delivery of an air compressor is in May 1933, so the car may have been fitted with a second-hand tram one at first. Originally Car 60 retained its painted glass partition screens, and did not have 600 Volt emergency lights. Lighting was still by bare lamp bulbs fed from the T-iron skids. Initially it had only a single headlight, and on the driver's side the circular window above a small rectangular one was retained from cable days – an arrangement which must have given a very restricted view ahead. The car was repainted in scarlet and cream livery with both panels and beading lined out. (See photograph opposite.)

The brake rigging under the car may originally have been something of an improvisation, because on 8th June 1933 a new 8-inch diameter brake cylinder, slotted crosshead, fulcrum bracket and 10-inch diameter by 24 inch auxiliary reservoir were received from the Westinghouse Brake and Saxby Signal Co.[9] The brake cylinder was underframe mounted, and acted on both bogies through pull rods. Tripcock gear and a control governor (the device whereby the car cannot be moved under power until the brake pipe is charged) were not fitted at first, but the first set of such equipment was received on 12th August 1933.[9]

Newly converted for electric traction, prototype Car No.60 has the unusual experience of being photographed in the open air at the north end of the Car Sheds. It retains its single headlight, and is wrong way round on the short stretch of electrified test track, for its current collector shoes are on the opposite side to the live rail. The telegraph pole still exists in 1996, and its location is marked (T) in Figure 5.1 on page 65. *SPT Broomloan Collection*

The driving cab of Car 60 after conversion for electric operation. Above the side window is a Metropolitan-Vickers circuit breaker, to its right in the corner is the air brake system pressure gauge and in the front are the restricted visibility round and oblong windows, with the two detachable doors to their right. From the left, the driving controls consist of the master controller (operated by the driver's left hand), with its spring-loaded deadman's handle, the air brake valve and handle and the handbrake wheel in the corner (with ratchet and 'dog' at the bottom). Later, the cars had a vertical stanchion adjacent to the air brake, from which was mounted a metal screen, partly to discourage passenger interest in the controls, but mainly to protect the driver from draughts from the front doors and the trellis gate. *SPT Broomloan Collection*

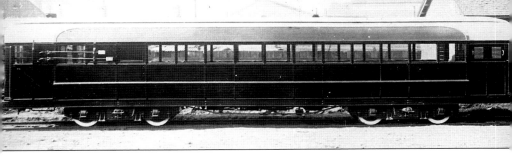

Since all 15 stations had island platforms, the left hand sides of the cars were never seen by the travelling public and were simply painted brown, later dark red. This view of No.60, with the driver's cab at the left hand end, also shows the T-iron skids in their retracted position, the two 'wooden windows', one of which was hinged to allow access to the skids from within, and the removable ventilated panel behind the electro-pneumatic control cubicle at the trailing end. A collector shoe is centrally mounted on the side of each bogie. The truss rods visible between the bogies indicate that the original underframe was adapted, rather than a new one provided as happened with the 'production' power cars, and subsequently with Car 60 as well. *SPT Broomloan Collection*

The adoption of a centre third rail, as envisaged by Mr Easton, was rejected on the grounds that it would not be possible to install it whilst the cable system was still operational. This meant an outside third rail was required, and various methods of support were considered, but the selected method was to use cast iron skewed brackets which supported the rail at a height of about $13\frac{1}{4}$ inches above the surface of the running rail, and some 20 inches outside it. Porcelain insulators were used, but different in form from those on London Underground or the Southern Railway.

Amongst the material required for the conversion of the track were some 440 skewed insulator brackets, some 50 pedestal type insulator stands, and some 654 insulator caps, 202 of which had lugs to anchor the live rail longitudinally. These items were delivered between September and December 1932.[9]

The first trials were in the Car Sheds North Yard where a short length of live rail had been installed,[12] followed by a number of experimental runs between Merkland Street and Copland Road (including Saturday night 11th March 1933) and from these details of the project were worked out. Most of the experimental work could only be done during non-traffic hours – from midnight on Saturday until 3pm on Sunday. For the experimental car to run over the test section hundreds of cable pulleys had to be removed, and replaced in time for the first cable-operated train to start the Inner Circle service on Sunday afternoon. The final test run on Sunday 19th March was with the train loaded with 10 tons of 56 lb weights[13] on loan from W. T. Avery.[9] As a result, the Municipal Transport Committee was given a demonstration run at 10am on Sunday 26th March with photo stops at Merkland Street (photograph opposite) and the Car Sheds pit. The committee must have been favourably impressed both by the demonstration and the electrification proposal submitted, because on 5th April it recommended authority be given to electrify the system at an estimated cost of £94,000. It was assumed there would be a reduction in running costs of £30,000 per year,[12] £10,000 by shutting down the Power Station, £10,000 in annual renewal of cables and £10,000 in other staff savings on train crews and track and rolling stock maintenance.[14] The 10 trains per circle required to provide the cable service with three crew members (gripman, conductor and gate [or 'smoker'] boy) could be reduced to six trains per Circle with two crew members (driver or motorman and conductor). It is likely the outline strategy for converting first one Circle then the other was included in the submission to the Committee. The scheme was to be financed by seeking Parliamentary approval for the

On Sunday 26th May 1933 members of the Municipal Transport Committee were given a demonstration run over the trial section of electrified track, in order to secure their approval of electrification of the whole system. They boarded Car 60 and trailer at the Car Sheds Lifting Pit, and the train then reversed to Merkland Street, where it is pictured prior to the run proper to Govan Cross and Copland Road. In the centre, with light coloured hat and cigar in hand is Lachlan Mackinnon, G.C.T. General Manager. To the left the cable and a pulley can be seen on the Outer Circle track, while to the right of No.60 is part of a large station name panel. Other features are a second station clock, additional to the one facing the stairs, and daylight illumination through the distinctive arches at the north end of the platform chamber.
Robert Grieves Collection

Corporation to borrow an additional £100,000 for transport purposes. At the meeting of the Corporation on 13th April a motion was put to re-consider the electrification in all its aspects, particularly proposals both for the abandonment of the Subway and for extensions to it. This motion was defeated by 78 votes to eight.[15] One of the advantages of the approved scheme over the 1924 proposals was that it avoided the need for buying new rolling stock or changing the track gauge. The fact that the wooden bodies of the coaches had not been subject to the elements no doubt contributed to the practicability of the scheme. In short it was a cut-price, 'no frills' scheme, but nevertheless soundly based, and capable of further development as will be seen later.

A cutting dated 15th March 1933 from a Glasgow newspaper, when circulated in the Ministry of Transport (which when formed in 1919 had taken over the railway interests of the Board of Trade), produced the comment from one Civil Servant: 'As far as I know we have so far heard nothing about this officially'. Whether prompted or not is unclear, but a letter was sent from 46 Bath Street dated 8th May, enclosing a document giving estimates etc. dated 5th April, which must have been one prepared for the Transport Committee deliberations.[16] Having lost the battle to keep the Railway status of the undertaking when the Corporation took over, the Ministry of Transport officials took solace in the fact that Section 29 of the Glasgow Order of 1905 provided 'the tramways shall not be opened for public traffic until the same have been inspected and certified to be fit for such traffic by the Board of Trade.'[16]

The General Manager sent three rolling stock drawings to the Ministry on 17th May, requesting approval 'at the earliest possible date so that the work . . . may be proceeded with.' In response to both communications arrangements were made for a meeting in London with the Inspecting Officers of Railways, and was attended by Messrs Mackinnon and Bruce for GCT and three out of the four Inspecting Officers of Railways, namely: Lt-Colonel Sir Alan H. L. Mount (Chief Inspecting Officer), Colonel A. H. C. Trench and Lt-Colonel Anderson.[16] Amongst matters discussed was the construction of the station platforms – the existing soft timber on brick piers was not in accordance with the Ministry's requirements on the grounds of fire risk, and the pitch pine treads on the platform access stairs were also unacceptable. In discussing the signalling the Inspectorate insisted on the provision of trainstops.[17] An outcome of the meeting was that Lt-Colonel Anderson and Colonel Trench, accompanied by Messrs Mackinnon and Bruce, visited the system on Sunday morning 18th June 1933,[16] to see it in its existing condition and to inspect the experimental length of track. The inspection consisted of two return trips on Car 60, when speeds of up to 26mph were achieved, followed by a trip round the Outer Circle in a trailer car propelled by the battery locomotive.[16]

Amongst other things the Inspecting Officers noted that the new steel wheels on Car 60 had flanges only 1 inch deep, and that the gates closed rather more powerfully than in London. They recommended use of wheels with railway style thick flanges to reduce the risk of derailment, and adjustment to the gate engines.[16] They were also critical of the barriers at station entrances erected at Colonel Yorke's instigation: they considered they represented a hazard if the station had to be evacuated in the event of fire. They noted that the Corporation's experiments with automatic ticket machines mentioned in Chapter 4, if successful, could assist in improving free egress in emergency.[16] They reported that: 'generally . . . the interior of the brick and concrete tunnels appeared to be in good order in spite of its age, a remarkable example, by comparison with other tunnels, of the deteriorating effect of the use of steam engines. Galvanised iron plates have been fixed to the soffit of the arch in some places to prevent leakage water dripping on to the rails. It would be desirable to remove these and stop the leakage by other means if possible . . . so that there is no possible chance of their falling and causing a short-circuit.'[16] Because of the requirement to alter the platforms, stairways etc. it was necessary for the additional borrowing powers to be increased to £150,000.[15] In preparation for the opening of the Inner Circle with electric traction, the trial length was used for driver training on Sunday mornings, though it was clearly very limited in scope.[16]

Car Sheds Extension

Because the bulk of the conversion work was to be done by direct labour at the Car Sheds, the under-cover accommodation had to be increased. This was achieved by extending the building into part of the open yard to the north, and involved:-[18]

> Removal of a lean-to building with six double leaf wooden doors across the north end of the West and Centre bays of the main building, but leaving the section of lean-to across the end of the East bay; building a northward extension some 130ft long to the West and Centre bays: the North gable and West wall to be brick and the East wall coated with corrugated iron. The greater part of the length of the Centre bay extension was to be higher and equipped with crane rails (but a crane was never fitted); construction of three inspection pits in the Centre bay extension; the building of an enclosed two-road paint shop at the northern end of the West bay; and strengthening crane rails in the original lifting bay.

On 1st November it was announced Brown, Fraser & Co. had won the contract at a price of £5,201.[15]

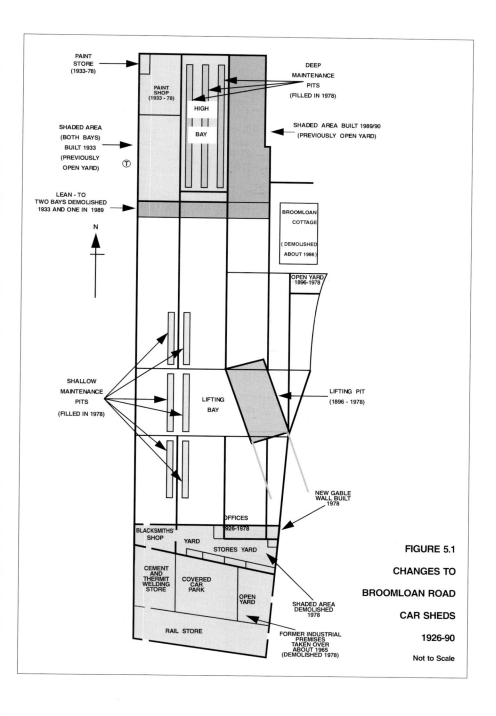

PAINT STORE (1933-78)

PAINT SHOP (1933 - 78)

HIGH

BAY

DEEP MAINTENANCE PITS (FILLED IN 1978)

SHADED AREA (BOTH BAYS) BUILT 1933 (PREVIOUSLY OPEN YARD)

SHADED AREA BUILT 1989/90 (PREVIOUSLY OPEN YARD)

LEAN - TO TWO BAYS DEMOLISHED 1933 AND ONE IN 1989

N

BROOMLOAN COTTAGE (DEMOLISHED ABOUT 1986)

OPEN YARD 1896-1978

SHALLOW MAINTENANCE PITS (FILLED IN 1978)

LIFTING BAY

LIFTING PIT (1896 - 1978)

NEW GABLE WALL BUILT 1978

OFFICES 1926-1978

BLACKSMITHS' SHOP

YARD

STORES YARD

CEMENT AND THERMIT WELDING STORE

COVERED CAR PARK

OPEN YARD

SHADED AREA DEMOLISHED 1978

RAIL STORE

FORMER INDUSTRIAL PREMISES TAKEN OVER ABOUT 1965 (DEMOLISHED 1978)

FIGURE 5.1

CHANGES TO

BROOMLOAN ROAD

CAR SHEDS

1926-90

Not to Scale

65

In July 1934 tender enquiries were issued to replace the 12-ton overhead crane. Sir William Arrol received this order and, on completion, the Safe Working Load became 22½ tons. A new lifting cradle had been acquired in November 1932 from Fleming Brothers – presumably because the old one could not cope with Car 60.

An electrically driven capstan with foot pedal control was installed in the original lifting bay for shunting cars at ground level in August 1935.[9] This was preferable in the circumstances to the 600-Volt overhead trolley jumper system used in London Transport and Southern Railway Depots whereby a cable suspended from a trolley is plugged into a socket on the car, which can then be moved under its own power. Both the crane and capstan had 600 Volt d.c. motors, and, together with the lifting cradle, remained in use until after closure of the system for modernisation in 1977.

Preparations for Converting the Fleet.

At this stage it is almost certain it was intended to retain only ex-gripper cars, 19 as motor coaches and 17 as trailers. Tenders were invited in September 1933 and February 1934 for equipment to convert 19 cars to electric motor cars as follows:-

- 19 steel underframes;

- 38 power bogies;

- traction equipment for motor coaches (quantities not specified but probably 19 sets.)

- 20 sets of pneumatic door engine equipment;

- 20 sets of air brake equipment.

The traction equipment specification included the following passage:-

Each set . . . shall be capable of accelerating a train consisting of one motor coach and one trailing coach, weighing approximately 32 tons, when loaded, at a rate of not less than 2 miles per hour per second from rest, up to a speed of 15 miles per hour over a level track with clean dry rail, and thereafter at a diminishing rate of acceleration to a free running speed of 30 miles per hour, with a line pressure of 550 Volts. The average rate of acceleration . . . must be such that a schedule speed of at least 17 miles per hour can be maintained over the Subway route. Stops of an average duration of 15 seconds are made at all stations. The average rate of retardation during braking is 2·75 miles per hour per second. Braking is by compressed air and acts on all wheels (motor coach and trailer).[18]

In November 1933 Hurst, Nelson of Motherwell won the contract for the underframes and bogies, the latter at a contract price of £3,329 15s[15] and later the same month the offer of £11,400 from Metropolitan-Vickers for traction equipment was accepted.[19] Westinghouse Brake and Saxby Signal Co. received the order for the air brake equipment and put in the lowest offer for the door – or more accurately "gate" – gear: however the order was placed with the firm putting in the second lowest bid – G. D. Peters. Surprisingly, since non-metallic brake blocks had been in use from at least March 1930, the bogie specification called for cast iron brake blocks, but the contract was probably altered before delivery.

The production motor bogies were built to the same drawings as the prototypes, but with some minor modifications. The shape of the top frame member was altered to eliminate the abrupt change in section as the photographs on page 60 show. Plain bearing oil-lubricated axleboxes were retained – roller bearing boxes did not come until the 1950s. Various templates, patterns etc., used for the conversion of Car 60 were loaned to Hurst, Nelson.[9]

There was one current collector shoe per bogie, on the non-platform (or T-iron) side: these ran on the top of the live rail and were continuously supported by it. They were spring loaded to give a downward force of 20 lbs.[14] to maintain firm contact with the rail and reduce arcing.

From the shoes current passed to the electrical control cubicle on the Conductor's platform at the rear of the car. That cubicle contained nine electro-pneumatic contactors (called unit switches in Underground parlance), motor reverser switches, a control rheostat, a limiting (or notching) relay, isolating switches and fuses for certain circuits. The main resistance grids were arranged in two banks on the underframe between the bogies. The master controller, incorporating a deadman's handle, was worked by the driver's left hand: it had "shunt", "series" and "parallel" positions, but notching (and hence acceleration) within the series and parallel ranges controlled automatically by the limiting relay. The master controller in the driver's cab and the equipment in the control cubicle were connected by control wiring which derived its voltage from a rheostat in the cubicle: unlike more modern stocks (including the present Glasgow Underground stock) there was no battery. The equipment was conventional by mid-1930s practice, although the layout was somewhat unusual. The control cubicle gave excellent access to the components and wiring within it, as there were pairs of removable panels both inside and outside the car.

There were four MV101DR motors connected in permanent parallel pairs in the then-normal axle-hung nose-suspended layout. The motors drove the wheels through 14-tooth pinions and 61-tooth gear wheels on the axles. When the master controller was placed in the 'shunt' position the motor pairs were connected in series with all resistance in circuit: when the controller handle was moved to the 'series' position, the five sections of resistance were successively cut out automatically as speed built up under the control of the limiting relay. When the master controller handle was moved to the 'parallel' position, the power circuit passed through a 'transition' step, whilst the motors were re-connected in parallel and four of the five sections of resistance were put back into circuit, then in three further steps progressively cut out the resistance again. The traction current return was through the wheels and axles to both running rails. (See Figure 5.2). The cars were not strictly multiple units, since each master controller only operated equipment on its own car, and traction control train lines were not required, as there was only one power car per train. Two 6-core jumpers with Reyrolle plugs and sockets at each end were provided between power and trailer cars. That on the non-platform side supplied the 600 Volt d.c. lighting circuits on the trailer, and the 250 Volt a.c. lighting circuits on the motor car from the T-iron skids on the trailer car: the jumper on the platform side was for gate control and indication circuits.

Brakes

As before, the two-pipe Westinghouse automatic air brake system was used, this time supplied with air from a 600-Volt motor-driven DH25 compressor under the car. This machine had horizontal cylinders, so was much 'flatter' than earlier designs of air compressor, which allowed it to be fitted under low-floored vehicles. The driver's brake valve was positioned for use by the driver's right hand. There was one brake cylinder per car mounted on the underframe beside the resistance grids, working one block per wheel through rigging. A tripcock[17] was provided on the right hand side of the front bogie of each power car: unlike most others (including on the modernised Glasgow Underground) the type of tripcock used did not have a re-setting mechanism, and since it could not be re-set from inside the train, the practice was to *isolate* it if a train was tripped, and re-set it and normalise the isolation the next time the train passed the Car Sheds Pit.

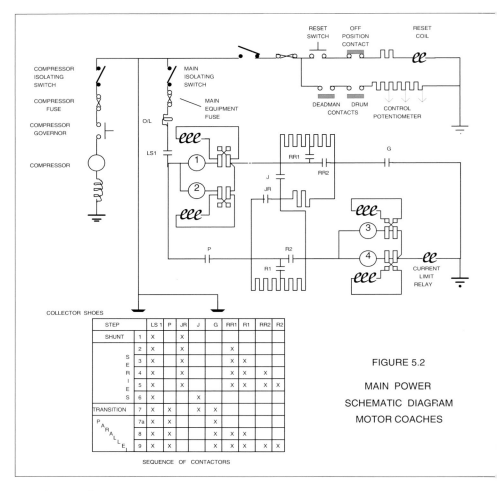

STEP		LS 1	P	JR	J	G	RR1	R1	RR2	R2
SHUNT	1	X		X						
S E R I E S	2	X		X			X			
	3	X		X			X	X		
	4	X		X			X	X	X	
	5	X		X			X	X	X	X
	6	X			X					
TRANSITION	7	X	X	X	X					
P A R A L L E L	7a	X	X			X				
	8	X	X				X	X	X	
	9	X	X				X	X	X	X

SEQUENCE OF CONTACTORS

FIGURE 5.2

MAIN POWER

SCHEMATIC DIAGRAM

MOTOR COACHES

Delivery of First Production Equipment

The traction motors, underframes and power bogies were delivered between March and October 1934. Six underframes were originally delivered to Barrland Street (Tramway) Permanent Way Depot, presumably because there was insufficient storage space at Broomloan Road.[9]

Twenty trailer bogie sets of brake gear – fulcrum levers, pull rods, etc. – were received in two consignments from R. Y. Pickering Ltd on 12th November and 3rd December 1934.[9] This was part of an order for 34 bogie sets.

The contract for 35 coach sets of leather (i. e. hide covered) seats and bucket backs was initially awarded to G. D. Peters,[19] but the local branch of the National Union of Vehicle Builders drew attention to the alleged unfair wages paid by that firm, and the contract was rescinded and awarded to Bennett Furnishing[19] who delivered the seats between January and June 1935.[9] Fourteen 3-seater cushion and back units were used in each short saloon (i.e. ex-gripper) car, red leather being used in motor cars and brown in trailers.

Ninety-six new 4-inch diameter axles with Millar 27-inch diameter chilled iron[20] double plate wheels were delivered between November 1934 and February 1937[9] for use on trailer cars. Although the motor cars had steel wheel centres with steel tyres shrunk on, the old-fashioned practice of using chilled iron for wheels was not finally abandoned in favour of steel on the trailer cars until the late-1960s.

Following the electrification decision, consideration had to be given to up-grading and modernising the 'way and works', and to automating the signalling system. Broadly the work could be divided as follows:-

1. Providing a traction power distribution system and live rails;

2. Upgrading the track to take heavier axle loads and higher speeds;

3. Providing an automatic colour-light signalling system with train stops;

4. Improving the safety of stations by removing timber platforms;

5. General improvement at stations.

Electricity Supply and Distribution

It was decided that traction power should be derived from the Tramway rectifier sub-stations at Dalhousie Street, Kinning Park (Seaward Street) and Partick (Benalder Street). These received an alternating current (ac) supply at 6,600 Volts 25 cycles per second (Hz) from the Department's Pinkston generating station alongside the Cowlairs incline on the railway line out of Queen Street (High Level) station. The supply was transformed and rectified to 600 Volts direct current (d. c.) in the sub-stations by means of rotary converters. Cables were run from the nearest sub-station to a green-painted cast iron traction pillar outside Cowcaddens (Dalhousie Street), Shields Road (Kinning Park), and Partick Cross (Partick) stations. For the positive feeders two 0·6 in² cables were run in parallel from the sub-stations to traction pillars outside the respective station entrances, and for the negatives there was a single 1·0 in² cable: these traction pillars contained knife switches of isolation purposes. The negative cable was jointed in the traction pillar to become two parallel 0·4 in² cables onwards to the running rails. Each sub-station fed about one third of the system by ring main cable, and each passenger station had switchgear feeding the live rails in two sections of tunnel, one on the Inner Circle and one on the Outer Circle, towards the next station in advance in each case. For all stations to receive a traction supply 600-Volt ring main cable was run round the system: this was in the Inner Circle tunnel, the one scheduled for conversion first, and looped into each station. The cable used was manufactured by the Craigpark Electrical Cable Co. Ltd, and was 0·6 in² single core cross section.

The four running rails were bonded together at 100 yard intervals where cross-passages between the tunnels permitted, and as close as possible to that standard elsewhere. The object was to limit the negative voltage drop to about 7 Volts to prevent trouble from electrolysis on water mains, gas pipes, etc. close to the tunnels.[16]

It was confirmed on 22nd November 1933 that British Thomson-Houston (BTH) had been successful in their bid for station switchboard panels.[19]

The station switchgear was mounted on 2ft 6in wide by 2in thick slate panels supported on a steel framework which formed a division between a specially constructed Station Masters office and Signal Relay Room at the end of each platform.

The upper panel was 2ft high, and the lower one 3ft high. Two circuit breakers were mounted side by side on the top panel, the one on the left supplying the Inner Circle, and the one on the right the Outer. These circuit breakers incorporated a handle for setting them by hand: tripping could be done either remotely by the tunnel telephone

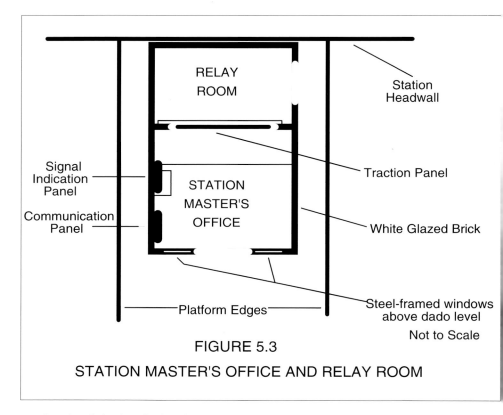

FIGURE 5.3

STATION MASTER'S OFFICE AND RELAY ROOM

wires (see below), or by hand using the same handle. Between the two circuit breakers there was a large fuse carrier for station emergency lighting and pump supplies etc. (Further circuits of lighting were from the public a.c. supply.) On the lower panel there were two rows of knife switches, hinged at the bottom, and with handles at the top. The upper row (which were slightly smaller) consisted of four track feeder switches, with a station supply switch in the centre: the lower switches were in the ring main, and controlled the supply to the panel. There was a considerable amount of metalwork on the front of the panel which was 'live' during normal operation, the only physical protection being a horizontal wooden pole with a framed 'Danger keep clear' notice hung on it! The switchgear was delivered in two consignments in March 1934,[9] and it is likely it was installed during traffic hours by direct labour.

The circuit breakers were arranged for remote tripping in emergency from bare wires stretched along the tunnels on the opposite side from the T-irons. These wires were supplied from a 12-Volt battery in each station, and when short circuited by a telephone handset, the trip coil of the appropriate station circuit breaker was energised which in turn opened the circuit breaker contacts. A relay controlled this, set up a speech circuit to the Station Master's office in rear, and sounded a klaxon when either circuit breaker opened. It was only after cases of damage to electrical conduit containing telephone circuit wiring and the like running above the roof of the Station Master's Office (or 'box' as it was more often known in Underground parlance) that arc chutes were provided for these circuit breakers.[21]

These two 1977 photographs were taken at Merkland Street just before the Glasgow Museum of Transport dismantled the stationmaster's office and relay room. *Left* Looking through the entrance doorway towards the traction panel, a wooden pole is the only barrier between occupants and the 600 volt circuit breakers and fuses. *Right* Having entered, on the left-hand wall is the telephone communications panel and the signal indication panel with the desk beneath it. The wooden pole mentioned above runs alongside the desk. *Glasgow Museum of Transport*

It has been claimed that the installation of at least some of the tunnel telephone wires was carried out during traffic hours, with the men concerned taking refuge in the cross-passages between tunnels to allow trains to pass.[22]

Many of the switching operations were carried out by the Station Masters, particularly re-setting the circuit breakers if they had opened on overload due to a faulty train motor or similar defect. During traffic hours the advance feed knife switches were closed and the rear feed switches were open (though initially it had been intended that both should be closed). One of the lower group of switches was kept open at the boundary stations between sub-station areas to avoid paralleling up two or more sub-stations which could have resulted in considerable current flows through the ring main cable due to imbalances in the tramway system.

After the last Inner Circle train at night, Station Masters would open the circuit breaker and then open the advance feed knife switch to make the Inner Circle safe for the Permanent Way Section to work. A 'Cash' Train normally ran on the Outer Circle after the last passenger train, to pick up the day's takings and keys from each station, so Station Masters would close the rear feed switches and open the advance feed switches after the last passenger train, so that the personnel on the cash train could open the circuit breaker and rear feed switch on arrival at each station and leave the tunnel 'dead' behind them. (It also meant that the Station Master could leave his station as soon as the Cash train had left, and not have to wait for its arrival at the next station in advance before switching off!) If movement of works trains requiring traction current was scheduled, a 'broadcast' was put out from the Car Sheds to notify Station Masters of the arrangements. (Works trains involving one of the bogie wagons invariably consisted of a motor coach hauling the wagon: the battery locomotive could only handle one of the four-wheeled wagons on the steep gradients under the Clyde and at Shields Road. Its usual partner was a small wooden wagon with one dropside, no brakes, and no springing known both as the 'wee wagon' and 'the tumbril': latterly at least its wheels did not all match, some having curved spokes and some straight!)

In the morning a 'staff' train ran round the Inner Circle to take drivers and others to Govan, leaving the pit area at 5.20am and a 'key' train ran round the Outer Circle delivering the station keys. Invariably by the 1960s at least, the staff train was driven by a Car Sheds Electrician, and on reaching each station the advance switches were put in on both Circles, ready for start of traffic.[23]

The Track

There were three main difficulties with the track:-

• sub-standard creosoted soft-wood sleepers;[16]

• too light a rail section to accept the heavier axle loads of the motor cars compared with the grippers; and

• dirty ballast impeding efficient drainage.

It was decided to replace the 60lb/yard flat-bottomed rail with British Standard Section 80R flat-bottomed rail of 80lb/yard weight. As originally laid this was jointed with mainly 6-hole fishplates and $7/8$ in diameter square headed bolts. The majority of the rail, was in 30ft lengths, but some 11% came 29ft 9in long. All was rolled by the Steel Company of Scotland and, together with the fishplates, was delivered between October 1933 and April 1934.[9]

Suitable lengths of the displaced 60 lb/yard rail were used as live rail. One of the difficulties during the trials had been to find a suitable position and method of support for the live rail. The position used in the trial was adopted as standard with similar skewed brackets and porcelain insulators. The insulators were attached to the brackets by inverted "U" bolts. The live rail brackets were fixed to steel sleepers which were placed at every fifth position – i. e there were four timber sleepers between successive steel ones. There was a 'dead' section of live rail at the approach to each station. This was about 25ft long – just over the shoe span of a motor coach – and ensured that a train could not bridge between two feeding sections.

There was a short section of live rail on each Circle at the Car Sheds pit which was controlled independently from the rest of the Copland Road to Govan Cross Section, and each had its own circuit breaker on the South headwall of the pit. These were controlled by Car Sheds personnel when cars were being lifted and lowered.

Two designs of pressed steel sleeper were produced, both made by Colvilles. Hardwood sleepers were either bevel ended, to fit into the cast iron segmented tunnel sections, or square ended for other sections, and were supplied by A. & J. Begg. The foot of the running rail was drilled and coach-bolted to the timber sleepers, alternately on the inside and outside of the rail web.

Check rails (i. e. an additional rail attached on the inside of the inside rail of a curve to bear on the back of the wheel flanges to reduce wear on the outside rail of the curve) were added to two curves of under 5 chain radius on the Inner Circle – i. e. at Bridge Street and Cowcaddens – before it was converted to electric traction.[16]

The Inspecting Officers recommended cleaning of the ballast once the cables had been removed, and, once the pulleys had been removed and the drains straightened, new ballast added to bring the level up to the sleeper tops to give an unimpeded evacuation route.[16] Considerable quantities of whin ballast were brought in for this purpose.[9] An open drum concrete mixer with 4 h.p. electric motor 'arranged for bogie mounting' was received in March 1934.[9]

In April 1938 authority was given to experiment with the Thermit welding of rails 'in an endeavour to decrease the noise and make for smoother running'.[24, 25] During the 1939–40 period the running rails were welded on site using the Thermit process, making the system one of the earliest railways to have continuously welded rail.

Signalling System

The original signalling system based on semaphore arms operated by the Station Masters was not considered adequate to cope with the additional traffic envisaged, and no doubt caused some concern to the Railway Inspectorate. It was clear that a modern automatic colour light system was required incorporating trainstops, which when raised engaged the tripcock arm on any train attempting to pass that signal, and fully applied the air brake on the train. There is no record whether track circuits were considered, but the decision to use steel sleepers at current rail bracket positions ruled out the possibility. An ingenious scheme retaining the T-irons, and adapting them to work the signalling automatically as well as supplying the car lighting was worked out and sent to the Railway Inspectorate for comment and approval in the Autumn of 1933. The Inspectorate asked for an additional relay in each section, making four instead of three as originally proposed. This idea was accepted and developed.

The scheme involved converting the original T-iron system from d.c., fed from the Subway Power Station, to a 250-Volt 50 cycle per second a.c. supply from the public network at each station: at that stage Pinkston operated at 25 cycles. Thought was probably given to adopting a 110-Volt 50 c. p. s. system, because a sample single element vane relay and trainstop wound to this voltage were acquired from the British Power Signalling Co. in November 1933, but the idea was not proceeded with.

The bottom T-iron had a 90ft. long insulated section cut into it at the notional braking distance past each signal: in most cases this was 200 ft, but was extended because of steep falling gradients leaving stations as follows:-[26]

Bridge Street	(Inner) 400ft	Govan Cross	(Outer) 600ft
Buchanan Street	(Inner) 400ft	Cowcaddens	(Outer) 400ft
Partick Cross	(Inner) 400ft	St Enoch	(Outer) 400ft
Merkland Street	(Inner) 600ft		

This 90 foot long insulated section was known as the 'clearing section'. The upper lengths of 'T-iron' were supplied from a phase connection off each station's domestic supply, but insulated at intervals so as not to parallel up the station electricity supplies. The main length of the bottom T-iron was connected through the coil of a vane relay known as the 'Blocking Relay'. The bottom T-iron in the clearing section was similarly attached to the coil of the 'Clearing Relay' – also of the single element vane type.

The current for the lighting load on a train passed from the upper T-iron through the top skid on the trailer coach, through the lighting circuit of both cars, through the bottom skid, bottom T-iron and the appropriate relay coil, thereby energising the relay. The blocking and clearing relays were of the Westinghouse 'H2' type (square in shape). The other two relays were of the 'jam jar' type and were respectively the Signal Relay (energised to give a green aspect), and the Proving Relay.

This piece of demonstration track shows two of the components used in the 1935 resignalling. On the left-hand rail is the treadle, which was depressed by the wheel flange on the train's leading axle and caused the adjacent signal to change to red and the trainstop arm, just outside the right hand rail, to rise to the position shown by the action of an electric motor in the box mounted between the rails. The flat bottomed 80R section rail is seen. If a train attempted to pass a red signal, the raised trainstop would strike the train's tripcock arm (illustrated on page 60) knocking it back, thus opening an air valve, which applied the brakes and brought the train to a halt. A similar system is used on the modernised Underground.
SPT Broomloan Collection

When a train left a station it operated a track treadle (see photograph above) which put the signal it had just passed to red and raised the trainstop: that signal could not go back to green until the train had drawn current from the next clearing section, typically beyond the next station. The blocking relay was arranged to illuminate a yellow lamp above the Station Master's Office when energised – i. e. when a train was approaching – so this was known as the 'Announcer' light. The station destination indicators fitted at the time of electrification were originally internally illuminated, and lit up when the announcer light came on.

Two specifications covered the supply of signalling equipment, one covering relays, trainstops, treadles and Station Master's signal indication panels, and the other for the supply of two- and three-aspect signal lanterns.

The bulk of this equipment was delivered by the Westinghouse Brake & Saxby Signal Co. between late May and early July 1934[9] under a contract authorised in December 1933.[19] A separate contract, authorised in February 1934 covered spare equipment[19] – two each of the four types of relay, a track treadle and a trainstop – delivered in early July 1934.

The signal lanterns were supplied by the British Power & Railway Signalling Co. The initial contract was for 30 of the two-aspect (green over red) type, and three 3-aspect signals (green over yellow over red) for use on either side of the Car Sheds pit, one at Govan Cross on the Inner Circle, one at Copland Road on the Outer Circle, and one on the Outer Circle some 1,600 ft on the pit side of Copland Road. Calling-on aspects, consisting of a back-lit letter 'C', were also provided some 75ft on the pit side of the 3-aspect signals at Govan Cross (Inner) and the intermediate between Copland Road and the Car Sheds pit on the Outer Circle. These aspects were operated by Car Sheds Electricians from a hut in the pit, and authorised a train to enter a section already occupied by trains, and were mainly used at the close of traffic.

The trainstops were of the Westinghouse 'F2' type, which were used on the Edgware extension of the Hampstead Tube. An electric motor drove the arm down when the signal cleared to green, and on reaching its lowered position, switched over to holding coils to keep it down against a large spring which caused the arm to rise when the holding coils were de-energised or there was loss of electrical supply. The motor, spring, and switching contacts were in a large cast-iron box positioned between the running rails, with the shaft to the arm passing under the right-hand running rail (see above photograph).

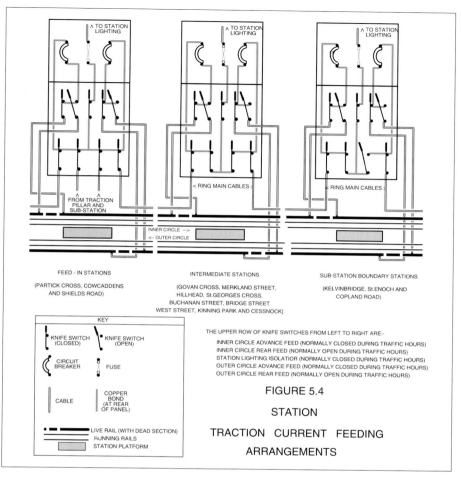

FEED - IN STATIONS

(PARTICK CROSS, COWCADDENS
AND SHIELDS ROAD)

INTERMEDIATE STATIONS

(GOVAN CROSS, MERKLAND STREET,
HILLHEAD, St.GEORGES CROSS,
BUCHANAN STREET, BRIDGE STREET
WEST STREET, KINNING PARK AND CESSNOCK]

SUB-STATION BOUNDARY STATIONS

(KELVINBRIDGE, St.ENOCH AND
COPLAND ROAD)

KEY

KNIFE SWITCH (CLOSED)
KNIFE SWITCH (OPEN)
CIRCUIT BREAKER
FUSE
CABLE
COPPER BOND (AT REAR OF PANEL)
LIVE RAIL (WITH DEAD SECTION)
RUNNING RAILS
STATION PLATFORM

THE UPPER ROW OF KNIFE SWITCHES FROM LEFT TO RIGHT ARE:-

INNER CIRCLE ADVANCE FEED (NORMALLY CLOSED DURING TRAFFIC HOURS)
INNER CIRCLE REAR FEED (NORMALLY OPEN DURING TRAFFIC HOURS)
STATION LIGHTING ISOLATIOR (NORMALLY CLOSED DURING TRAFFIC HOURS)
OUTER CIRCLE ADVANCE FEED (NORMALLY CLOSED DURING TRAFFIC HOURS)
OUTER CIRCLE REAR FEED (NORMALLY OPEN DURING TRAFFIC HOURS)

FIGURE 5.4

STATION

TRACTION CURRENT FEEDING

ARRANGEMENTS

A panel giving a series of signalling system indications for each Circle and emergency trainstop lowering switches – the latter normally sealed – was provided in each Station Master's 'box'. A similar panel was provided in the hut under the stairs in the Car Sheds Pit from where trains were 'called on' for parking at night.

The Craigpark Electrical Co. supplied the Signalling and Telephone cable on 16 drums between February and April 1934.[9]

On their inspection of the Inner Circle on 3rd March 1935 the Inspecting Officers pointed out that since the trainstop and tripcock were so important, it followed that the tripcock should be checked at frequent intervals,[16] so a tripcock tester was acquired from London Passenger Transport Board in April 1935 for installation on the Inner Circle at Copland Road: this proved the tripcock arm on every passing train to be in its correct position. Subsequently one was put on the Outer Circle at Govan.

Fixed tunnel lighting was not installed at the time of the electrification, but since the T-irons were normally energised continuously, they formed a useful power source for night-time maintenance operations, particularly lighting.

Stations

The platforms had to be resurfaced to eliminate the wooden planking, and the Signal Relay Room-cum-Station Master's Office built at the end remote from the access stairs. At least new stair steps, and in some cases the whole stairway structure, were renewed. All the platforms remained of the island type of original width and length.

The material chosen for the platform surfaces was ferro-crete slabs, which were laid by direct labour. The Station Master's Office structure was built from white glazed bricks, and was done under contract to a specification issued in September 1933.

The gantry-mounted destination indicators above the centre of the platforms were renewed, and new clocks supplied by Gent Limited of the 'Pul-Syn-Etic' type operated from a master pendulum clock at Kinning Park were fitted.

Converting the Rolling Stock – the First Phase.

Since the electrification programme was done without closure of either Circle, sufficient cars had to remain available for cable operation as the conversion proceeded: the Inner Circle was dealt with first. To keep a balance of Inner and Outer Circle cars available, four odd-numbered and three-even numbered gripper cars (in addition to Car 60) were selected for conversion to motors to work on the Inner Circle when it started electric operation. Dates, believed to be those on which conversion was completed, are given in Appendix 6. The cars were virtually identical to Car 60 in appearance after conversion, except that they had double headlights placed one above the other on the non-driving side, there was a 600-Volt interior emergency lighting circuit, and the painted internal partition glasses were replaced by uncoloured patterned panes.

Newly converted electric motor car No.24 receives an inspection and polish in the Car Sheds early in March 1935, in preparation for the start of electric service on the Inner Circle on Sunday 31st March. The original small headlamp has been replaced by a pair of larger and more powerful lights, the upper fed with direct current from the live rail and the lower using alternating current from the T-irons on the tunnel walls. The separate round and oblong front windows on the driver's side remain, but at a later date the dividing woodwork will be removed to allow better visibility. The handle of the tripcock isolating cock is to the left of the left foot of the man attending to the headlight. No.24 is standing on what is No.17 Road today, and the high roof and heavy girders intended to support the rails of an overhead travelling crane – planned, but never installed – are noticeable. *Evening Times*

Meanwhile Car 6 was re-axled and re-wheeled and emerged as a trailer coach on 2nd March 1935, and Car 60, which of course already had been converted for electric operation, was given new wheels and axles on 22nd March – no doubt in response to the Inspecting Officer's comment on flange depth already noted.

Inspections by Railway Inspectorate

In preparation for the public opening Colonel Mount, the Chief Inspecting Officer, and Colonel Trench, the nominated Inspecting Officer of Railways for the project, made an inspection on Sunday 3rd March which 'dealt with the structural condition of the tunnel, the reconstruction of the permanent way and the third rail . . . the signalling arrangements generally, and the power control arrangements in stations. Also the reconstruction of the stations to render them adequately fire proof, and finally a brief inspection of the new rolling stock'. The Inspecting Officers considered that at least two of the motor coaches should be fitted with speedometers and that all motormen should have some instruction on these during the trial running period[16] – this was tried but was not satisfactory.[27] They also suggested that 'gradient notice boards should be provided in tunnels at all important changes of gradient',[16] and that was done, some of the notices still surviving at the time of writing (September 1996).

For the change-over on the Inner Circle it was proposed to withdraw the pulleys and rope on Sunday 24th March, and to arrange for drivers to work electric trains on the Monday. The line would be ready for inspection by Lt-Colonel Mount and Colonel Trench the following day. It was the intention to continue the practice running on the Wednesday, and open the Inner Circle for public traffic on Thursday 28th. The Fire-master arranged inspection of all appliances on the Monday. Colonel Trench detailed his plans in a letter dated 22nd March saying on the Tuesday morning he and Colonel Mount would like to see the driver practice service in operation, watch the signalling, and take some trips on the trains. He continued 'Thereafter . . . you should stop this instructional service about 11am so that we can have a full and unhampered occupation of the majority of the Circle for further trials of one train, fully loaded (with sand bags, brake blocks etc) to the equivalent of a packed Saturday afternoon train, the trials being mainly in connection with: (a) normal operation of the brakes, (b) emergency and trainstop operation of the brakes and (c) starting on one or two of the steepest gradients.

'If we cannot do all the trials we want on one trip round the Circle, we would then abandon the fully laden train which would be at the tail of the queue (at the Car Sheds Pit), and walk forward to an ordinary train at the head of the queue and go on again. I shall remain in Glasgow . . . with a view to looking at the rolling stock and a number of other points . . .'[16] Just before Colonel Trench left on the Wednesday a train broke down and had to be propelled (pushed) to the Car Sheds by the following train, but he could not wait to see if the operation was successful, which in fact it was. A number of Councillors and members of the Press visited the system on the Wednesday, an event which went off without a hitch. Colonel Trench submitted a brief report recommending approval on 28th (by which time it had been decided to defer the public opening) but also recommending a temporary speed restriction of 20mph throughout. The main reason for this was concern about the structural integrity of the tunnel in places, and worries about the track stability in other areas because of water inflow: the solution was seen to be concreting the track on the sharper curves and the worst areas of water penetration, after which the speed limit could be reviewed. The Corporation had decided against widespread replacement of the ballast formation by concrete to save cost. A copy of this report, together with a 'certificate permitting opening of the Inner Circle . . . subject to certain conditions' was sent to GCT on 29th March.[16, 19] In fact public electric operation did not start until 31st March.

Colonel Trench noticed that shoe fuses were not fitted and that main cables under the seats of the motor coaches were protected by rubber hose: he was unhappy about this, and discussed the matter with London Underground personnel, and, having done so, wrote on 30th March to say that the shoe fuse was of doubtful value, but that as far as possible all cables, and especially unfused lengths of main cables, should be carried in heavy gauge steel conduit, which is effectively earthed to the body of the car. He continued 'if there is to be a short circuit it is much better to ensure that it will be heavy enough to pull out the breaker at once, rather than . . . setting fire to insulation and causing smoke.'[16.] GCT responded on 9th April saying: 'arrangements have been made to cover all the main cables with armoured flexible hose. Some of this work has already been done, and the remainder will be completed without delay.'[16]

Public Electric Service Starts

The electric service on the Inner Circle started on Sunday 31st March 1935, apparently without ceremony. The Mondays to Fridays service was provided by seven trains,[28] there were six trains on Saturdays and six or seven over a shorter working day on Sundays. Eight motor coaches (Nos. 2, 3, 11, 12, 15, 24, 25 and 60) were available for this: it is not clear what the trailer car position was, other than Car 6 being available, but it is probable that some ex-gripper cars and possibly even some ex-4-wheel trailers had been adapted though not fully re-conditioned.

The Evening Times carried a light-hearted piece on Saturday March 16, claiming, amongst other things, that the 'old' Subway had been extremely successful in one of its aims – to make every passenger a critic! The piece ended with what was claimed to be a song (with concert and bathroom rights reserved):-

> Folks used to shout out for the gore,
> Of the poor town councillor.
> Because he never did a thing
> People said "He ought to hing,
> Ought to be sent back to college -
> The Subway's still on cable haulage!"
> He just slumbered at George Square,
> Every Thursday he was there -
> At least that's what the voters said,
> And then he proved he had a head.
> Now all our wrongs are rectified -
> The Subway is electrified![29]

The old cable operation Rule Book had to be substantially re-written, and the resulting smart red hardback publication contained several photographs and operating instructions for the new equipment – unusual in Railway Rule Books.

During the summer or autumn of 1935 there was one case of passengers having to be de-trained in the tunnel. A crowded train failed on a steep gradient, and the Station Master in rear detained and emptied the following train, and sent it on with instructions to propel the faulty train forward. The driver of the propelling train should have coupled up to the failed train, and having found it on a rising gradient should have run back beyond the foot of the gradient, so that he could have a 'run' at the hill. In this case the driver did not run back, and was unable to re-start the two trains without the circuit breaker opening. The passengers were then de-trained from the front train and walked forward to the next station, some illumination being provided by the emergency 'T'-iron light fittings carried on each train.[16]

Converting the Rolling Stock – the Second Phase.

The start of electric traction on the Inner Circle released a number of odd-numbered gripper cars. Seven additional motor coaches (Nos. 1, 21, 23, 27, 29, 55 and 59) were available when the Outer Circle started electric operation on Thursday 5th December 1935, though most if not all would have seen some service on the Inner Circle by then. (See Appendix 5)

Meanwhile the need for more trailer coaches was receiving attention, which probably involved fitting new brake gear to the existing bogies, fitting new wheels, leather seats and 600 Volt d.c. emergency lighting. Four coaches (all ex-grippers) were dealt with between July and September 1935. (See Appendix 5).

Electric service on the Outer Circle.

The General Manager wrote to the Ministry on 6th November saying that the conversion work on the Outer Circle had taken longer than anticipated, the reconditioning of the rolling stock being the main cause, but that sufficient vehicles would be available by 25th November, and he would like the change-over to be about the end of the month.[28] Colonel Trench suggested his inspection be on Tuesday morning 3rd December, and a trial service start at 2pm that afternoon, during which he could go round the system, observe the signalling, inspect the completion of the station alterations, and continue this if necessary on the Wednesday morning. These arrangements were confirmed by the General Manager, who intimated 'it is intended to invite members of the Transport Committee to make a trip on the Outer Circle on the forenoon of Wednesday 4th December, after which there will be a simple informal luncheon in the City Chambers . . . we shall be very glad to have you join us on that occasion.'[16]

As planned the last cable trains ran on the Outer Circle on Saturday 30th November 1935. The whole system was closed on Sunday 1st December, but the Inner Circle opened again on Monday 2nd December. The Outer started electric service on Thursday 5th December – to programme and in accordance with previously published posters – with seven trains, Train Route Nos. 1 to 7. Providing sufficient rolling stock each day must have been something of a headache with only 15 motor cars available.

Mr. Bruce found time to present a paper to the Institution of Engineers & Shipbuilders in Scotland on 3rd December. Colonel Trench was in the audience, and participated in the discussion.[13] The main recommendation from the inspection was that the speed limit of 20mph be retained and extended to the Outer Circle as well.[16] A certificate dated 6th December 1935 stating that the Outer Circle was fit for traffic was issued by the Minister of Transport.[30]

Tenders were invited for the removal of the Power Station Equipment, and the offer of Messrs David Smith (Govan) Ltd was accepted on 18th March 1936. Some thought was given to conversion of the Power Station to a bus garage, but after a period of lease on a month-by-month basis to Young's Express Deliveries, it was leased to James Howden & Co, Ltd for 10 years from about October 1939, at a rental of £650 per annum.[31] Howdens was an engineering firm occupying adjoining premises.

Converting the Rolling Stock – the Third Phase.

The balance of motor cars to make up a total of twenty available were converted more slowly as work on re-axleing and re-wheeling trailer cars gathered momentum. The last motor coach conversion was not completed until September 1936. Between December 1935 and February 1937 nine former gripper cars were reconditioned as trailers.

It is significant that by the middle of 1936 the decision had been made to retain at least some of the ex–4-wheel trailer cars, of which No. 45 was the first to be reconditioned, and by August 1937 five others had also been done.

Thus it would appear that 20 motor coaches and some 16 trailers were available for use by the end of 1936, though some unreconditioned coaches must have been used as trailers behind electric power coaches, but to a decreasing extent.

Changes at the Top

Lachlan Mackinnon retired on 21st March 1936 after 49 years' service with the Corporation, the last nine of which had been as General Manager of the Transport Department. He was replaced by James N. Wilson at a salary of £1,500 per year, but he in turn retired on 13th November 1937,[32] and was replaced by the Deputy General Manager, Mr Robert F. Smith. The post of Deputy General Manager was advertised, and Mr Eric R. L. Fitzpayne, aged 33, Deputy Transport Manager with Edinburgh Corporation Transport, was appointed.[33]

In March 1939 the General Manager proposed to a Special Sub-Committee set up to consider proposals for a re-organisation of the Transport Department, that, in anticipation of the retirement in February 1940 of the Superintendent at Coplawhill Car Works, Mr. Bruce be appointed to that post with a corresponding reduction in his Underground responsibilities. As a result the engineering side of the Underground was split four ways as follows:-

Signalling, switching and lighting . . . to the Electrical Section
Permanent Way and Tunnelling . . . to Permanent Way Section
Construction and Maintenance of stations and buildings . . . to Buildings Section
Underground Workshops . . . to stay with Mr Bruce[34]

Improvements to Service – 1936/7

With two more motor cars available the Saturday service was increased to 8 trains per Circle from 22nd February 1936. In view of the small number of spare motor cars it must have caused concern when Car 23 developed flats on the wheels of the front bogie, requiring them to be changed on 11th March 1936.

The basic Mondays to Fridays service was 7 trains per circle from Monday 27th July 1936, and was increased to 8 trains per Circle from Wednesday 13th January 1937.

Nine trains were run on each Circle on 9th July 1937 in connection with a Royal visit to Glasgow.

On Saturday 11th September, for one day only, a tenth train was operated on each Circle. Train Route 10 ran on the Outer Circle from 10·45am until 8pm. and Train Route 20 worked on the Inner from 11·15am to 8:30pm. Twenty trains were again in service on Wednesday 8th December. This would have meant that all motor cars were in service with no spares.

Station Facilities

At its meeting on 5th February 1936 the Municipal Transport Committee, after hearing a number of suggestions from the Manager, decided to stop referring to the system as "the Subway", and adopt the term "Underground".[30] Some 60 years later Glaswegians (including estate agents) still refer to the system as "the Subway".

In June 1937 a specification was issued for the supply of two neon pole signs, with the wording 'UNDERGROUND' on them in a style reminiscent of the London Underground, with large 'U' and 'D' letters. They were to be box type signs, with, in at least one case, the letters reading vertically. The signs were intended for Dumbarton Road at the end of Merkland Street and Paisley Road West at Cessnock Street. The latter was to be mounted on a tramway fare stage pole.

This official photograph, looking south, records the state of St Enoch platform chamber soon after electrification. At the top of the steps twin staircases connect the landing to street level, that on the right descending from the ticket-issuing side of the booking office. On the landing are two British Automatic Company vending machines, one for Swiss milk chocolate and the larger for 'Sweetmeats', including Beech Nut chewing gum. Station lighting was not much improved from cable days, wall advertisements had not yet appeared and wooden station name signs were affixed to the T-irons only at occasional intervals; by some time in the 1950s these had gone forth and multiplied into clusters, usually of five, which could be more readily seen from inside the trains. Litter was becoming a problem, hence the sign positioned beneath the live rail and the track being flushed to top-of-sleeper level to make sweeping up easier.

The initial success of the electrification and the impending Empire Exhibition (q. v.) stimulated further station improvement works in 1937–8. Some 14 specifications for station improvements at Bridge Street, Shields Road, Kinning Park, Cessnock, Copland Road, Merkland Street, Partick Cross, Hillhead, and St. Enoch were issued between May 1937 and May 1938.[18]

On 29th September 1937 the Municipal Transport Committee awarded a contract to Rex Publicity Services Ltd. for an experimental period of two years to use station walls for advertising purposes:[33] this certainly helped to dispel the 'whitewashed cowshed' image complained about by a shareholder in Company days. When the contract fell due for renewal, it was awarded to Cowan-Ad Service for 5 years to run from 1st October 1939, at an annual rental of £125 per station.[34] A few days after the outbreak of war, Cowan asked if the start of their contract could be delayed until 1st January 1940, but at the Municipal Transport Committee meeting on 4th October, it was agreed they should be relieved of their contract.[34] Despite these setbacks, commercial advertising has remained a feature of the stations and cars ever since.

The General Manager reported in June 1938 that the hoist (lift) at Kelvinbridge Station was in an unsatisfactory condition. Approval in principle to renewing the hoist had been given in December 1937, but a sub-committee was appointed and visited the site on 5th September and agreed that the hoist should be closed, but instructed the Manager to establish the cost of installing an escalator: there was also a proposal to install a 'verandah' outside the South Woodside Road entrance. After due time for advising the public, the hoist was closed as from 18th November, when the last tickets (from 'Kelvinbridge High Level') were sold.[35] Nothing came of the escalator or verandah proposals, and the South Woodside Road entrance remained the only one until the hoist was reinstated in 1967, which is dealt with in Chapter 7.

It had originally been hoped that electric trains would make their way round the circle in 23 minutes, which with a 3 to 3½ minute headway, would have required seven trains per circle. Largely because of the 20 mph speed limit it was soon discovered that this was over-optimistic, and with the prospect of additional traffic for the Empire Exhibition in mind, the Municipal Transport Committee recommended in January 1937 the conversion of 6 more motor cars and 4 more trailers.[33] Tender enquiries were put out early in 1937 for equipment to convert the six motor cars.

Five firms tendered in April 1937 for the supply of seven sets of traction equipment (six for installation and one spare). The firms in price order were:-

G.E.C.; Crompton Parkinson; Metropolitan-Vickers Electric Co.; English Electric; British Thomson-Houston.

Despite a plea from Mr Bruce pointing out that if gear other than Metro-Vick were bought, a spare set of M.V. equipment would still have to be acquired, and that G.E.C. equipment was more bulky, the decision was still made to buy G.E.C. gear at £1,000 per equipment. Mr Bruce did manage to arrange for a number of the smaller parts to be common with the Metro-Vick equipment: contact tips and magnet valves were cases in point. The equipment incorporated WT28 traction motors (also similar to those used in some Glasgow trams), but the principles of the circuitry, motor configuration, contactor sequence etc. were the same as on the M.V. cars. The master controllers incorporated a different type of deadman's handle device: on the Metropolitan-Vickers controllers downward pressure had to be maintained on the whole handle, and if it was released in any position it sprang upwards and released air from the brake pipe, whereas the G.E.C. arrangement consisted of a button protruding out of the top surface of the wooden knob, and had to be depressed by the palm of the hand, which quickly became uncomfortable. The twenty eight WT28 motors were delivered between March and early May 1938.[9]

Four firms also tendered in April 1937 for the supply of seven steel underframes and 14 power bogies. Six of the underframes and twelve of the bogies were for the six cars to be converted, whilst the seventh underframe was earmarked for Car 60, and the remaining two bogies would be spares. The firms in price order were:-

R. Y. Pickering & Co. Ltd, Hurst, Nelson & Co. Ltd, P. & W. McLellan Ltd, and The Brush Electrical Engineering Co. Ltd.

R. Y. Pickering of Wishaw received the order. The underframes were delivered between February and May 1938, and the bogies during April and May.[9] The only significant difference was that the 1937 specification called for non-metallic brake blocks, whereas, as already noted, the 1933 specification called for cast iron. The specification for the non-metallic blocks seems crude by modern standards, and was as follows:-

The brake blocks shall be made to Drawing No. CS296. They shall be of the laminated type, built up with five thicknesses of 'Ferodo' brake lining and held together with six wire nails of suitable size. The lamination to be pressed en bloc to radius given and thereafter the nails to be driven and clinched. All as shown on drawing.

The trailer car brake blocks were of similar construction.

Also in March 1937 tenders were invited for sets of brake gear for trailer coaches and air brake and horn equipment for motor coaches, and in May for door engine equipment and upholstered seating for coaches – six-coach sets in crimson leather for motor coaches and three coach sets and odd 2- and 3-seater sections and backs in brown leather for trailers. The odd seats allowed four coach sets already delivered for short saloon trailers (ex-gripper cars) to be made up to five car sets for long saloon (ex–4-wheel) trailers.

R. Y. Pickerings also won the order for the trailer car brake gear, but Westinghouse received the contract for the air brake and horn equipment. R. Y. Pickering won the order for the seats, delivering all the brown seats and backs on 28th September 1937, and the red ones on 31st May 1938.[9] G. D. Peters provided the door gear again, and the bulk of the equipment was delivered in February 1938.[9]

Converting the Extra Cars

Four former gripper cars already re-conditioned as trailers and two which appear not to have been so treated were converted to motor cars as follows:-

No. 18 28/4/38*, No. 14 20/5/38*, No. 6 2/7/38, No. 30 15/7/38, No. 17 4/11/38 and No. 28 31/12/38

* No record of previous re-conditioning as trailer car.

The last two of these coaches did not enter service until after the Empire Exhibition had closed.

Simultaneously eight trailer cars were re-conditioned by strengthening underframes, mounting on new bogies and fitting brown upholstered seating as follows:-

No. 35 12/3/38, No. 43 8/4/38, No. 36 25/4/38, No. 52 26/4/38, No. 39 3/6/38, No. 31 23/8/38, No. 34 2/12/38 and No. 32 6/12/38

To accomplish this conversion, two more batches of Miller wheels on new axles were delivered, 12 pairs each in May and October.[9]

A change to more conventional non-metallic brake blocks of the TBL type supplied by James R. Chisholm & Co. was marked by the arrival of a batch of 24 such blocks on 29th December 1937.[9] By 1939 it had evidently been decided to adopt these as standard and three orders each for 300 were delivered during that year.[9]

The Battery Locomotive

Presumably because of wear and tear and experience gained during the electrification period, it was decided to rebuild the 1927 battery locomotive. This took the form of removing the jackshafts and coupling rods between the wheels, and substituting an internal chain drive to the axles through a central gear box. The treatment also involved a new steeple cab and battery boxes. Several photographs of the locomotive in rebuilt condition survive, one of which appears on page 84. About the same time in 1936 a new battery was authorised for the locomotive.[30] Latterly yellow and black 'wasp stripes' were applied to the buffer beams, which retained railway-type side buffers until after the closure of the system for modernisation.

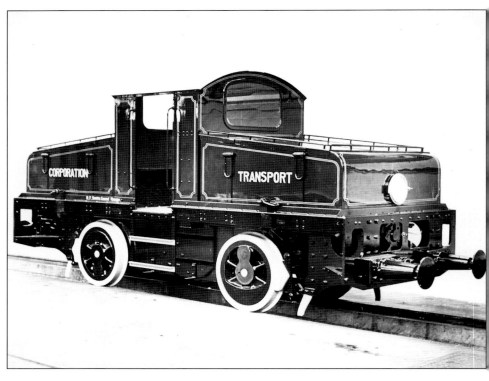

The British Electric Vehicles battery locomotive as rebuilt and repainted in 1938. The nearest wheel betrays the former jackshaft drive by reason of its counterweight and the offset location for the former coupling/connecting rod pin. The locomotive, now in dark red, is one of the exhibits in the Glasgow Museum of Transport's Subway Gallery. *SPT Broomloan Collection*

Train Services for the 1938 Empire Exhibition

No doubt to cater for the additional traffic brought about by the Empire Exhibition in Bellahouston Park, which had been opened by King George VI in a ceremony at the nearby Ibrox stadium on 3rd May, the 'Saturdays' nine-train per Circle service was run on weekdays from Monday 9th May, but from 14th May the Saturday service became 10 trains per Circle, and the weekdays service followed suit from Monday 16th May: this produced a weekly scheduled train mileage of 31,507.

Until Car 14 was completed on 20th May this service must have been run with only one spare motor car. Matters were still further complicated by a number of motor cars suffering flatted wheels.

To assist with the operation of these intensive services, an additional 2-aspect signal was placed in each tunnel between Govan Cross and Merkland Street from 11th July 1938. At the same time the Outer Circle signal at Govan Cross and the Inner Circle signal at Merkland Street became 3-aspect (green over amber over red). A notice of the same date told drivers to keep the lighting skids of trailer cars on the T-iron rails during reversing.[36] The reason for this is not known, but latterly the practice was always to retract the skids.

Presumably because of the Glasgow Fair holiday period the service was revised from Sunday 17th July 1938 as follows:-

Sundays   6 trains per Circle
Weekdays   9 trains per Circle
Saturdays   10 trains per Circle

Damage was caused to the tunnel between Kelvinbridge and St George's Cross by flooding on 28th July, and the system 'lost' about 3,000 train miles that week.[37]
The mid-July reduction in frequency was short-lived, however, because from Friday 5th August the weekday service reverted to 10 trains per Circle, then on Wednesday 24th August all trains ran additional journeys so the last train reached the Car Sheds at 1·06am next morning: this was repeated on Saturday night 27th August and Wednesday night 31st August. Late running continued every Saturday and Wednesday night, but possibly not so long as on the previous Saturday and Wednesday nights.
From Monday 17th October 1938 the weekdays and Saturdays services were reduced to eight trains per Circle and nine trains per Circle respectively. Ten trains per Circle ran again on Saturday 29th October (the last day of the Exhibition), and the service ran about an hour later than usual, and to the same times as on 24th August. This resulted in the highest weekly patronage figure since electrification – 586,549. Three staff buses were arranged to take Underground personnel home on Saturday night/Sunday morning 29/30th October.
The Exhibition only attracted some 12½ million visitors, against a predicted 20 million: the shortfall was put down to the Munich crisis and the threat of war, and cold, wet and windy weather for much of that summer. It is interesting to speculate how the Underground might have coped if larger crowds had been attracted.[38]
On 10th November the General Manager issued a staff notice quoting at length a letter from Lord Elgin, Chairman of the Council of Management of the Empire Exhibition which gave praise to the GCT staff who had successfully carried heavy traffic to and from Bellahouston Park over the six month period of the Exhibition.

Train Services 1938–39
Friday 11th November 1938 was the 20th Anniversary of Armistice Day, and was probably the last time that the two-minute silence was generally observed on a weekday. As far as the Underground was concerned, d. c. power was cut off from the sub-stations for two minutes from 11·00am to 11·02am The gate control circuit on the trains was such that loss of power resulted in any trellis gates which were open closing automatically. The notice which was issued on 8th November read:-

. . . drivers will endeavour to avoid being brought to a standstill between stations when power is cut off, by delaying their departure, if need be, from a station, until the 2 minutes have elapsed. They will also see that all gates are isolated at any convenient time between 10:50 and 10:55am so that gates may not close automatically when power is cut off.
All conductors will please stand at attention during the 2 minutes' silence.
It has been requested that members of the Uniform staff should wear naval and military decorations.

On Sundays 18th June and 9th July 1939 experimental five train per Circle services were tried: the Car Sheds must have been badly congested with 30 cars, the battery locomotive and Permanent Way wagons stored in it!
From Sunday 10th September – a week after the outbreak of World War II – the Sunday service was started approximately one hour earlier – at 8·00am This arrange-

85

ment was made at rather short notice, the first week being covered by overtime as duty sheets had not been prepared: this resulted in a weekly scheduled mileage of 25,933. Also, from Sunday 17th September a staff train started to run on the Inner Circle leaving Govan Cross for Merkland Street at 7·30am and returning for Govan Cross at 7·40am; two minutes were allowed for the journey back to Govan. From Sunday 5th November services were stopped about half an hour earlier each night, and a staff train was run after close of traffic from Govan Cross to Merkland Street and back: these changes reduced the weekly mileage to 25,146.

The service remained at this level until at least 10th February 1940, the last week for which detailed records of this period survive, but on Saturday 23rd March only, ten trains were run on each Circle. The Sunday starting time was brought forward to 7am from 26th May.[39]

Rolling Stock

By the end of December 1938 all fifty cars had been modernised for electric operation. Under the original – and too optimistic – plan, it seems likely the intention was to scrap all of the surviving 14 ex-4-wheel cars. As it was all 14 lasted until 1968, when Car 31 was scrapped, and Nos. 38, 39, 43 and 52 survived to run on the last day of the pre-modernised system – 21st May 1977.

Even before conversion of the fleet had been completed, general overhauls of the coaches were commenced, Trailer No. 7 being the first, completed on 5th November 1938. It is not clear exactly what was involved in the overhaul, but it was probably fairly light in nature.

There is reason to believe Car 60 had a general overhaul on 27th February 1939, and that all wheels were removed for turning. It seems most likely that at this stage it was mounted on the seventh Pickering underframe.

Whether as a result of an accident or otherwise is not recorded, but 245 ivorine notices measuring 5ins by 3¼ins and reading in red letters on a white background 'PASSENGERS ARE WARNED TO STAND CLEAR OF THE GATES' were delivered on 19th November 1937.[9]

During its first overhaul after conversion to electric operation, completed in September 1939, Trailer Coach 9 was fitted with sliding doors in place of the original trellis gates: this involved creating door pockets for the doors to slide into when open. The cost was £243 11s 9d, but it was many years before any other cars were so treated. (See photograph opposite.)

In the early stages before conversion of the Inner Circle some trouble was experienced with flats on the commutators of the motors, leading to flash-overs: this was attributed to drivers applying power before the brake was released.[16] It is not known whether the problem diminished as the drivers gained experience, or whether the current settings of the notching relays had to be adjusted downwards.

The braking rate was not as good as hoped for in the early stages, but this improved once the oil residue from the cables was cleaned off the rail surfaces by the passage of trains.[16]

A record of only two defects in 1936 has survived: Car 2 had to have the wheels of its rear bogie removed for re-profiling and to rectify a torn journal on 4th August 1936, and Car 29 suffered flatted wheels on its front bogie some four months later, and had the wheels changed on 11th December.

Car 30 suffered flatted wheels on both axles of the front bogie requiring the wheels to be changed on 7th March 1939, then trailer Car 35 had one pair of wheels changed for flats on 30th April 1939.

Trailer Coach No. 9, suspended from the crane, has cleared the collapsible railings at the edge of the Car Sheds lifting pit and is steadied for its descent to the Inner Circle track. In September 1939 No. 9 was the first car to have trellis gates replaced by sliding doors, and this December 1948 photograph shows them clearly. In the background the steep staircase to the floor of the pit and the top of the Inner Circle tunnel from Govan Cross can be seen. *Glasgow Evening Citizen*

Seven more motor cars suffered flatted wheels between July and November 1939, and two trailer cars had similar problems in November. Although the incidence of flatted wheels was not as great as in the previous year, the problem had evidently not been fully solved. The fact that the passenger carryings had been significantly higher in 1938, influenced by the Empire Exhibition, may well have been a factor. Probably in an effort to improve matters, eight 'Chekko-V10' brake blocks $1\frac{7}{8}$ins thick were supplied for a free trial by Cresswells Asbestos Co. Ltd on 20th June 1939.[9] No reported findings have come to light.

Car 55 was involved in a collision in May 1940 between Govan Cross and Merkland Street during night shift operations, but no other details have been found.

The flatted wheel problem seems to have been largely overcome by 1940, and this may have been associated with the arrival of a large consignment of TBL brake blocks during 1939.

In 1934–5, in the depths of the Depression, the Underground carried some 14.4 million passengers. In the years to 31st May 1937, 1938, 1939 and 1940 the statistics had improved somewhat[40] to 21.5 million, 24 million, 25.8 million, and 26.7 million respectively.

In the 1936–8 period the energy used to propel the trains was about 3. 5 KW-hr/mile, or 23 KW-hr/train journey round the system[41]: this compares with about 50 KW-hr/train journey for a modern 2-car train.

Chapter 6

1940–1965 – The Crowded Years

Sometime between 2·20am and 3·08am (accounts differ) in the morning of 18th September 1940 a German high explosive bomb from a lone aircraft, possibly intended for the nearby docks or other strategic riverside targets, landed on Beith Street bowling green, south of Merkland Street, penetrated the soft ground above the tunnel and exploded either above or inside the Outer Circle tunnel.[1] A further bomb from the same aircraft crippled the cruiser HMS Sussex at Yorkhill basin.[1] The explosion shattered the cast iron segments of both tunnels allowing silt and sand to enter (see photo below) and clog up the pumps at the Clyde Manhole. Piles had to be driven down in two stages round the bomb crater in very unstable ground. The piles were braced apart by wooden frames. When this had been done excavation was started and proved difficult as the water-bearing silt started to rise in the excavation. Eventually the broken segments were removed, and sufficient undamaged ones salvaged to rebuild the base of the tunnels. Brick arches, four rings thick, were built followed by concrete 6 inches thick on top of the arches. The work had to be stopped for 12 days at the end of December and beginning of January 1941 because of severe frosts. By 26th January 1941, all the necessary repairs to the tunnels, track, live rail, electric cables, signalling system etc. had been sufficiently completed to allow traffic to commence. A thorough examination of the tunnels and track was made and a train taken round both circles for testing purposes. On the following morning, 27th January 1941, the Underground was re-opened to traffic, having been closed for 131 days.[2] The Manager reported on 25th November that he was 'preparing a scheme for the operation of a service on sections of the Underground for the approval of the Ministry of Transport'[3] – presumably some sort of shuttle working, but it is unlikely it was ever put into operation.

The blocked tunnel south of Merkland Street after a High Explosive bomb penetrated it.
SPT Collection

The period from 1940 to 1965 was the most successful so far in the life of the system. Traffic levels built up from 17.07 million in 1940–41 (the year of the bomb damage) to 28.5 million in 1941–42, to 34 million in the 1944–5 financial year, peaked at 37.3 million in 1948–9, remained at over 30 million until 1958/9, and did not fall below 20 million until 1968–9. The annual train miles were of the order of 1.5 to 1.3 million throughout this period, and for several years the Underground made a surplus, including each year from 1941/2 to 1957/8 and 1959/60 and 1960/1. The lost mileage was usually less than 0.25%. Receipts in 1946/7 were three times what they had been in 1934/5, but the working expenses had only doubled.

For most of the period the standard Mondays to Fridays service was nine trains per Circle, the Saturday service ten trains per circle, and the Sunday service 7 trains per circle.

After the bomb damage the service resumed, with, it is thought, 6 trains per circle on Sundays, 8 on weekdays and 9 on Saturdays. From Tuesday 18th until Saturday 29th March 1941 the service was augmented because of disruption to tram services caused by bombing: the Monday-Friday service was run on the Sunday, and the Saturday service on all other days.[4]

A lunchtime scene at St Enoch about 1950. Just how labour intensive the system was in those days is evident by the number of staff visible. In the foreground are two ticket collectors, beneath the gantry, which has internally illuminated route displays on each side of the Pul-Syn-Etic system clock, are two conductors and an inspector, and in front of his 'box' the station master has words with the driver of the left hand (Inner Circle) train. *Glasgow Museum of Transport Collection*

From 16th May 1943 the Sunday service was augmented to 7 trains per Circle, and ran from the earlier time of 6·38am until 10·21pm, and from Monday 17th May the Saturday service was run on Mondays to Fridays with 9 trains per Circle from 6·43am until 11·31pm – it is not clear what changes, if any, were made on Saturdays.[4] The Sunday service soon changed again and from 30th May was extended to 10·47pm. From 6th September 1943 the same timetable was used Mondays to Saturdays, with 9 trains per circle starting at 6·43am, but finishing at 11·03pm.[4] From Sunday 5th March 1944, the starting times were adjusted, to 6·51am on Sundays and 6·08am Mondays to Saturdays – in the latter case the last train leaving St Enoch for Copland Road at 11·03pm. The Sunday starting time was again altered from 13th August to 7·07am[4] with the last train at 10·47pm.[5]

	FIRST TRAIN		LAST TRAIN	
	Weekdays and Saturdays	Sundays	Weekdays and Saturdays	Sundays
Govan Cross to St Enoch (* OUTER)	6 08	7 07	10 47	10 31
Govan Cross to St Enoch (* INNER)	6 35	6 56	10 49	10 28
Copland Road to St Enoch (* INNER)	6 15	6 33	10 50	10 29
St Enoch to Copland Road (* OUTER)	6 21	7 19	11 03	10 47
St Enoch to Govan Cross (* INNER)	6 23	6 40	11 01	10 40
* OUTER CIRCLE CLOCKWISE, INNER CIRCLE ANTI-CLOCKWISE				

Starting on 16th October 1949, following a census of passengers entering the system up to 9am carried out on Sunday 4th September,[6] the Sunday service was adjusted to run with 7 trains per circle from 7·49am until 11·16pm.[4]

Between Monday 17th October 1949 and Saturday 7th January 1950, a 10-train per circle Mondays to Fridays and Saturdays service starting at 6·23am and running until 11·30pm with running times reduced from 28 to 27 minutes was tried but was not successful,[4, 7] in part because trains encountered more red signals.

Further changes took place from Sunday 8th January 1950 as a result of complaints from passengers about the later start on Sundays, poor patronage of late-night trains revealed by censuses carried out in late October, and the desire to save staff.[8] The Sunday service was now from 7·29am until 11·03pm, the Monday to Friday service reverted to being different from that on Saturdays, and ran with 9 trains per Circle from 6·21am to 11·03pm, and the Saturday service remained at 10 trains per circle starting at 6·23am, but as on other days stopped at 11·03pm: all three timetables had a running time of 28 minutes.[4] Commencing Monday 17th March 1952, the running time for a journey in the peaks on weekdays and Saturdays was increased from 28 to 30 minutes resulting in a slight reduction in scheduled mileage.[4, 9] Apart from holiday services, and unforeseen interruptions to the service by flooding or industrial action etc, this remained the standard timetable for the next 13 years or so.

Christmas Day fell on a Friday in 1964, and the service was reduced to 7 trains per circle, in recognition of the increasing observance of Christmas as a Trades Holiday in Scotland.[10] Christmas Day and New Year's Day services, at a reduced level, continued until after the Modernisation.

The Monday to Fridays service was reduced to eight trains per circle from 15th February 1965, and the Saturday service to nine trains per circle from the same week.[11]

Other Operational Matters

The General Manager, R. F. Smith, reached the age of 65 in January 1943, and was succeeded by the Deputy General Manager, Eric R. L. Fitzpayne at a salary of £1,500 per annum, and on similar terms to those of Mr Smith.[12]

In 1943 Fitzpayne wrote to the Ministry of War Transport suggesting that the requirement to log the times all trains passed each station should cease, and be done only at the timing stations, thereby saving the paper of 13 reports per day. The Railway Inspectorate would not agree to this until the telephone system had been improved. This had been done by May 1944, when the following notice was issued:-[13]

GLASGOW CORPORATION TRANSPORT

NOTICE TO UNDERGROUND STATION MASTERS,
TIMING OF TRAINS

ON AND AFTER SUNDAY, 14TH MAY RECORDS OF TRAIN RUNNING WILL ONLY BE KEPT FOR ST. ENOCH AND GOVAN CROSS STATIONS.

IN THE EVENT OF AN ACCIDENT OR BREAKDOWN, STATION MASTERS OF ADJACENT STATIONS MUST IMMEDIATELY BE INFORMED BY TELEPHONE OF THE CIRCUMSTANCES, SO THAT THERE CAN BE NO POSSIBILITY OF ANY MISUNDERSTANDING.

46, Bath Street,   BY ORDER.
11/5/44.   E.R.F.

As noted previously, West Street station had been closed on Sundays since February 1932, but this practice ceased from the spring of 1953.[7]

The requirement dating back to 1898 that no more than 50 passengers be allowed on to a platform at any one time, was given as the reason for not adopting concourse automatic ticket issuing machines in reply to a public letter in January 1948.[14]

Traffic staffing levels were generally about 230 plus 60 Booking Office Assistants until 1949 when the numbers increased to around 240. The basis of the Maintenance staff figures given in the GCT annual reports changed over the years, particularly with regard to the Permanent Way Section. In the mid-1950s there were 90 men and 6 women employed in the Workshop, which would include electricians, fitters, handymen, bodymakers, welders, tinsmiths, riggers, coach painters, pumpmen and car cleaners. This went up to 100 in 1967. The Permanent Way section at this stage was about 57, almost exclusively on night shift. The Permanent Way squad increased to an incredible 93 in 1964, probably associated with the disbanding of the Tramway Permanent Way workforce, but it remained in the 73 to 84 range until 1973.

Part of the reason for the success in this period may well have been that the fares were reasonably stable, until about 1959. Movement of population away from the areas served by the Underground to outlying housing schemes or later to new towns such as East Kilbride and Cumbernauld, together with increased car and television ownership were the main reasons for the drop in ridership from the early 1950s, accelerating in the 1960s when industrial decline in the traditional industries such as shipbuilding became a major factor.

Strikes, Weather and Public disorder

On Friday 10th November 1961 Glasgow was in the grip of ice in the morning and dense fog in the evening which brought chaos to road transport: the Underground, however, ran without any interruptions, and carried what was said to be a record 104,947 passengers.[15] In fact daily figures in excess of 100,000 must have been carried in the 1949–52 period.

During the week ending 11th April 1964 there was a strike which curtailed Corporation bus services, and as a result the Underground carried additional passengers. On the Wednesday the additional heavy traffic delayed both circles by 10 minutes during the morning and evening peak periods, but over the week there was a 48% increase in revenue.[16] That week's loadings may well have been a 'last fling' for the pre-Modernised Underground, because by mid-June 1964 Harland & Wolff's shipyard at Govan (a major source of traffic) had permanently closed.[17]

The service on both circles was brought to a standstill for nearly 20 minutes shortly after 3pm on Sunday 1st November 1964 when a band of some 30 youths brandishing knives and sticks descended on Partick Cross Station, jostling passengers waiting for trains. The live rails had to be de-energised when one youth jumped from the platform and made off up the tunnel towards Hillhead station. The police made four arrests.[18]

Owing to a dispute about wage rates, GCT busmen imposed an overtime ban and work-to-rule from midnight on 22nd November 1964. The Underground staff joined in this action, and in order to avoid disruption to services by staff shortage the Fair Holiday 7 trains per circle service was introduced for Mondays to Fridays, and the normal Mondays to Fridays 9 trains per circle service on Saturdays. The Sundays service also operated as usual. This continued for a fortnight until the overtime ban and work-to-rule was lifted, but during that period the Underground, despite the reduced service with resultant over-crowding, coped with the additional passengers who had deserted the infrequent buses. The Underground revenue for week ending 28th November was £10,511, an increase of £631 over the previous week.

Floodings

On 24th May 1946 the Outer Circle was flooded between Shields Road and Kinning Park due to a sudden inrush of clear water thought to be from a deep spring. About 200 to 300 yards of track were flooded to a depth of 2ft. With the assistance of pumps from the Fire Service, the tunnel was cleared and traffic resumed the following morning.[7]

Probably the most spectacular incident in the period under review occurred at about 2.40pm on Friday 26th June 1953, when Glasgow was struck by an unprecedented rainstorm which lasted until about 4.30pm: the rainfall in Springburn Park in the north of the city was recorded as 1.39 inches (35mm). The normal street drainage could not cope, and at Govan Cross station water from the flooded street flowed down the stairs and passage to the tunnels. Unfortunately construction work was in progress on the new office, canteen and exit building and the excavations were flooded by water from the adjacent railway goods station (now the site of Broomloan Workshop building and staff car park), which also poured down into the tunnels. The water flowed down the 1 in 18½ gradient to the lowest point under the River Clyde, where it reached a depth of 6 feet and completely submerged the pumps in the cross-passage between the tunnels (known as the Clyde Man-Hole in Underground jargon). Traffic had to be stopped at 4pm when water started to gather. Pumps and pipelines (some of which were lent by the Fire Brigade) had to be acquired and installed to pump the large quantity of water the distance of some 400 yards and raise it some 80ft from the low point to the platform chamber and then to the surface at Govan. By round-the-clock working it was possible to re-open the Outer Circle (which is slightly higher than the Inner at the lowest point) by 3pm on Tuesday 30th June: the Inner Circle was cleared for start of traffic at 6·03am next day.[19, 20]

During the repair work an alarming incident occurred when a 4-wheel bogie with two men on it ran out of control down the gradient from Merkland Street (Inner Circle) platform, narrowly missed two electricians working in the tunnel, and collided with another bogie standing at the water's edge. One of the men on the bogie was pitched into the water, and was slightly injured.[21]

An account of this incident would not be complete without reference to the legendary use of a boat, borrowed from Hogganfield Loch, to transport personnel through the tunnel to and from the Clyde Man-Hole.[22]

There was a severe storm during the evening and night of Saturday 2nd September 1961, and not for the last time the St George's Cross to Kelvinbridge area proved vulnerable.

At 8·30pm the Station Master at Buchanan Street reported flickering on the electricity supply, causing intermittent failure of signals over much of the system: this was attributed to the effects of the electrical storm. At 10·15pm a dog was injured on the line at Cessnock – perhaps it had thought the tunnel safer than the storm outside! A few minutes later reports were received of flooding on the stairs at West Street and Bridge Street stations.

At 10·55pm flooding of the Inner Circle between St George's Cross and Kelvinbridge at Manhole (i. e. Cross-passage) No. 15 was reported, and an hour later water was running down the T-irons at St George's Cross. By 12·34am next morning the situation was still deteriorating, but by 1·50am the water was receding, and an hour later the crisis was over. On the Sunday evening after traffic there was further trouble with the T-irons at St George's Cross, but the nocturnal activity on this had to be stopped abruptly when the Car Sheds crane stuck with a car suspended half-way down the pit![23]

Rolling Stock

A series of brake block tests was carried out between October 1946 and November 1951: the earlier ones were a service comparison between Top Dog blocks made by Hubert H. P. Trist & Co. and TBL blocks, and involved Cars 6, 17, 23 and 24. The 1951 test was a comparison between Duron and TBL blocks, and involved Cars 12 and 17. The conclusion of all three series of tests seems to have been to continue with TBL blocks,[24] and indeed this firm remained the supplier until the system closed for modernisation in 1977.

Over the years there were problems with skids becoming de-railed from the T-irons for a variety of reasons, such as the skid plate breaking or coming adrift, or joints in the T-irons becoming misaligned. Another occasional problem was of parts of trains coming into contact with the T-irons – usually either the Klaxon or the retracted skids on the leading car. Here are some examples over the years.

On 9th January 1947 Route 12[20] broke a T-iron skid plate at 6·40am because the skid had not been placed correctly on the T-iron, and caused a delay of 10 minutes.

On 11th June 1948, for the third time since 4th June, a car broke a top skid in the Cessnock to Copland Road (Outer Circle) section, causing four top and three bottom T-iron insulators to be broken at a point about 520 yards from Cessnock. Although only one journey was lost, the incident extended over a period from 8·40am to 9·40am. The section concerned was under repair by the Permanent Way Department at the time, so a speed restriction of 5 mph was imposed to prevent further trouble.

There were various instances of parts of trains making contact with the T-irons and causing failures. On 6th July 1949 the Klaxon horn on the Motor Car of Inner Circle

A down-at-heel Partick Cross. Compared with the scene on page 44 little seems to have changed over 50 years or so apart from commercial advertising, a new destination gantry and a live rail instead of cable and pulleys. *R. Adams collection*

Route 16 worked loose and struck the T-iron in the Govan Cross to Copland Road section, resulting in 35-minute delay. On 3rd February 1951 the metal cover behind the contactors on the rear platform of a motor car became dislodged and fouled the T-iron on the Outer Circle near Hillhead: this blew the T-iron fuses and caused a delay of one journey.

On 31st January 1951 the front skids of Motor Car 17 working on Route 12 became dislodged from their retracted position, and damaged the rear skids of its trailer car (No. 22). Six T-iron insulators were also damaged. There was a one journey delay, although repair work took from 1·20pm until 2·45pm: clearly this involved men working in a tunnel section, and trains passing through under the Caution Order procedure.

Between June and October 1961 there were six cases of inter-car air connections giving trouble, all in the St George's Cross to Cowcaddens section of the Outer Circle, where the sharp right-hand curve contributed to the problem. Trailer Car 41 was involved in four of the incidents, and Motor Car 24 in three. Between January and early November 1962 there were 16 more cases of Outer Circle trains suffering inter-car brake hose problems in the same section. In the majority of cases the hoses became uncoupled. The incident on 17th August seems to have been more serious than usual, as pipework was damaged on Trailer Car 8, and a plumber had to be directed to the Car Sheds on Saturday 18th August to carry out repairs. The reason for the hoses disconnecting was thought to be over-speeding on the sharp curve approaching Cowcaddens.[26] There were two other cases of trouble with inter-car air couplings during June and July 1962, but at other locations.

The hook of the overhead crane broke whilst the lifting frame was attached to Trailer Car 32 on 8th April 1954 (see photograph on page 107). Extensive damage was done to the roof of the car, and the opportunity was taken to rebuild it with a pair of centre doors. In this form it was used as the middle car of the experimental 3-car train. By an extraordinary coincidence the same car was involved when the hook broke again in 1972 (see photograph on page 120).

One persistent problem was the over-heating of plain axle-box bearings. Records of some 43 incidents have been found for the 1947–55 period, but this is probably incomplete. The fitting of SKF roller bearing axleboxes started in 1952, Motor Cars 18, 25, 58 and 15 and Trailers 52, 44, 32 and 19 being the first converted. Eventually all cars were converted, the last being done in the 1960/1 financial year. The last recorded overheated plain axle-box bearing was on 16th July 1959 on Trailer Car 13.

The conversion did not, however, go without incident, because on 23rd May 1954 trainstop arms at West Street and Hillhead (Inner Circle) were broken by the rear car of Route No. 16 (Car 19) which, on being lifted from traffic, turned out to have a broken axle. Car 19 is also recorded as having suffered a broken No. 1 axle (T-iron side) on 4th February 1954. Both of these axles had been fitted with roller bearings.[20, 27]

Other broken axles occurred on 16th November 1954 and 27th May 1955. In the first incident Trailer Car 52 was the culprit in the Merkland Street to Partick Cross section of the Outer Circle at 5·01pm The line was eventually cleared at 9·15pm, after a delay of 4 hours and 10 minutes. In the second, Route No. 13 (Cars 1 and 36) was involved between Partick Cross and Merkland Street (Inner Circle) at 11·50am. Traffic was not re-started until 5·30pm. It is recorded that two live rail insulators were damaged, but not which car was involved.[20]

As stated in Chapter 5, Trailer Car 9 was experimentally converted to solid doors in 1939. This scheme to replace trellis gates was revived about 1948, and by May 1953 a further three trailer and four motor cars had been done. The programme began in earnest in 1956, but although priority was given to power cars (presumably to improve the drivers' lot) it took about 9 years to complete these cars. The programme was abandoned in 1968 after a further three trailers (Nos. 13, 26 and 45 in that order) had been converted, bringing the total to 10. The cars had carried a metal plate on the roof panels close to the trellis gates reading in white letters on a red background:-

PASSENGERS
ARE WARNED
TO STAND CLEAR
OF THE GATES

Although a stock of plates with the word 'gates' altered to 'doors' was acquired, the new plates were not always fitted at conversion.

The conversion involved the creation of door pockets – a double skin arrangement – for the solid doors to slide into, rather than fold up against the pillar as was the case with trellis gates. This involved a fair amount of body-building work, including moving the seats adjacent to the pockets, resulting in the narrowing of the central gangway, and forming an inner 'skin' with hinged casement windows. The Peters door engines were retained, but with modified linkages. On the motor cars the vertical strengthening plates running the whole length of the saloons above the solebars had to be cut back on the 'platform' side to make way for the bottom door runner: this structural alteration caused problems later, particularly if the car had been in a collision or 'heavy shunt', and often the solebars became cracked and required riveted strengthening pieces.

Once all the motor cars had been converted, at least two of the trailers had the internal bi-parting doors at the ends of the saloon removed, and one of these (Car 35 treated in 1964) had glazed draught-screens fitted, which gave a much more spacious appearance, particularly when associated with fluorescent lighting – Car 13 had the doors removed, but the original bulkheads left with the slots for the doors blanked off. The rear door of Car 13 was of experimental lightweight construction, featuring a rubber-mounted window, and probably a refinement of the type of door referred to in the 1960/1 Annual Report, where a weight reduction from 150 lbs to 78 lbs was claimed.

Car 28 during modifications in 1965 to replace gates by doors, as described above.
Ian Maclean

By 1949 at the latest, and probably earlier, the practice of lining out the exterior panels ceased, but the beading continued to be picked out in black.[28]

Between 1955 and 1958 the whole fleet was repainted in a simpler style, with the former cream-painted panels painted red to match those originally painted red. The original style of gold, blue-blocked, black-shaded numeral and letter transfers remained, however, together with the Glasgow Corporation crest on the centre side panel, with the words 'GLASGOW' and 'CORPORATION' on the larger panels. On both panels adjacent to the gates/doors the fleet number appeared with the prefix Nº. About 1969 the 'Nº' transfers ran out, and were not replaced, and only about one car (No. 13) retained them to the end.

At first the brown colour was retained for the 'unseen' side of the cars, but from about November 1962 this was painted plain red as well,[7] and from about 1964 roofs became black, leaving the portion between the 'rain strip' and the clerestory grey.[51]

Many of the trailer cars, which had retained the trussed type of underframe, were showing signs of bowing, so the opportunity was taken to carry out extensive work by fitting new 40 ft long composite 'side-sills' (presumably solebars) and new tensioning devices.[29] at Coplawhill Tram Works before it closed. All 24 trailer cars were sent there between April 1959 and January 1963, for periods of up to 5 months, the last one being Car 32, which returned to Broomloan Depot on 11th April 1963. The pattern was for the car to be jacked up off its bogies, and the body only transported to Coplawhill by Pickfords Heavy Haulage:[30] usually there was only one car away at a time, and bodies were transported each way on the same day. There was a period between August and October 1961 when two cars at a time were at Coplawhill. It is a pity that the opportunity was not taken to fit solid doors to the cars still outstanding when this work was being done.

Trailer coach No. 7 at Coplawhill Tramcar Works in May 1962 for new solebars and frame tensioners.

The 3-car train (of which more later in this chapter) required a different type of inter-car jumper from the twin 6-way plugs and sockets, fitted on either side of the communicating archways (they were not 'doorways', because there were no doors!) at the rear of the motor cars and leading end of the trailers. The 6-way plugs were evidently not very secure, and taping the plugs into the sockets had become standard: this of course could only be done when cars were on the track at the pit, a considerable inconvenience. Having gained some experience with the 19-way jumper used for the 3-car train, it was decided to adopt this as standard, and the rest of the fleet was converted between 1959/60 and 1962/3. For some unexplained reason these became known as 'Transport Sockets' in Underground jargon.

Some 32 new trailer bogies were produced at Broomloan between about 1956 and 1963 – presumably to replace pre-electrification ones still in service. These bogies retained the unusual arrangement of having no primary axlebox suspension: the axle-boxes were constrained within hornguides for vertical movement, but the only springing was between the bogie transom and the bolster.

In the 1950s a programme of rewiring the lighting circuits on the trailer cars was started, twenty cars having been done by May 1958, and three more by May 1959. Just before the programme on the trailer cars had been finished, a change was made to neoprene-insulated cable, so a start was made on re-wiring the trailers cars again, and the motor cars had the equivalent work done to the new standard: by May 1962 12 motors and 15 trailers had been completed.[31]

Motor Car No. 55 was experimentally fitted with 14 exposed fluorescent lighting tubes in 1948, but this was found to be too expensive to maintain, so was removed again.[32] In June 1964 Trailer Car 35 was fitted with 14 fluorescent tubes behind diffusers at the same time as it was fitted with solid doors and glazed draught-screens at the vestibules. As part of this scheme the side ceilings were flush panelled, and the horizontal grab rails were fitted with flexible hand grips – the only car so fitted – see photograph below. The fluorescent lighting installation became standard, but some cars had the centre ceilings flush panelled as well. An even lighting level of 20 foot candles at seated passenger reading height was achieved, twice that obtained from the Atholl fittings with filament lamps previously used.[33] It was claimed only three tubes had to be changed in the course of the first year's operation of Car 35.[34]

Motor Car 17, converted during an overhaul which was completed in March 1968, had a different type of fitting, designed to take back-illuminated advertisements: similar fittings were provided on a batch of Atlantean buses delivered about this time. Though Car 17 retained these fittings until the end, no other cars received them. The four small partitions in the centre of the saloon were modified: the patterned glass and chromium plated brass rods were removed, and decorative laminate with an oval aperture in it (similar in shape to a Pullman Car lavatory window) was fitted to each side of each partition. (See photograph below.) Car 18, which was the next to receive fluorescent lighting, received similar treatment to the partitions, but after that no others were subjected to this indignity. Both cars retained this feature until scrapped. By the time the programme was abandoned in 1971 some 28 cars had been fitted with fluorescent lighting – see Appendix 5 for details.

Early in the conversion programme two cars fitted with fluorescent lights were not allowed to run coupled as a train: this was because the reduced lighting current would not reliably operate the signalling system. In due course this restriction went when the circuitry was modified to increase the current.

Facing page Looking forward in Trailer Car 35 towards Motor Car 25. Points of interest in 35 are the match-striking panels on the centre glazed partitions, fluorescent lighting with flush side ceilings, the unique toggle type strap hangers, the setting-in of the foremost right-hand bench seat to accommodate a sliding door in place of a trellis gate and the open platform arrangement which resulted, with the two half doors removed and clear glass above the waist in the end bulkheads. No.25 retains the half doors at both ends of its saloon, and the handwheel for the Conductor's handbrake can be seen on the right hand side. Passengers who wished to smoke were obliged to travel in the trailer cars. *G Watson*

Below The interior of Car 17 after overhaul in March 1968. *G. Watson*

Stations

A start was made to fitting fluorescent lighting on the stairs at Buchanan Street in July 1947.

The most significant station renovation scheme during this period was the construction of the new exit and Depot Office building at Govan in 1953. The Depot Office – the place where drivers and conductors reported for duty, and to which cash from all 15 stations was taken – was on the ground floor of a tenement building on the west side of Greenhaugh Street, adjacent to the public entrance/exit for the station. The platform chamber was actually under Railway-owned land on the opposite side of Greenhaugh Street, and was reached by a subway under the street. Partly because Govan Cross was the busiest station on the system at the time, and partly to increase the inadequate Depot Office accommodation, it was decided to build a new structure on the east side of Greenhaugh Street, incorporating an exit from the station, and Depot Office facilities on the ground floor. The land required was part of Govan Goods Station, and belonged to the Railway Executive: purchase arrangements for 250 square yards of ground valued at £750 were put in hand in June 1951.[35] On completion the building had on the upper floor a canteen – also available for tram and bus staff – and a locker room. The stairs to the new exit left the original passageway at the top of the first flight of stairs from the platform. The original entrance/exit became an entrance only, with two separate ticket kiosks, and the former Depot Office became the Signals Workshop. As already described, the building works contributed to the serious tunnel flooding on Friday 26th June 1953. This building was demolished before the system closed for modernisation to allow preliminary work on the new Govan station site.

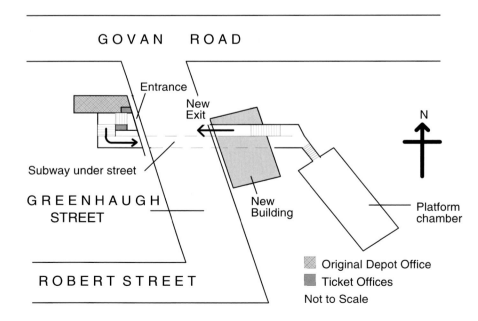

GOVAN CROSS STATION

Above The Shields Road station entrance in Scotland Street, with its surrounding tenement having been demolished in preparation for the westward extension of the (elevated) M8 motorway (in the background). *George Watson*

Left The basement entrance to Cessnock station in about 1974. *George Watson*

In November 1964 the old ticket office at St Enoch was replaced by a more modern arrangement with its window on the opposite (i. e. west) side, reverting to an arrangement superseded some 14 years before.[18] About a year later the wooden steps were replaced by concrete ones.[36]

The Track
Following the successful trial of Thermit welding of the running rails in 1937, it remained the standard method of jointing rails. 30ft long rails of British Standard section 80R (80 lbs/yard flat-bottomed) remained standard until modernisation. In general these came from Scottish steelworks. In the mid-1960s trials of more modern rail fastenings were carried out, first with a spring clip, but the final choice was the Pandrol system.

Pinkston Generating Station
As noted in Chapter 5, the Underground obtained its traction supply from the Transport Department's own generating station at Pinkston. After the Second World War it was decided to renew some of the equipment and install a further turbo-generator with associated boilers. At this time, shortly after nationalisation of the Electricity industry and with a general shortage of materials, the consent of the Electricity Commissioners had to be obtained, and a condition they laid down was that the new equipment must operate at the standard frequency of 50 Hz rather than 25 Hz as hitherto. For the new boilers to work satisfactorily it was necessary to build a large cooling tower, the outer shell of which was complete by May 1954. The tower, which became a significant landmark on the Glasgow skyline was 310ft high, on what was already an elevated site.[37] Changing over the frequency was a complex project, and involved work in the rectifier sub-stations as well as at Pinkston. This, however, permitted easier exchange of energy between the British Electricity Authority network and GCT.

Pinkston Power Station was taken over by the South of Scotland Electricity Board (SSEB) on 31st October 1958, and initially continued to supply the Underground sub-stations. The distribution arrangements were gradually integrated into the SSEB network, and Pinkston was closed as uneconomically small in the early 1970s, being demolished about 1976.

Legislation
Following the abondonment of the Tramways, of which the Underground was legally a part, its position was regularised in the Glasgow Corporation Consolidation (Water, Transport and Markets) Order Confirmation Act, 1964. This was a tidying up measure and re-stated many of the existing Corporation obligations from earlier Acts. The route of the line was described in relation to the streets above as they then were, but interestingly the system was described as a 'subway' throughout.[38]

Accidents and Incidents
On Saturday 14th March 1959 at about 4.55pm the first known collision since 1920 occurred at St Enoch on the Outer Circle. A disabled train being propelled by the following one had stalled on the rising gradient approaching Bridge Street, and was running back to St Enoch in reverse when the collision occurred at St Enoch with a stationary train. Trailer Car 4 was damaged in this incident, but repairs were complete about six weeks later.[39]

About 8.55am on Friday 24th August 1962 there was a failure of the electricity supply affecting a wide area of the city, and the Underground signalling failed. The proper procedures were not followed in the Underground, and Route 8 consisting of Cars 55 and 35 was allowed to depart from Hillhead station on the Outer Circle whilst the preceding train (Route 7, consisting of Cars 17 and 8) was still standing at Kelvinbridge. The approach to Kelvinbridge includes a reverse curve so the train standing in the station correctly protected by its battery tail lamp was invisible to the driver of the approaching train until too late for him to avoid a collision, fortunately slight although five people (including two employees) were taken by ambulance to the Western Infirmary but none was seriously hurt. Unfortunately there were to be more collisions before the system closed for modernisation and these are covered in Chapter 7.

Railways have never been run without risk to life and limb of the people employed on them, and the Glasgow Underground is no exception. Fatal accidents occurred to employees in 1941, 1954, 1957 and 1960, as follows:-

1. At about 5·30am on 16th May 1941 whilst removing car sweepings from the rear platform of Trailer Car 44 of Route 5, a fitter called Ernest Conner, was crushed by the front of Motor Car 11 of Route 6 which had been stopped about 10 yards away, but moved off. He received severe injuries to both legs and was removed by ambulance to the Victoria Infirmary, where he died at 7·20am.[40] This presumably happened either at the Car Sheds pit, or in the adjacent tunnel: the reason for Route 6 moving is not known, but there is a slight down gradient from the pit to Govan Cross, so it is possible it had not been correctly secured after earlier shunting.

2. At about 3am in the morning of 10th October 1954, C. Kennedy, a Permanent Way burner, was electrocuted in the Merkland Street to Govan Cross section of the Inner Circle when leaving the side of a car to climb on to a wagon.[20]

   The bare tunnel telephone wires could be switched at night to provide a 240 Volt mains supply for special light fittings similar to those which fitted over the T-irons and were carried as part of the trains' emergency equipment. With both types in use good illumination of worksites was achieved. When the telephone wires were at 240 volts a small red lamp was illuminated near the tunnel entrance to warn drivers not to attempt to clip a telephone handset on to the wires. On the night in question, the back of the burner's neck came into contact with the energised wires. After this accident the battery locomotive had warning notices painted near the cab doorway.

3. A second fatal accident in the pit area befell Arthur Mooney, a Shift Fitter, at about 11.40pm on the night of 8th December 1957. He was working at track level in the lifting pit area and was run over by a reversing train and died later the same night. A safety procedure involving coloured lettered tablets for each of the four tunnels (which were coded to match) was introduced from 13th April 1962. The letters were allocated as follows:-

A	Inner Circle from Govan Cross	(Red)
B	Inner Circle to Copland Road	(Blue)
C	Outer Circle from Copland Road	(Green)
D	Outer Circle to Govan Cross	(Yellow)

   Anyone going into the tunnel to carry out shunting operations had to take the appropriate tablet from its holder at the tunnel mouth. Removal of the tablet revealed a notice reading 'Men in Tunnel'.[41]

4. About 9·03pm on Sunday 26th June 1960, Thomas Hamilton, the Conductor of Route 11 was going forward from his disabled train to Buchanan Street (Inner Circle) to report loss of power to his train and to Route 12 which had been sent forward to assist. Before he reached Buchanan Street the trains started to move again, and the Conductor was trapped: unfortunately his injuries proved fatal.[42]

A strange incident, fortunately without serious consequences, took place at Bridge Street at 3·49pm on 10th February 1949. William Warnock, a 16½ year old Ticket Collector, had been collecting tickets from the rear gate of Inner Circle train Route 16. He gave the Conductor the 'all clear' signal in the normal way, who in turn gave the Driver the 'all clear', and stepped on to the rear platform of the motor car to close the gates. As the gates were closing, the Ticket Collector noticed two boys playing with the brake wheel on the rear platform of the trailer car, and moved towards the train to get them to stop, obstructing the closing gate as he did so. A corner of his coat caught in the gate, and the train moved off. He managed to grab the outside gate handle with one hand, and his whistle from the lapel of his coat with the other and started blowing it. The Station Master, contrary to instructions when trains were in the platform, had gone into the 'box' at the end of the platform to sign a labourer's time book, and, attracted by the shouts of passengers opened the Inner Circle advance feed knife switch instead of tripping the Circuit Breaker.

A passenger attracted the Conductor's attention, and he ran through the front car and told the driver to stop, then back to the rear of the train where he found the lad hanging on to the gate, and standing on the rear buffer beam. In the meantime another Underground driver travelling as a passenger in the rear car went to the Conductor's platform and operated the emergency brake valve. When the train stopped the Conductor opened the gate and helped the lad into the train. The Ticket Collector was taken to the Victoria Infirmary, but found to be unhurt, and resumed normal duty the next day![43]

On Saturday 8th August 1959 a train in the charge of Driver Sam Louden over-ran the trainstop at St Enoch (Outer Circle). The driver left his cab to isolate the tripcock, and the train moved away on the steep down-gradient, and trapped him at the mouth of the tunnel. The Fire and Ambulance services experienced much difficulty in removing the injured driver, and a delay of 62 minutes resulted.[44]

1950 Ideas for Replacement Rolling Stock

About 1950 consideration was given to replacing the rolling stock. On 3rd June the General Manager wrote ot the Town Clerk pointing out that the present stock "has been in service for over 50 years, and its replacement will be necessary in the near future".[41]

The General Manager went on to recommend that a prototype 3-car train of modern construction be built in GCT workshops. Although 3-car trains of the existing stock could not conveniently be run because of the limited length of some station platforms, the arrangement of doors on the proposed train would overcome this difficulty. He considered 3-car trains would ease the problems in peak periods caused by the Underground having become so popular, and would be more economical to work than 2-car trains. Each train would accommodate 158 seated passengers compared with 84 in the existing trains. He estimated the cost of the train consisting of front and rear motor cars and centre trailer need not exceed £5,750: this was on the basis that the equivalent number of cars of the existing stock would be scrapped, and the electrical equipment and bogies would be available.[45]

Alexander Reid, who was based at the Underground Car Sheds, was allocated the job of developing the design: on 14th September he wrote to the General Manager listing some 10 difficulties in operating 3-car trains, and advocating the building of 2-car trains with some 15 to 20 more seats than the existing trains.[46] His message evidently impressed Mr R. D. Ewen, the Tramways Engineer, because he wrote to the General Manager on 2nd October in the following terms:-

I would remind you that you agreed to the argument that the depositing of the number of passengers carried by a three-car train at a station with say a train unloading at the other platform at the same time would over-stress the capacity of stations, and probably lead to accidents. You agreed, therefore, to consider a two-coach train provided that the capacity of the system as a whole could be increased. On close examination of this, I came to the conclusion that the capacity of the system could be increased by increasing the number of signalling sections. I have had a word with the Electrical Engineer, and he now informs me that such an alteration is practicable.

Say you intend to increase the present maximum number of trains per circle from 10 to 15, it would mean increasing the number of sections in the ratio of 3 to 2, which would give us a number of 24 sections per circle.

A rough sketch is submitted herewith, showing the proposed seating arrangement . . . of the proposed two unit train. You will note that the rear vestibule of the leading coach, and the leading and rear vestibules of the trailing coach have now been incorporated in the passenger accommodation space . . . The leading coach provides seats for 47 passengers, the trailing coach for 50.

Mr Fitzpayne considered that since the proposed cars would not greatly increase the capacity compared with the existing ones it was not opportune to continue with the project.[47]

The 3-coach Train Experiment

Later in the 1950s when traffic was still buoyant, and the system was subject to considerable overcrowding, particularly between Govan Cross and Merkland Street, and to and from Copland Road when Rangers were playing at Ibrox Stadium, a scheme for a trial 3-car train consisting of 2 motor cars and an intermediate trailer – all adapted from existing vehicles – was conceived.

BTH had supplied camshaft traction control equipments of their design for many years to London Transport, and the Southern Region of British Railways was planning to use the English Electric version on its Kent Coast stock, so it is likely that Metro-politan-Vickers was keen to have a test bed for its equivalent design. From GCT's viewpoint adaptation of the existing contactor equipment would have been simpler, but it seems the project involving the use of camshaft equipment was considered, initially at least, as a joint venture.

Design work seems to have started in the spring of 1955. The equipment on each motor car consisted of a pneumatically operated camshaft, and eight electro-pneumatic unit switches. The camshaft driving engine consisted of two opposed air cylinders, air to which was controlled by two magnet valves, an advance magnet valve and a return magnet valve. There was also a hydraulic damper system which controlled the speed at which the camshaft moved, and this in turn was electrically linked to the current limit relays. The camshaft had six power and six control cams operating finger contacts, but no more than four of the control cams were used, and in the early stages one of the power cams was also unused.

New resistor grids and master controllers were needed, and because train control wires between the equipments were required (making the vehicles true multiple units) new-style 19-way jumpers were provided, but the original motors, shoegear and compressors were retained. The camshafts and associated equipment were housed in the equipment cubicle on the rear platform like the previous contactors .

Two Metropolitan-Vickers equipped motor coaches – Nos. 3 and 56 – were selected

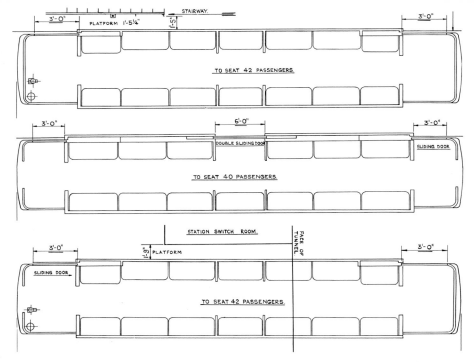

Drawing dated December 1958, showing the difficulty of fitting a 3-car train into one of the stations with short platforms – Hillhead. This drawing shows the layout of the 3-car train as run experimentally, but confined to the Outer Circle.

for conversion. Because the overall layout of the cars was not changed, and there was no need for a cab at the rear of the train, the rear car's cab was adjacent to the trailer. Trailer Car 32, the one damaged when the crane hook broke in 1954, was chosen as the intermediate trailer: it was rebuilt with a pair of additional doors in the centre, losing 4 seats. At this stage Car 32 retained filament lighting, but was fitted with 19-way through control lines for multiple control of the two power cars. Car 3 normally ran as the trailing car, and had the bodywork altered and the T-iron skids brought to the rear to suit. In this form the 3-car train had a seating capacity of 124. The main items of equipment for the first car arrived from Metropolitan-Vickers during January 1958, and that for the second car in April.

After conversion Car 56 was taken for test runs on Saturday 29th March 1958, possibly on Wednesday 30th April, and on Thursday 1st May – presumably at night. Following these tests it was decided to increase the number of notches from 21 to 23, which involved modification to the camshaft equipment and the resistance grids, and alteration to some of the wiring. Cars 56 and 32 were tested on 1st November 1958, then all three cars had test runs on 16th November and 7th January 1959. Three days (or nights) later what is recorded as an "MoT Test Run" took place.

During loaded test runs it was found necessary to increase the trip settings of the station circuit breakers. The notching current in series was about 240–250 Amps per car, and in parallel about 440 Amps per car. The station circuit breakers on the Outer Circle had their trip settings increased from 700 to 800 Amps. On the level the train reached 19 mph in 12 seconds.

The 3-car train started operation on the Outer Circle – to which it was confined

Trailer car No. 32 being rebuilt in November 1955 in the Car Sheds, in preparation for use as the centre car in the proposed 3-car train. It had been damaged on 8th April 1954 when the crane hook broke and dropped the lifting frame on to its roof. The framing for the new centre doorway can be made out half way down the body side. *Ian Maclean*

throughout its career – as Route 9 on Monday 23rd February 1959. It gave satisfaction to the operators in clearing peak period traffic, but loading and unloading times were slightly extended on the first day, amounting to a running delay of 6 minutes between 7·02am and 9·07am. Minor adjustments were needed, and this extended the delay by a further 3 minutes up to 11·05am, but 6 minutes of the lost time had been recovered by 2·45pm. Lack of experience in handling the new formation by drivers and station staff (no doubt particularly at Hillhead and West Street which were particularly tight for length) was the official explanation for most of the delay. On the Tuesday it gave every satisfaction and ran to schedule.[48] The train was lifted again on Saturday 28th February, by which time further modifications to the control equipment had been found necessary.

On Tuesday 8th September 1959 the 3-car train was put into service with the some of the cams modified, and other changes. The leading motor car performed satisfactorily, but the control gear on the rear one was erratic. Next day the problem was established as occurring if power was shut off before the train had completed the accelerating sequence, and this was put down to too low an air pressure to operate the pneumatic engine. Next day the train performed satisfactorily during the morning with an electrician on board to deal with any problems, but the rear car was lifted about midday for adjustment of the air pressure, and the other two cars remained in service in 2-car formation. Car 3 was returned to service about 4·20pm, and the train performed satisfactorily until close of traffic about 11pm.

There were two other developments on 10th September: it was decided that the 'No Exit' notices at the rear door of Car 3 were not sufficiently conspicuous, and as an initial measure a temporary large notice was fitted up overnight. It was also agreed that '30-day' probationary drivers should be precluded from instruction on the 3-car train.

The train evidently ran uneventfully on Friday 11th and Saturday 12th September. It was arranged for the train to be lifted on the Saturday night, and returned to service on Tuesday morning 15th September. Car 56 failed during the afternoon of Tuesday 15th, however, and was lifted because of a contactor fault. The other motor car had to be lifted at 11·15pm.

At some stage the train earned the nickname 'Sputnik', after the first artificial earth satellite launched by the USSR about this time, because the train spent more time up (in the sheds) than down (on the line).[6]

After further modifications, it was decided to test each motor car for 10 days running in a 2-car formation, then after 20 days to run the whole 3-car train.

On 6th October Cars 56 and 32 were put into service, and ran satisfactorily that day and the next, but on 8th October gave two small interruptions to service due to contacts welding together and air bubbles in the hydraulic fluid. It was decided the train should not be risked in service next day, so it was lifted after traffic on 8th October. On examination next day it was discovered hydraulic fluid had found its way into the air system.

After further attention it was decided to give the car a test run out of passenger service on Sunday 18th October from 10·30am until 4pm, but on examination on completion of the test it was found sufficient hydraulic fluid had passed into the air system to cause problems if it were to run for 10 days, so it was not returned to service. Bench tests of the air engine system were then set up in Coplawhill Tram Works. The equipment was re-assembled to the train, and tests carried out on the night of 8th December, and the train was put back into service next day for what was hoped to be a 10-day trial, initially accompanied by a GCT or AEI (as Metropolitan-Vickers had by then become) tradesman. By 15th December only small quantities of hydraulic fluid

The 3-car train lying out of service in the car sheds.

had had to be added, and the train had accumulated 1,602 miles running. The 11-day test on the 3-car train was concluded on 19th December, but on static tests it was found the timing of notching on Car 3 had gone out of adjustment, so it was kept out of service. About this time it was decided to move the Outer Circle trainstops at Buchanan Street and St Enoch to allow the train to stop balanced on the crest of the hump, instead of hanging back down the approach gradient.

On 26th December 1959, Car 56 running with Car 32 as a 2-car train failed with a fused contactor. A meeting was held with AEI, and it was decided more major modifications were necessary, and the train remained out of service for nearly 18 months.

The train next ran in passenger service on Sunday 7th May 1961, but next day Car 56 suffered a power defect, but no delay occurred as power from the trailing motor car was used thereafter and enabled scheduled running to be maintained.

On Wednesday 10th May the 3-car train had to be taken out of service at St Enoch at 3.11pm with a motor defect. The train reached the Car Sheds Pit at 3.23, and Car 56 was lifted. Car 3 then propelled Car 32 for one journey, and on reaching the Pit again at 3.55 the two cars were switched over, and the train re-entered service in 2-car form from Kelvinbridge at 4.12, by which time the Circle was running 15 minutes late.

On Friday 12th May, repairs having been carried out to Car 56, the 3-car train resumed service and ran successfully all day.

By Saturday 27th May the Southern Area Superintendent was able to report that the 3-car train had completed 8 consecutive days in passenger service without incident.[48]

The three cars seem to have been in service either in the 3-car formation, or with one or other of the power cars, reasonably regularly, though not without minor incident, from August 1961 until the end of January 1963, when Car 32 was sent to Coplawhill for underframe strengthening. It returned to Broomloan in April, received the rest of an overhaul, and was back in service by the end of September. Meanwhile Cars 56 and 3 ran in 2-car formation with Nos. 2 and 4 motors on each cut out.

The cars continued in service through 1964, 1965, 1966 and the first seven months or so of 1967.

A slight mystery surrounds the last workings of the 3-car train. According to the surviving weekly mileage returns Car 3 did not run in service after some date prior to 20th August 1967. Car 3 was shunted out of the Paint Shop on 5th August 1967, having been completely re-painted inside and out, but retaining the older style of interior decor with dark stained ceiling ribs. The whole 3-car train was put in running order on 23rd September for test: presumably the tests revealed a defect. All three cars received a 10-daily overhaul on 7th October. *Scottish Tramlines* recorded the last date the whole train was in service as Monday 23rd October 1967, but even then it was withdrawn with mechanical faults. The Electricians' report for Sunday Night Shift of 22nd October states they accompanied the train for one journey before they went home. The Back Shift Electricians' report for Monday 23rd October reported that the train was on half power, and that Nos. 1 and 2 contacts on the top were stuck in (but on which car is not stated). The electricians evidently cleared this, and the train lost no time. The weekly mileage returns credit Cars 56 and 32 (but not Car 3) with 447 miles in Week Ending 28th October. In preparation for what turned out to be the last outing of Car 56, all three cars had a 10-daily overhaul on Wednesday 10th January 1968. The electricians were called to Cars 56 and 32 running as Train Route 8 during the Back Shift on 11th January 1968, because the train was slow in picking up top speed. The electrician cleared and adjusted some contacts and improved matters somewhat; however the next day the cars broke down – further details have not survived, but Car 56 does not appear to have been in service again. *Scottish Tramlines* confirms that Cars 56 and 32 last ran on 11th and 12th January, but had to be withdrawn with mechanical faults. The mileage returns credit cars 56 and 32 with 446 miles in Week Ending 13th January.

Looking north on Greenhaugh Street in 1959, the entrance to Govan Cross Underground Station is beneath the illuminated half-circle-and-bar sign on the left hand tenement, while the 1953 depot office and station exit, with similar sign, are to the right of VKV 99, a Daimler-Willowbrook demonstration bus working on service 4A while on loan to Glasgow Corporation Transport. (This bus was later purchased by McGill's Bus Service and worked for several years on their Barrhead to Paisley routes). *Ian Maclean*

What might have been

The General Manager wrote to Pressed Steel Co. Ltd. of Linwood Works Paisley in January 1961, following an earlier meeting to discuss a tentative proposal for replacing the Underground stock. It will be remembered that Pressed Steel built the two batches of AM3 (later 303) 3-car units (originally better known as the 'Blue Trains') for the B.R. Glasgow suburban electrifications, and production of these would be drawing to a close in 1961.[49]

An undated GCT drawing[50] shows what was clearly intended to be a new steel framed and steel panelled centre trailer car, with two 5ft 3½ins wide double leaf doorways on the platform side at 11ft centres. This allowed for 4 seats on the platform side between the doorways, and nine seats at the ends on the non-platform side – on the non-platform side there were 30 seats, giving a total of 52 in all. (See page 109.)

In 1966 a scheme was drawn up for conversion of the whole Underground fleet to 3-car trains. The intention was to convert most of the remaining cars into 13 3-car trains (in addition to the prototype): this would have involved the conversion of two ex-gripper trailer cars to motor cars, and included the cost for the additional motor bogies, motors etc. The trailer cars would have had centre doors cut into them as on Car 32. Presumably the remaining 8 ex-gripper trailer cars would have been scrapped. It seems likely the figure of 14 trains was chosen because of structural difficulties in cutting centre doors into ex-gripper trailers. Two versions of the scheme were costed, one involving merely the new traction equipment and conversion of two trailers to motors, and a more grandiose one involving the same number of cars, but also fitting automatic train operation (ATO) equipment! No doubt the latter was the current "fad" with London Transport conducting trials for their ATO system subsequently installed on the Victoria Line about that time. The costs of the two schemes were £91,000 and £210,000 respectively. Justifying the fitting of ATO equipment to 70-year old rolling stock would have been no mean task, but by that time traffic figures were declining, so the scheme was taken no further.

In conclusion, the demise of the 3-car train marked the end of an interesting project, which probably accumulated about 250,000 train miles of running, but it is doubtful if either GCT or Metropolitan-Vickers (by then part of AEI) learned much of practical use from it. It was the last major attempt by GCT to keep the Underground abreast of modern technology. The motor cars were scrapped (except for the motors and bogies) but trailer Car 32 ran on as a conventional trailer, using the double doorway and with the rear one usually locked out of use. It was not until November 1980 that the Underground was to see 3-car trains again, but that was after the Modernisation.

Chapter 7

The Years of Uncertainty, 1965–1977

The period from the mid-1960s until closure of the Underground for modernisation was one of decreasing standard of service. This, of course, stemmed from the increasing age of the equipment, and, in the early stages, no clear idea of how the cost of replacement or improvement could be funded, or indeed whether expenditure could be justified. Fewer and fewer people in the senior or middle management of GCT had electric traction knowledge and expertise, and this trend accelerated after abandonment of the trolleybuses in 1967. On a day-to-day basis the operation of the Underground was left to those who had found ways to make it work, rather than with knowledge of the principles involved. Passenger figures dropped from 25 million in 1964/65 to 14 million in 1972/73 (the last year of GCT ownership) and to 7 million in 1976/77. The early 1970s was a period of national industrial unrest, and the Underground did not escape: it was affected by power cuts, and industrial relations in GCT and GGPTE reflected the mood of the times. The train service had been progressively reduced, reliability was becoming steadily worse, and towards the end the stations were depressing places with peeling paintwork and a general air of dilapidation, but despite all this the trains were always clean. There were two collisions warranting Railway Inspectorate Inquiries, and the tragic deaths of a driver and station master. On the Traffic side, many long service tramway employees had been drafted into the Underground, but as they retired and were replaced by 'outsiders' standards fell.

In 1969 E. R. L. Fitzpayne retired as General Manager after some 27 years in the post and was replaced by Mr William (Bill) Murray, who remained in the post until the end of Corporation ownership, and, as will be seen in Chapter 8, went on to become Director of Operations of Greater Glasgow Passenger Transport Executive.[1]

A five-day working week commenced for Underground drivers (and probably conductors) from 22nd November 1970, and for station staff from 7th February 1971.[2]

The station improvements at Kelvinbridge in 1965 and 1967 were the last significant investment in the Underground undertaken by GCT: St Georges Cross station was rebuilt in 1970, but this was associated with motorway slip road construction and the forming of pedestrian underpasses rather than improving the Underground *per se.*

Stations

About 1965 the Corporation acquired from British Railways the former goods yard at Kelvinbridge, and converted it into a 250-space Park-and-Ride car park. The car park itself came under the jurisdiction of the Roads Department which supplied the attendant, who issued joint parking and Underground return travel tickets. The facility came into use on and from Monday 22nd November 1965.[3]

In late 1966 or early 1967 work started on rehabilitating the passenger lift at Kelvinbridge, which had been out of use since 1938. This brought intending passengers down from Great Western Road to a level approximately mid-way between South Woodside Road and the platform: a short passage led from the lower lift landing to a landing on the stairway between the South Woodside Road entrance and the platform. Previously tickets had been issued by the attendant in the lift, but in its reconstructed form the lift was passenger operated, so the booking office was moved from its position just inside the South Woodside Road entrance to the intermediate level so that one booking office assistant could issue tickets to passengers entering by both routes. The new ticket office came into use during the summer of 1967, and the lift from 20th November.[4] The old booking office became a staff bothy, mainly for use by night shift Permanent Way personnel.

About the same time as the Kelvinbridge hoist scheme was being planned, consideration was given to installing an escalator at Buchanan Street station: this would have been under the buildings on the east side of Buchanan Street itself, but the scheme was abandoned before work on site started.[5]

Late in 1970 the station building at St Georges Cross, which had until some time previously been incorporated in a tenement building was demolished, and a new entrance was brought into use on 11th January 1971.[6] This entrance was formed at a landing in the stairway down to the platform, where it took a 180° turn. Access to the new entrance was down external steps from Great Western Road which also gave access to a pedestrian underpass. Since the entrance was practically invisible from the surrounding streets, the new building was surmounted by a tower with prominent 'U' signs mounted on either side. The lower flights of stairs down to the platform remained essentially as before.[2]

Cowcaddens Street and the Underground station were both greatly affected by the road schemes. A new road, Cowcaddens Road, was built parallel to and south of Cowcaddens Street and at a higher level. Much property had to be demolished to accommodate the new road, including the tenement above the station. The entrance and booking office were replaced by a Portakabin in 1973 and remained on Cowcaddens Street, which became a dead-end, whilst access to the station from the south and west was thereafter by pedestrian underpasses below the new road.

Preliminary work for the westward extension of the M8 Motorway necessitated the closure of both Circles during the Glasgow Fair of 1973. The work entailed building a new sewer below the Underground tunnels just east of Kinning Park station. Work commenced on Sunday 15th July, and was sufficiently complete to allow train services to resume on Thursday 26th July – four days earlier than forecast. Whilst the line was impassable, shuttle services were run on both Circles between Kelvinbridge and St Enoch and Govan Cross and Partick Cross.

Excavations alongside St Georges Cross for new low-level access. *Glasgow Museum of Transport*

The South Woodside Road entrance to Kelvinbridge in the late 1940s, with the 'iron stair' on the left. This was the only Underground station to use 'GCT' in its identification, and did so because another Kelvinbridge station, on BR's Glasgow Central Railway, lay just across the way. No.74 was, and still is, a "close", or entry passage, to the tenemental flats above. The booking office was just inside the doorway at No.76, on the left, and faced the street.

In a comprehensive scheme completed in 1967, the passenger lift was reinstated, with a new passenger-operated car and a rebuilt entrance on Great Western Road. The old booking office was closed, and the frontage, the entrance and the stair down to the intermediate landing were all modernised; the top of the handrail for the stair can just be seen through the doorway.

Halfway down, the stair made a right-angled turn and then continued towards the landing, at the far side of which was built the new booking office. This had two issuing windows, with the Automaticket machine installed in the angle between, and thus was able to serve passengers coming along the passage from the lift as well as those who had used the stair.

Facing the passage was another stair which descended to a short tunnel leading onto the platform. Here on 3rd May 1977 Motor Coach 15 and Trailer 7 form an Outer Circle train. *G. Watson*

In the 1977-80 rebuilding of the station, the pedestrian tunnel and the stairs became the emergency exit, and a new staircase was built at the west end of the platform, where the Station-master's box had been. The lift was removed, the shaft decked-over at the Great Western Road entrance level and the space gained, together with the former entrance, became an extension to a shop, and the passageway from the shaft was bricked-up at the intermediate landing. This photograph was taken on 24th December 1995 from the same view-point as the one above; the early morning 'key train', made up of refurbished power cars 127, 119 and 114, is about to continue its pre-service journey. *Ian Maclean*

Broomloan Depot

About 1965 a business which had occupied a range of buildings in Broomloan Road to the south of the Car Sheds closed down, and GCT leased them for use as an extension to the Car Sheds. A track was projected into the building from the 'smithy', so materials could readily be moved in and out. Most of the buildings were used as a Permanent Way store for rails, Thermit Welding materials and so on, but part was used as a covered staff car park – a facility becoming ever more necessary at that time. As will be seen in Chapter 8 these buildings were demolished about 1978.

Permanent Way bogie wagon No. 2, one of three similar vehicles, in the south west corner of Broomloan Depot, with the Blacksmith's shop and building occupied in the mid-1960s and used as a Permanent Way Store through the doorway in the background.

Several small wagons, all unnumbered, were built on single bogies from overhauled or scrapped passenger coaches. This one – an ex-motor bogie – carried electric and gas welding equipment, and is being lowered on to the Outer Circle on 28th January 1977. *G. Watson*

Train Service

The weekdays service was reduced from Monday 15th February 1965 to 16 trains (Route Nos. 1 to 8 and 11 to 18 on the Outer and Inner Circles respectively) running every 3 to 4 minutes with a time of 28, 29 or 30 minutes for a circuit, depending on the time of day. The last trains on each Circle became Route Nos. 8 and 18. As far as the passengers were concerned the effect of the adjustment was small, and the new service operated very successfully. It remained the standard weekday service for nearly 10 years, until 28th February 1975, although only 14 trains ran from early October 1974, but to the original timings. Returning to February 1965, the Saturday service was reduced from 20 to 18 trains, thus Route Nos. 10 and 20 no longer operated. The Sunday service was not altered at this stage.[5]

On Wednesday 3rd May 1967 there was an evening Rangers vs. Slavia football match at Ibrox Stadium. During the afternoon an additional train was put into service on each Circle, and ran until the end of service. The arrangement proved successful, so was repeated on Wednesday 16th August for a Rangers vs. Celtic match and on Wednesday 8th November for Rangers vs. Cologne.[7]

To enable shorter working hours for traffic staff, the Saturday service was reduced from 18 trains to 16 as from 10th February 1968. The new timetable, although using the same number of trains as the weekday service, retained the same Saturday start and stop times: this had the effect of reducing the scheduled weekly mileage by about 460 to 25,133.[8, 9] As from 4th August 1968 a new 12-train Sunday service was introduced, giving a 5-minute frequency – this lasted until February 1972, and reduced the weekly scheduled mileage to 24,643.[8, 9, 10]

Because of the acute axle shortage brought about by the measures to resolve the breakage problem (see later in this Chapter) the Mondays to Fridays and the Saturday services were reduced to 6 trains per circle from 3rd November 1975. The service was not re-timed; Route Nos 3, 5, 6, 13, 15 and 16 simply did not run.[11]

As we are now in the period when GCT (including the Underground) began to use the 24-hour clock, from now on this will be used in the text.

Cars 57 and 37 at Shields Road in January 1977. *George Watson*

Incidents

On 13th February 1965 there was a problem with Car 55 colliding with the tunnel roof on the Outer Circle where the track levels out after passing under the General Terminus Quay branch of British Railways, just west of Shields Road station. The problem was caused by the track ballast being packed too high. The rails were lowered and re-laid in concrete, and a temporary 10 mph speed restriction imposed.[12] The re-railing contractor experienced difficulties with clearances in the same area during Modernisation, the results of which manifested themselves in 1985.

At about 15:20 hrs on Wednesday 20th April 1966, part of the brake rigging of an Inner Circle train became dislodged and dropped on to the track between West Street and Bridge Street and became wedged between the running rail and a check rail. The following train composed of Cars 27 and 41 hit the obstruction and both cars became derailed near the entrance to Bridge Street station. Nobody was injured, and passengers were taken along the tunnel to Bridge Street. The cars were re-railed and repairs carried out to the live rail, and services were resumed on the Inner Circle by 21:00 hrs, the Outer Circle having been suspended for about 15 minutes.[13]

Two days later, at 19:03 hrs on Friday 22nd April, there was a particularly unpleasant incident at Partick Cross. A man fell from the platform on to the track and whilst climbing back was hit by an oncoming train and trapped by the legs between the train and the platform. The Fire Brigade and emergency personnel together with doctors and nurses from the Western Infirmary were involved in the rescue. The car had to be jacked up to release the man's legs. As a result of this incident the Fire Brigade produced an internal instruction on how to deal with such incidents, but fortunately it never had to be put into practice. The original instruction is, of course, out of date, but procedures are now in place for a wide variety of scenarios, some of which have been the subject of simulated exercises (see Chapter 9).

On Saturday 27th August 1966, Trailer Car 41 was again in trouble, when a wheel cracked whilst the car was working on the Outer Circle near Hillhead. The train completed another circuit before the car was lifted and replaced. Fifteen days later the same car suffered a similar failure, which was ascribed to faulty metal in the chilled-iron wheels. The General Manager quickly directed that all such wheels should be replaced by conventional forged steel ones. The replacement wheels were ordered from the North British Steel Foundry at Bathgate, and were fitted between May 1967 and June 1969. The change, however, had its problems as three of the new wheels moved on their axles and caused derailments on 5th June and 29th August 1969 and 7th March 1970.[4, 14] A shuttle service was put on during the resulting suspensions on the first two occasions – the first time this is known to have been done.[15]

Broken axles were all too frequent in the last years before Modernisation. About 17:52 hrs on Thursday 17th October 1968, Motor Car 17 fractured an axle on the Cowcaddens curve and became derailed whilst working on Route No. 14. Passengers had to de-train and walk along the tunnel, and the Inner Circle was suspended for the remainder of the day.[10] Five further broken axle incidents occurred in 1970 (2), 1973 (1) and 1975 (2),[16] all but the 1973 one being on motor cars. Following the first broken axle incident in 1975 arrangements were put in hand to ultrasonically test all the axles – a procedure which had not previously been carried out. The second incident occurred before the arrangements had been finalised, and when the testing was eventually carried out, (initially under contract by British Rail) some 40% of motor axles and 32% of trailer axles were found to be suspect, which inevitably affected the number of trains available for service, and resulted in the service reductions already mentioned. It was impossible to obtain the required number of new axles from normal sources quickly enough, but it was discovered that certain types of British Rail diesel multiple unit axles, even if dimensionally sub-standard for their original purpose, were adaptable for Underground use. British Rail was scoured for these axles, some even coming from Swindon! They were turned down to size at the Underground, at the PTE's Larkfield Bus Works and by contractors. The wheels and gears were pressed off the old axles and remounted on the new ones at British Rail Engineering Limited's Glasgow Works, better known locally as St Rollox or 'the Caley'. For ease of identification, the axleboxes of axles which had passed the test were painted white, and those which had failed were painted red.

Unusual precautionary measures had to be taken on Monday 29th March 1975: early in the afternoon it was noticed that the glazed ceramic tiles on the lightwell adjacent to the stairway at St Enoch were bulging dangerously above the Outer Circle track. The bonding had failed after about 40 years in use. The Outer was suspended, and a permanent way wagon was lowered, coupled to a car, and hauled round to St Enoch. As much of the track and platform as possible were protected, then the tiles were knocked down into the wagon.

At about 09:24 hrs on Thursday 23rd December 1976 an incident which could have had much worse consequences occurred at St Georges Cross. A train composed of Cars 55 and 13 was pulling away from the platform in the normal way, and the conductor was stepping from the rear platform of the motor car to the trailer, when the cars parted, throwing the conductor on to the track between the cars. Fortunately the automatic air brake operated correctly, and both cars were automatically brought to rest, with the conductor between them. The conductor was able to stand up, and was assisted on to the platform. It transpired that the coupling pin at the rear of the motor car had worked up and been forced out, allowing the coupling link between the cars to become detached from the adjustable fork-end of the motor car: this was mainly caused by wear on the pin and in the holes[17] (see Figure 7.1 below).

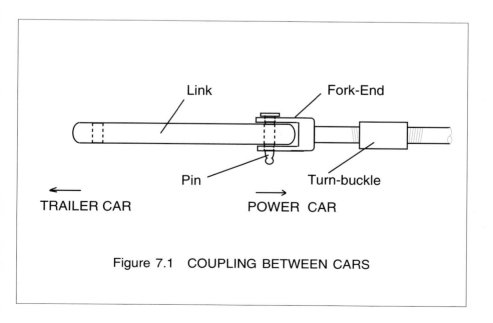

Figure 7.1 COUPLING BETWEEN CARS

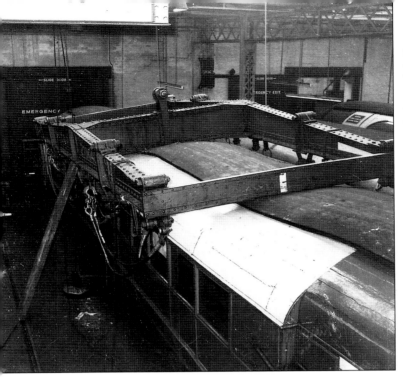

Upon the dissolution of the three-car train in October 1967, No. 32 was temporarily withdrawn, but returned to service as a normal trailer car on 12th March 1968 on the Inner Circle, its first time there for many years. On 30th January 1972 the replacement crane hook also failed, and again the lifting frame fell on a coach, and again it was trailer 32. The extent of the internal damage is shown in the lower photograph. The coach was repaired once more and continued unscathed in service until the closure of the system for modernisation. *J. McTavish*

Collisions in Passenger Service

A collision occurred between Merkland Street and Govan at about 15:50 hrs on Sunday 10th August 1969. A train became disabled, and the following one was emptied of its passengers and sent to assist. The assisting train collided with the disabled one, and the passengers were walked through the tunnel to Govan. A motor car was lowered from the Car Sheds, and used to tow the damaged vehicles out. The Circle was running again by 18:05 hrs. The motor car from the assisting train (No. 59) was out of service for some five weeks.[9, 15]

The second collision in this period occurred on Friday 22nd May 1970 at Merkland Street (Inner Circle) when a train (Cars 2 and 10) which had left Partick Cross on a red signal collided with a stationary train (Cars 55 – again! – and 42). One female passenger on the moving train was taken to the Western Infirmary, but damage to the cars was slight.[15]

On Tuesday 4th February 1975 Route No. 17 (Cars 25 and 35) collided with the rear of Route No. 16 (Cars 24 and 41) which was standing at a red signal in Bridge Street platform because men were working on pumping equipment between St Enoch and Buchanan Street. Route No. 17 had a probationary driver, but an off-duty driver came into the cab whilst the train was standing at West Street, and offered to take over the controls, an offer which was accepted. The conductor closed the doors, and as the train left West Street it was tripped by the trainstop arm, which was correctly in the raised position. Evidently neither driver had seen the signal aspect, and they assumed the train had been tripped on a 'bobbing' trainstop. The probationary driver isolated the tripcock, and the train resumed normal speed towards Bridge Street. By the time they saw the tail lights of Route No. 16 it was too late to avoid a collision, which fortunately was not severe. Luckily the trains were lightly loaded, and there were no serious injuries. Lt-Col Townsend-Rose of the Railway Inspectorate conducted a Public Inquiry into the incident, and whilst he placed the blame mainly on the off-duty driver, he criticised the propensity for trainstops to bob up and down with the signal at green, which, though not dangerous in itself, tended to discredit the signalling system.

About 11:48 hrs on Glasgow Fair Monday, 19th July 1976, an Inner Circle train with a dozen or so passengers on board developed a motor fault whilst ascending the 1 in 20 gradient approaching Govan Cross. This caused the circuit breaker at Merkland Street to open on overload. After the circuit breaker had been reset the train was unable to re-start, so the driver sent his conductor forward along the tunnel to Govan Cross to summon assistance. The station master telephoned the nearby Car Sheds and then Merkland Street, telling the station master there to de-train the passengers from the following train which was delayed there. The conductor returned to his train with a line inspector who happened to be at Govan Cross at the time. The shift fitter and two electricians walked through the tunnel from the Car Sheds to Govan Cross, and on down the tunnel to the front of the disabled train.

The electricians identified and isolated the defective motor, but because there was risk of wheelspin and consequent 'dishing' of the running rails when trying to re-start on three motors, they decided to run the train back to the bottom of the gradient and attempt to climb to Govan Cross from there – a perfectly normal practice at that location. The shift fitter took over the controls for this operation – again accepted practice.

Meanwhile, another line inspector, whilst carrying out a ticket check on an Outer Circle train at Merkland Street, heard the horn associated with the circuit breaker operation, and went to the station master's box. Shortly afterwards a train arrived in the Inner Circle platform, and the telephone message from the Govan Cross station master was received. In a well-intentioned attempt to save time, the line inspector at Merkland Street instructed the crew of the train to de-train passengers, and prepare the train to push the casualty. The station master issued the driver with a Caution Order, but told him not to proceed. Shortly afterwards the line inspector took over the controls, and moved off. The train was, of course, tripped on the trainstop, but after isolating the tripcock, the train moved off again. As it rounded the left-hand curve near the lowest point, the duty driver saw the tail lights of the other train approaching, and shouted a warning, but it was too late to avoid a collision. The duty driver and line inspector were trapped in the wrecked cab for a time, and the conductor of the same train was knocked unconscious, but there were no obvious injuries amongst the passengers on the originally failed train. Although the two cars were telescoped by about 4 feet, there was no derailment. Cars 2 and 42 were not repaired, though the underframe of Car 2 has seen further service as a rail-laying wagon. There was a Public Inquiry held by Major P. Olver into the incident, one of the recommendations of which was that Engineering personnel who were required to drive trains in the course of their duties should be passed out by the Traffic Section.[10] The primary cause of the collision was the line inspector at Merkland Street moving off, contrary to a notice of long standing in the 'box' at Merkland Street to the effect that assisting trains were to await the arrival of the Car Sheds staff before moving off.

Research carried out at the request of Major Olver revealed that over the previous four years there had been ten cases of trains having to be assisted by a following train out of the Merkland Street to Govan Cross section. Over the same period there had been some 22 cases of trains becoming stalled, but being moved out under their own power, usually with Engineering assistance.

Of some 160 incidents affecting the running of the trains recorded in 1969, there were 42 cases of motor cars having to be lifted from service, 11 of trailer cars having to be lifted, and 46 cases (some included in the above) where trains had to be pushed by the following train.[15]

The number of cars lifted in 1975 was more than double the equivalent figure for 1970, despite a reduction in train mileage of about 14% – one measure of the increasing difficulties in maintaining the life-expired equipment. Cars lifted during traffic hours for faults or damage amounted to 153 motor cars, 9 trailers and 4 complete trains – total 170 cars. These figures compare with about 50 cars in 1961.

During 1975 and 1976 the rolling stock and other difficulties were compounded by a shortage of traffic staff (particularly drivers), so it was ironic that a poster campaign on both cars and stations extolling the advantages of becoming a PTE bus driver was in full swing.[18]

In the 28-day period between Thursday 24th February and Wednesday 23rd March 1977, there were only five days with no incidents recorded in the Car Sheds Diary: there were another 7 days on which no lost time was recorded, but one defective car was lifted. The worst day in this period was Friday 4th March when three complete journeys were lost on the Outer Circle and two on the Inner Circle, and no fewer than four defective motor cars were lifted, two from each circle.

Fires in Nearby Properties and Demolitions

A fire in a supermarket in Cowcaddens Street on Friday 16th September 1966 caused interruption to the Underground service.[4] The fire started about 09:30, but when water and foam started seeping into the tunnels, and showed no signs of abating, traction current was switched off about 12:17. Service was resumed about 15:30 with trains running under Caution Orders between Cowcaddens and Buchanan Street on both Circles, but water and foam continued to enter the tunnels and started to gather north of Buchanan Street (presumably because the gravitation pipe under the station 'hump' was running at full capacity), and north of St Enoch. An additional pump was brought from the Car Sheds to St Enoch in the wide centre doorway of Car 32 (see Chapter 6) and worked all night. The gutted shell of the building was demolished on the Saturday and Sunday, which required service suspensions at certain times.

Another fire in adjacent property, this time near St Georges Cross on Saturday 18th November 1972, had even more serious effects. The Outer Circle tunnel was badly affected by water flowing in west of St Georges Cross station, presumably from the basements of the burning buildings. Both Circles were suspended from about 14:30 on the Saturday and all day Sunday. The Inner Circle resumed at 11:30 on the Monday, and the Outer on Thursday 30th November. Shuttles were again run in an attempt to provide some sort of service.[19]

On Sunday morning 19th September 1976 the cooling tower at the former Pinkston Power Station, the development of which is mentioned in Chapter 6, was demolished by explosives. It was feared that vibrations might be transmitted through the bed-rock and damage the tunnels in the Cowcaddens area, so trains were not allowed to run on either circle during the time of the detonation. In fact no damage was sustained.

Power cuts

During the electricity workers' dispute in December 1970 supplies from the domestic circuits which fed individual stations and thence the station and train main lighting and signalling system were subject to rota power cuts on the south side of the system. On 8th December the service was maintained between West Street and Govan Cross from 16:00 until 23:00 in darkness apart from the 600-Volt emergency circuits in both stations and trains. The trains were controlled by telephone, without mishap. A similar situation arose on Thursday 10th December.[6, 20]

When, in 1973, the Government became embroiled in a conflict over pay with the miners, a State of Emergency was declared and a 3-day working week was imposed on most of industry and commenced from 17th December. Three-hour rota power cuts were re-introduced in January 1974. A General Election was called as a result of which the Conservatives were unable to form a Government, and the new Labour administration called off the State of Emergency and 3-day week from 8th March. Unlike the situation three years before, planned reductions in the service did not take place.

Because the State of Emergency banned the use of floodlights at football grounds, a Rangers vs. Dundee match was re-scheduled for Sunday 17th February 1974. Four extra trains were lowered into service from about 11:00: this was the only fixture requiring extra trains during the State of Emergency.[21]

Accidents to staff

A driver, Thomas Egan, was run over by his own train and killed when approaching the Car Sheds pit on the Outer Circle at close of traffic on 5th April 1971. Apparently he had been attempting to remove the front gangway half door whilst the train was in motion and overbalanced.[6] It was normal for the drivers to remove the doors to allow train crews to walk through the cars to the Car Sheds Pit, and because they were outward opening it was easier to do this before the train joined the end of the 'queue'.

1974 got off to a grim start with the death of Station Master George Wallace at Copland Road on 4th January. He had been remonstrating with some boys playing about at the bottom of the stairs leading on to the platform. As an Inner Circle train was leaving the station past the stairway balustrade the driver heard the sound of breaking glass, stopped and found some windows in the passenger saloon of the leading car broken. After he had reversed his train back into the platform, the station master's body was found on the track. It seems he was drawn into the narrow gap between the departing train and the balustrade, but it remains a mystery how it happened.[22]

Facing page A selection of tickets used before modernisation (1–12) and after (13–22).

1. GCT (Subway) punch-type ticket issued on the hoist at Kelvinbridge by the attendant.
2. GCT (Underground) punch-type ticket issued from the booking office at Kelvinbridge.
3. GCT punch-type ticket with station identification number overprinted.
4. GCT punch-type excess fare ticket with Outer and Inner Circle stations named.
5. GCT Automaticket – first issue.
6. GCT Automaticket with station of origin only.
7. GCT Automaticket with station identification overprint.
8. GCT Automaticket with decimal fare.
9. Greater Glasgow Passenger Transport Executive Automaticket.
10. GGPTE Automaticket Concession.
11. GGPTE punch-type excess fare ticket with station identification numbers only and inverted fare. Until the 1977 closure, late evening travellers were issued with excess fare tickets, on the platforms or on the trains, because although the stations remained open, their booking offices were closed during the time the trains were completing their last journeys.
12. GGPTE double Automaticket prepared for issue during the last week of operation before modernisation in 1977, but never issued because of the premature closure of the system.
13. Strathclyde Passenger Transport Executive Rapid Mini Printer ticket (roll stock). "77" does not represent the year 1977, but was the identification number of Cowcaddens, the issuing station.
14. SPTE Crouzet concourse passenger-operated machine ticket (roll stock).
15. SPTE Crouzet booking office portable machine ticket (pre-cut stock). "Exchange" tickets were issued per journey to pass-holders – e. g. police – to operate entry barriers.
16. SPTE Westinghouse Cubic roll stock ticket.
17. SPTE Westinghouse Cubic pre-cut stock ticket. "No Value Seasons" were, until January 1994, issued to Zonecard passengers to operate entry barriers. They had no monetary value, but were validated to match the expiry date of the Zonecard.
18. GGPTE Rapid Mini Printer (RMP) pre-cut Underground Transcard.
19. SPTE RMP pre-cut Underground Zonecard.
20. SPTE RMP pre-cut stock Underground Season. The St Enoch Transcentre continued to sell RMP Season tickets for some months after implementation elsewhere of the Westinghouse Cubic system, hence the "10/10/91" commencement date. Upon presentation at an Underground booking office, a correspondingly-validated Westinghouse Cubic "No Value Season" ticket would be issued in exchange.
21. British Rail Edmondson (non-magnetic) return ticket issued at Springburn to cover the complete rail journey from there to Ibrox on the occasion of the Papal visit to Glasgow on 1st June 1982. (Ibrox BR station closed on 6th February 1967.)
22. Front and rear of exit barrier tokens for the Park and Ride car park at Bridge Street station. Similar tokens are issued at Kelvinbridge, West Street and Shields Road stations.

Early Effects of Modernisation

A few weeks after the Secretary of State's announcement of the Infrastructure Grant (see Chapter 8) Glasgow and Strathclyde Universities' Joint Audio-Visual Service was deputed to make an archive film of the Underground before its character and equipment were displaced by modernisation. The film, which was very comprehensive, covered the operation from lifting cars, driving trains, handling football match crowds, Thermit welding of rails, through to carrying out emergency procedures. The producer wanted to depict the days of cable operation but could find no original sequences, so Trailer Car 41, which still had trellis gates and filament lighting, and was being overhauled at the time, was repainted externally in Glasgow District Subway Company colours. Sequences were shot at night in Merkland Street Outer Circle platform with PTE staff as 'passengers' dressed in Edwardian costume. After the filming the car continued to run in GDS livery, and was ultimately selected – in short 4-wheel form – to become a feature at the modernised Buchanan Street station (see Chapter 8).

This was by no means the only film made. In the 15 months following the Modernisation announcement no fewer than 22 film and television teams visited the system. Perhaps the most notable was the BBC 'Blue Peter' team, including the children's hero Peter Purvis who appeared in sequences including lifting a car from the tunnel.[23, 24]

1 Wh 9728 — Glasgow Corp. Transport (Subway) — FARE — KELVINBRIDGE (High Level) — 1d.

2 R 1543 — Glasgow Corporation Transport (Underground) — 1½d — KELVINBRIDGE (Level) — To ANY STATION on One Circle

3 T 5114 — Glasgow Corporation Transport Underground — 1d — PARTICK CROSS

4 B 0678 — EXCESS FARE — Glasgow Corporation Transport (Underground)

5 648853 — FARE 2D — ST ENOCH TO ANY STATION ON ONE CIRCLE — GLASGOW CORPORATION TRANSPORT (UNDERGROUND)

6 887746 — FARE 3D — COPLAND ROAD — GLASGOW CORPORATION TRANSPORT (UNDERGROUND)

7 232435 — FARE 1/- — HILLHEAD — GLASGOW CORPORATION TRANSPORT (UNDERGROUND)

8 182345 — FARE 6p — SHIELDS ROAD — GLASGOW CORPORATION TRANSPORT (Underground)

9 213092 — FARE 12p — COPLAND ROAD — GREATER GLASGOW P.T.E. (Underground)

10 160724 — FARE 1p — CONCESSION — GREATER GLASGOW P.T.E. (Underground)

11 C 1958 — EXCESS FARE — G.G.P.T.E. [UNDERGROUND SECTION]

12 07824 — FARE 15p — MERKLAND STREET — GREATER GLASGOW P.T.E. (Underground)

13 ADULT — Underground

14 IBROX 06-07-94

15 Strathclyde Transport — EXCHANGE — 15813

16 Strathclyde Transport Underground — SUBJECT TO PUBLISHED CONDITIONS

17 Strathclyde Transport — Underground U — TICKET TYPE — VALID UNTIL — ISSUED FROM — JOURNEY LIMIT — PRICE

18 UNDERGROUND TRANSCARD — Valid only when accompanied by card and current season ticket — No 346377

19 Strathclyde Transport — UNDERGROUND SEASON — Valid from 27 OCT 1989 — VALID ONLY WHEN ACCOMPANIED BY I.D. PHOTOCARD — ZONE — 063328

20 Strathclyde Transport — UNDERGROUND SEASON — Valid from 10|10|91 ADULT 4 — VALID ONLY WHEN ACCOMPANIED BY I.D. PHOTOCARD — 016931

21 0748 — 2nd — PAPAL VISIT 1st JUNE 1982 — To IBROX From SPRINGBURN — OUTWARD & RETURN — 0748

22 STRATHCLYDE TRANSPORT — MERKLAND ROAD

Prototype Track

During the first week of the Glasgow Fair holiday period of 1974, a 100 metre length of Outer Circle tunnel just south of the Car Sheds Pit was stripped of its ballasted track and replaced with track on concrete sleepers held in place by concrete poured round them. This was to develop ideas of track design in the unique tunnel conditions, and to estimate the effects of noise and vibration. 100 precast concrete sleepers were ordered, but 10 were rejected, so were not used: the remaining 90 were spaced out more widely, and seemed to give satisfactory results. The track design was based on 80R rail (not the 80A subsequently used) and did not incorporate base plates, merely Pandrol shoulders set into the sleepers as on most main line ballasted track. Drainage was by twin 6 inch plastic pipes below the centre of the sleepers with rodding boxes cast in at about 10 metre intervals. Signalling block joints were cut into the running rails near the ends of this length, so electrical resistance data could be obtained for track circuit design purposes.

It was decided to carry out noise and vibration tests over the experimental length with loaded cars at speed on the night of Wednesday 11th September, but part of the stretch concerned was normally used for stabling the Outer Circle trains at night. To clear this section for the tests all eight trains were shunted back to positions between Cessnock and Copland Road stations. The trains left the Pit area in reverse with one man from the Engineering Section on each, but the leading one (which had been Route 8) went further than had been intended, and was followed by Routes 7, 6, 5, 4 and 3. Routes 2 and 1, however, stopped at their intended positions. The men on the trains which had gone too far were told to close up to the rear of Route 2. As Route 5 was about to park behind Route 4 the Outer Circle circuit breaker at Copland Road (which was feeding the section on a rear feed) opened on overload. The battery tail lamps had all been removed for re-charging as usual by the train conductors at close of passenger service, and the T-iron skids had been retracted for the reverse movement, extinguishing in the process one of the two fixed tail lights. Opening of the 600 Volt circuit breaker extinguished the second fixed tail light, and with no system of tunnel lights, the trains were in total darkness. A few seconds after the Copland Road circuit breaker opened Route 6 collided heavily with the rear of Route 5, and shortly afterwards Route 7 collided heavily with the rear of Route 6. The collisions resulted in the stationary trains being pushed into one another. Three of the Handymen driving the trains were slightly injured and had to be taken to hospital. The tests, needless to say, were abandoned for the night, but were successfully completed a week later.

As a result of the tests it was decided to place perforated concrete slabs supported on a single course of bricks in the 'four foot' in an attempt to absorb some of the noise.

Structural Problems

On Monday evening 24th May 1976 the driver of an Inner Circle train felt a lurch between the Car Sheds Pit and Copland Road. On investigation it was found the invert had subsided at a point corresponding to where bored piles for the South Turn-out Chamber were being installed from the surface, and the services on both Circles were suspended. The tunnels run through sand at that point, and the piling operations were thought to have created a void under the tunnel. Shuttle services between Govan Cross and Partick Cross were run on both Circles until Sunday 30th May.

From Monday 31st May shuttle services were to be introduced between Kelvinbridge and St Enoch on both Circles as well as the usual ones between Govan Cross and Partick Cross. Back-up trains were to be positioned at Hillhead on both Circles. All three Inner Circle trains had to reverse from Govan Cross to their respective starting positions – i. e. St Enoch, Hillhead and Partick Cross. On the first morning when, just past Merkland Street, the train for St Enoch (Route No. 11) ran on to the section of live rail normally supplied from Partick Cross it lost power because the circuit breaker at Partick Cross was open. There was some delay in restoring power because the station master at Partick Cross was late in reporting for duty. In the meantime Route No. 12 bound for Hillhead, passed Merkland Street running in reverse, and collided with the stationary Route No. 11. A few minutes later Route No. 13 en route to Partick Cross also ran through Merkland Street, and collided with the other two. Fortunately no passengers were involved, and there were no serious injuries to the staff. Four cars were extensively damaged, of which Nos. 16, 58 and 45 were never returned to service, but the underframe of Car 16 has seen further service as a works wagon. The cause of the problem was the station master at Govan Cross allowing the trains to depart when they were ready, without ascertaining where the previous one was. A substitute bus shuttle service was operated via the Clyde Tunnel, but the Outer Circle operated the shuttle services as intended. The two sets of shuttle services operated as planned from Tuesday 1st until Sunday 6th June.

The Outer Circle resumed normal operations on Monday 7th June with a speed restriction between Copland Road and the Car Sheds Pit, but the Inner only operated a shuttle service from Partick Cross to Govan Cross. On Friday 11th June the Inner Circle resumed operation, but with a speed restriction between the Car Sheds Pit and Copland Road. Unfortunately it was only possible to provide 5 trains for the Inner Circle service, which situation continued for the next ten days or so.[11, 20]

Because of the subsidence, investigations were carried out under the tunnel invert on the site of the North Turn-out Chamber before the main work started. This was done between 15th and 21st June, and voids were found under the Outer Circle tunnel, so, less than a fortnight after the previous incident the Outer Circle was suspended as a precaution from start of traffic on Tuesday 22nd June. A Govan Cross to Partick Cross shuttle was put on, whilst the Inner Circle ran with its normal 6-train service, but from the Thursday this was augmented to seven trains. Grouting operations were put in hand, working round the clock, and an attempt was made to resume the Outer Circle service on 28th June. However a sand burst occurred, apparently caused by a wooden plug put in during the grouting operations working loose; the full 6-train per circle service resumed on Tuesday 29th June.

On Sunday 25th July 1976 the Inner Circle was unable to start because of a leak of sand and water into the tunnel between Govan Cross and the Car Sheds Pit. A crack had developed in the base of the drainage channel between the rails close to Govan Cross station, but it proved impossible to stem the inflow by packing the crack with oakum. A bus shuttle service was put on between Partick Cross and Govan Cross: this operated at the Underground fare of 8p, but 9p tickets were issued as there was no stock of 8p bus tickets! It was decided that the Outer Circle should also be suspended in the affected area, so a Govan Cross to Partick Cross shuttle train was organised.

It was decided to call in contractors to effect a repair, and de-watering equipment was installed in the Inner Circle tunnel to reduce the level of the water table in the surrounding ground. The Permanent Way Section removed the rails in the affected area, and the contractors renewed a section of the tunnel invert.

Both Circles resumed normal service from about 17:20 on Wednesday 11th August, after a few hours of trial running round the system, but only carrying passengers between Govan Cross and Partick Cross.

A period of torrential rain occurred in Glasgow during the late afternoon of Tuesday 28th September 1976, when 3½ ins of rain fell in four hours. Both circles were suspended during the early evening because water was pouring in at a number of points. Half way along the Inner Circle tunnel from St Georges Cross to Kelvinbridge, water was rushing in through the tunnel wall and striking the rail on the other side, and at Kelvinbridge the water nearly reached platform level. The trains, however, all reached the Car Sheds.

Shuttle services between Govan Cross and Partick Cross began operating on Wednesday 29th September on both Circles, probably during the afternoon.

Water continued to cascade through the wall into the Inner Circle tunnel between St Georges Cross and Kelvinbridge until Thursday 30th September when it eased, and by 7th October the repair work on the track was virtually complete. However, further problems had arisen in the Govan area. Further test bores had revealed there might be a large void under the Inner Circle near the site of the proposed North Turn-out Chamber; grouting resumed on 14th and was complete by 17th October.

On Thursday 24th March 1977 cracks appeared in the roof arch of Govan Cross station, attributed to piling activities by the contractors working on the site of the new Govan station. The service was suspended at 12:30, all trains being stabled by 13:15, and a substitute bus service was put on, at first by Partick Garage (which was within weeks of being closed), and then from 24th April by Ibrox Garage. The Underground remained closed until Monday 2nd May, by which time the contractors had exposed the whole of the outside of the station arch, and steel beams had been fitted as external support with tension bolts passing through the arch to steel plates inside.

Final Closure.

In view of some of the above problems it was decided in October 1976 to abandon the original intention of keeping one circle running whilst the other was modernised, then changing over. It was considered that complete closure would allow the work to be completed in 16 to 18 months, instead of 12 months for the first circle and 9 months for the second.[25] As events turned out these estimates were over-optimistic, but the difficulties of trying to operate the system safely while converting and commissioning the new one with passenger trains operating in the other tunnel, would have been verging on the insuperable. A policy of no compulsory staff redundancies was adopted, but nonetheless it was difficult to find jobs on the bus side for some people, and many, particularly Traffic staff, opted for voluntary redundancy. This, together with the periods of suspension, led to a drastic decline in morale. Recognising that expertise would be required when the new system opened, ten Traffic employees were retained in the Underground to drive the PTE-owned battery locomotives for the cabling contractors, and a nucleus of (mainly) craftsmen was retained by the Engineering section to maintain the battery locomotives, convert old coach underframes into wagons and to assist in setting up the new Workshop facilities.

During the April period of closure it was announced that the final day of operation would be Saturday 28th May, with a special service operated on Sunday 29th May from 10:00 until late afternoon when a special last train on the Inner Circle was to uplift invited guests at Buchanan Street, and convey them the 'long way round' to St Enoch where an official closing ceremony would be performed outside the station. On the last week of operation, from Sunday 22nd May, souvenir tickets were to be issued; these were of double length, and indeed were printed, but as will be seen they were never used.

As time went on it began to look doubtful if the system would re-open before the official closing date. Eventually, however, trial operation was carried out on both circles on Saturday 30th April from 09:15 until 14:40, and the structural engineers considered it was safe to resume service.

Copland Road station clock is at 12:50 on Saturday 21st May 1977. The Station Master has just received a telephone call from the Line Inspector to tell him that the service is being suspended because of cracks appearing in the roof at Govan Cross platform chamber. Passengers are leaving the old red trains for the last time, for on 23rd May the Executive decided not to resume the service, and cancelled the 'last train' arrangements planned for Saturday and Sunday, 28th and 29th May. *G. Watson*

Thus, on Monday 2nd May, operations re-commenced with a 5-train per Circle service. Even this proved difficult to staff as some of the traffic personnel had already departed, and those who had opted for redundancy had to be given time off to look for new jobs, and so from about 12th May only four trains per Circle operated.

On Saturday 21st May after some train problems at about 08:30, and a simultaneous pump problem, the traction current was cut off from both Circles in the Cowcaddens to Buchanan Street area because of a defective live rail insulator from 08:40 until 10:18 (Outer) and 10:50 (Inner). Then, at 12:50, both Circles were suspended by the duty line inspector because further cracks were seen developing at the north (stairway) end of Govan Cross platform arch, and a piece of rendering fell out on to the track. Neither the Executive's Civil Engineer nor the consulting Civil Engineers could be satisfied that a more major failure would not develop. On the Monday the Executive decided not to re-open the system until after Modernisation, and cancelled the 'last week' arrangements.

For the record, the cars put into service on the last day were:-

Outer:	Route No. 2	Car Nos.: 17/19	Inner:	Route No. 12	Car Nos.: 55/ 9
	4	29/ 8		14	57/52
	6	24/ 5		16	25/39
	7	27/38		17	11/43

Car 27 on Route No. 7 was the last car to be lifted for a defect, and was replaced by Car 20, resuming service at 08:44.

As a low-key substitute, a semi-official last train was operated on the south side of the Inner Circle on Wednesday 25th May to which selected guests were invited. Among the travellers was Mr Campbell Douglas, aged 84, who as a boy had been taken by his father for a 'hurl' on the Subway on its first day of operation.

Chapter 8

Modernisation, 1974–80 – New Wine in Old Bottles

Following the upheavals in public transport in the Greater Glasgow conurbation during the 1950s and 1960s, in which the principal suburban railway lines were either electrified or closed, and the trams and trolleybuses were replaced by diesel buses, the Greater Glasgow Transportation Study (GGTS) was commissioned. After the recommended transport plan was published in March 1968 the Corporation commissioned consultants to examine the capacity of the Underground and identify factors meriting examination in greater depth: the Stage 1 report was published in January 1970. Further reports were then commissioned from the GGTS team and the consultants. By January 1973 it had been decided that the estimates should make provision for modernisation of the stations.[1] As the 1970s dawned the possibility of a Passenger Transport Authority being established under the provisions of the 1968 Transport Act (as had been done with Merseyside, Tyneside, SELNEC and West Midlands) became another factor.

The Greater Glasgow Passenger Transport Authority was set up with representation from 21 local authorities in Lanarkshire, Dunbartonshire, Renfrewshire, Stirlingshire and the Scottish Office as well as Glasgow, and its functional body, Greater Glasgow Passenger Transport Executive (GGPTE), came into being on 1st June 1973. This body took over the direct operation of the Glasgow Corporation Transport Department and a transport co-ordinating role in an area including all or parts of each of the 22 local authority areas. The first Director General was Ronald Cox, the former General Manager of Edinburgh Corporation Transport, and there were four other directors, William Murray (Operations, last General Manager of GCT), Andrew McKay (Planning and Development, who came from British Rail), Norman Stirling (Finance, who came from a Lanarkshire local authority) and Joseph Coyle (Industrial Relations, whose background was in the mining industry). The Executive set up its headquarters in leased property at 48 St Vincent Street, Glasgow, the former Corporation Transport offices at 46 Bath Street being retained as the operational headquarters.

One of the early questions before the Executive was on the future of the Underground; broadly there were three options:-

1. To close the system completely.

2. To authorise work to keep the system going for another five years or so.

3. To carry out a comprehensive modernisation.

The Executive decided to recommend to the Authority a comprehensive modernisation scheme, and set about preparing an Infrastructure Grant application document for submission to the Secretary of State for Scotland. To this end Sir William Halcrow and Partners, who had produced some of the earlier reports, were asked to recommend a suitable firm of mechanical and electrical engineering consultants, and suggested Merz & McLellan of Killingworth, near Newcastle-upon-Tyne, who had worked with them on hydro-electric schemes in the 1950s. The Holfords architectural partnership was also invited to assist in preparing the estimates and documentation for stations etc.

In the course of developing the scheme, the various firms of consulting engineers carried out preliminary investigative work to assist in estimating costs and preparing contract documents; the most notable were ground investigation works, particularly at St Enoch Square, and test running of two power cars coupled together to establish realistic journey times. They also began the process of discussing their ideas with interested bodies such as the Railway Inspectorate, and the Dean of Guild (now Building Control Department of Glasgow City Council).

The policy was that the modernised system should be capable of further development in the future, so the station platforms were to be lengthened to accommodate 3-car trains, and the signalling was to be capable of operating trains at 2-minute headways. The quantity of rolling stock, however, was to be capable of providing a 3-minute headway of 2-car trains. The Infrastructure Grant application document had various options, but the estimated cost of the recommended version was £11·717m. The document was submitted to the Secretary of State in November 1973, and his approval to a 75% Infrastructure Grant for the recommended option was announced on 25th January 1974. The remaining 25% of the cost was to be raised by the Authority, either by Stock Exchange Finance or by a precept on the rates.

Concurrently with the Underground Modernisation scheme, the new Executive was pressing the Scottish Region of British Rail to develop a scheme for electrifying and re-opening the Central Low Level line from Rutherglen to Stobcross and providing a new non-conflicting junction to Partick Hill on the Queen Street Low level line. Most of this scheme was approved for Infrastructure Grant before the end of 1974: the part which was not approved was another connection between the Central and Queen Street Low Level lines at Bridgeton. Later this scheme became known as the Argyle Line.

To raise public awareness of these two major schemes, the PTE arranged an exhibition of models, displays etc in the Scottish Design Centre in St Vincent Street during December 1973; to what extent this influenced the authorisation of both schemes is difficult to judge.

Model of the original concept for the modernisation of Buchanan Street. *Ian Maclean*

To facilitate the Underground Modernisation and the Argyle Line projects, the Greater Glasgow Passenger Transport Order Confirmation Act 1975 was passed by Parliament.

The scope of the Underground Modernisation was broadly to renew everything except the tunnel structures and the sub-stations and their equipment, the latter of which was deemed to have 10 years' useful life left. The main elements of the scheme were as follows:-

1. Provision of 33 new passenger cars equipped for one-man Automatic Train Operation (ATO), and capable of a journey time of 22 minutes;

2. Complete renewal of the signalling system;

3. Modernisation of the rolling stock maintenance facility, provision of a new Stabling Shed and ramped track access to and from the tunnels;

4. Complete renewal of the track – fully on concrete but retaining the 4ft (1220mm) gauge, together with renewal of the pumping system;

5. Complete architectural refurbishment/rebuilding of all 15 stations including interchange facilities with British Rail at Partick Hill / Merkland Street and Buchanan Street / Queen Street stations and with PTE buses at St Enoch and Govan Cross, and provision of escalators at the busiest stations (the Underground platforms at Merkland Street would be on a new site to ease interchange);

6. Improved station facilities including new automatic ticketing equipment, closed circuit television (CCTV) monitoring and a public address (PA) system;

7. Renewal of power supply cables;

8. Provision of a new battery locomotive for use during the Modernisation and for general maintenance duties thereafter.

Once the scheme was formally approved the same firms of consultants were retained to oversee the preparation of contract documents, tender evaluation, and project and design management of the contracts within their respective scopes. One of the first of the specifications completed was that for the passenger rolling stock by Merz and McLellan.

As the scheme was developed other areas requiring attention emerged, such as the need for a Control Room, only given passing mention in the Infrastructure Application document. The signalling contract was extended to include communications equipment such as radio, internal telephone system and CCTV. Access to and from the Depot was changed to a double track ramp requiring two junction and cross-over (or turn-out) chambers to be formed in the tunnel between the Car Sheds pit and Copland Road station.

Many of the additional items did not qualify for the 75% grant, but one of those that did was probably the most significant in financial terms – namely the Fire Brigade insistence that each platform should have an emergency exit separate from the normal entry/exit. Because all the existing platforms were island (though some flank platforms were planned), and had stairs leading down to one end, the only place available for the emergency exit was at the other end of the platform: this meant that the traction switchgear which was housed in the Station Master's office had to be found a new home. In many cases this involved excavating larger subterranean switchrooms than had been previously envisaged, quite apart from providing the stairways to (with one exception) ground level.

At first the idea was to close one Circle for modernisation whilst the other one remained in use, and after the first to be modernised had been commissioned, close the other one. By about 1976 it was recognised the Modernisation process would be quicker if the system were closed completely and a substitute bus service provided.

In 1974 a contract was let for a survey of the tunnels to establish their line, level and cross-sectional dimensions. The survey included the station buildings. This assisted with the preparation of contract documents by the Civil Engineering and Architectural Consultants, and has remained a useful reference ever since. The contract, which extended into 1975, was awarded to Messrs Oliver of Sale, Cheshire

At the time of the Electrification, signalling based on track circuits had been rejected because of the need for steel sleepers. Because it was intended during the Modernisation to provide some flank platforms (i. e. on the left in the direction of travel) and pointwork to reach the Depot, the T-iron system could not be retained. Effectively the choice for train detection was between conventional track circuits and an axle-counting system. In order to establish the feasibility of track circuits, a length of the Inner Circle track just west of Partick Cross station had the steel sleepers supporting the live rail brackets changed for timber ones in the spring of 1974: this enabled typical ballast resistance readings to be obtained.

Numerous contracts were let for the diversion of pipe and cable routes belonging to a variety of undertakings including gas, telephone, and the water and sewerage authorities. This was particularly the case at Broomloan Road, Govan, where the turn-out chambers and tracked ramps to the surface were to be constructed, and at Buchanan Street.

Prior to excavation for the new platform chambers at Govan Cross, Partick, St Enoch, Copland Road, and the two turn-out chambers, piles of various types had to be driven from the surface, and much of this work started before the system closed in May 1977. In February 1976[2] ten piles were driven down between the two cast-iron tunnels to form the central supports for the roof of the new chamber at Partick; this had to be done at night when the system was closed, but fortunately was uneventful.

When the system closed for modernisation in May 1977 six motor coaches were purchased by the North of England Open Air Museum and transported to its location at Beamish in Co Durham. There they were progressively stripped for spares for the museum's tram and trolleybus exhibits and then scrapped. Two of the bogies, complete with motors, later found their way to Falkirk, where the Museums Department was restoring Falkirk and District Tramways Company No 14, the only remaining example of that Company's fleet, which had also been of 4ft gauge. On 25th September 1977, Cars 14 (right) and 30 are nearest the camera, while in the background Gateshead and District tramcar No 10, a survivor of two system closures before being acquired for preservation, approaches on the Beamish main line. *G. Watson*

134

Closure for Modernisation

As described in Chapter 7, the system closed a week earlier than intended, on Saturday 21st May 1977. The official hand-over date of the tunnels to Taylor Woodrow had been set for Monday 6th June, and this date was retained, though they removed the glass roof from Bridge Street station earlier than would have been the case had the system remained open for another week.

One of the first priorities after the closure of the old system was to clear the tunnels of the old rolling stock, but not before equipment to be retained from the stations had been recovered. The traction switchgear boards, complete with circuit breakers and knife switches which were to be re-used, were the main items, and Car 32 with its wide centre doorway was ideal for collecting and transporting such items. Since there was no adequate road access for lorries to position themselves under the crane, cars were removed from the building by knocking a doorway through the brickwork of the southernmost building of the complex (one of those acquired about 1965), and extending a track on to the waste ground outside. All the cars destined for scrap, the six power cars bought by the North of England Open Air Museum at Beamish and those destined for preservation or further use as site huts etc left this way, and were craned on to lorries outside.

In August 1977 a public sale of redundant equipment was arranged at Broomloan over a weekend, and realised about £16,000. On these days rides were arranged up and down the shed in trailer car 39 powered by the battery locomotive – probably the first time it had performed a passenger working since the 1933 Railway Inspectorate inspection described in Chapter 5. Among the last cars to leave were Power Car No. 1 for the Glasgow Transport Museum, then at Albert Drive, and Trailer Car No. 7, purchased by Sir William McAlpine and destined for the National Railway Museum at York.[2]

The equipment provided, and changes to stations and other buildings carried out under the Modernisation programme between about 1974 and 1980, are now described; more recent changes and developments are covered in Chapter 9.

Above left What a wealth of nostalgia is contained in this late 1940s view of St Enoch Square, looking north west! On the south face of the Underground station building, 'Glasgow District Subway' can just be made out above the station name, and on the roof 'Corporation UndergrounD Transport, Trains Every 3 Minutes' has almost faded away. In the foreground a wonderful display of mainly ex-London taxis dating from 1933 includes one with its spare wheel carried on the roof, and behind them a Western SMT AEC Regal setting off from its North Drive terminus for Largs pauses to allow a jay-walker to escape, and will then pass a mounted policeman. To the left of the station is a branch of The National Bank of Scotland; beyond is the Art Deco Municipal Information Bureau, and on Argyle Street 'Standard' and 'Kilmarnock Bogie' tramcars pass in front of a branch of Birrell's sweet shops. *Robert Grieves Collection*

Left In the lower view, looking south west during modernisation, the 'little castle' has been jacked up 8mm and is supported on reinforced concrete beams while excavation and construction of the enlarged station chamber proceeds beneath, with the Inner Circle track already in place. The amazing quantity of timber required for concrete shuttering is apparent on the left; it was about this time that a 'sidewalk superintendent' was heard to say, "I hope they don't lose the drawings for this." The temporary car park on the left replaces the massive bulk of the St Enoch Hotel and main line station, and will in turn be succeeded by the St Enoch Shopping Centre. Other features now changed or gone are Skinner's baker's shop on the west side of the Square, Cooper's name on the modern grocer's-cum-office building at the corner of Howard Street and Dixon Street, and the green, white and yellow of the GGPTE double-deck buses. The 'UndergrounD' sign beneath the clock face lives on – it is now above the stores issuing counter in Broomloan Depot. *SPT*

Taylor Woodrow's operational base for re-railing the system during modernisation was Bridge Street station and an area of surrounding ground. The roots of Alexander Findlay's 1896 steel roof girders remain, but the station chamber is exposed to the elements. At about this time the two Taylor Woodrow Clayton battery electric locomotives, which much later would be purchased by the Underground, gained the nicknames of 'Roger' and 'Claus' – the latter because of its habit of giving drivers little "presents" and "surprises", mostly unwelcome – and here 'Roger' rumbles out of the Outer Circle tunnel from St Enoch with wagons of spoil. *SPT Broomloan Collection*

Here on 4th July 1977 the Govan Cross platform chamber has been demolished, the island platform has gone and on each side of the tracks the ground has been excavated to make room for the flank platforms and escalator passages. At the north-west end of the station the top of the stair from the former platform survives between the tunnel mouths, and to its left is a hole in the side of the subterranean passage which led under Greenhaugh Street from the station entrance, which is just visible with its 'UndergrounD' sign peeping above the fence. On Govan Road, the Clydesdale Bank and the Royal Bank of Scotland compete for business, side by side beneath the caretaker's house and meetings hall of the adjacent Church of Scotland. To enable the larger civil engineering contracts to start it was necessary to demolish some operational buildings, and provide temporary alternative accommodation. At Govan the 1953 Depot Office building went, and its functions were transferred to a group of Portakabins. Similarly at Copland Road the main building was largely demolished, and replaced by a 'double deck' arrangement of site huts. *Balfour Beatty Construction Ltd*

Rolling Stock

The 33 passenger cars supplied were identical and were designed and built by Metro-Cammell of Birmingham with GEC traction equipment for use as 2- or 3-car trains. Like their predecessors, they have all longitudinal seating, but unlike the old cars, have doors on both sides – two double doorways on each side on the same 7·016m centre line as the bogie pivots. Floor height is about 695mm above rail. Each axle is powered by a 35·6KW GEC 312AZ nose suspended axle hung traction motor, driving through 13:71 reduction gearing. The wheel diameter is 688mm and the minimum permissible diameter is 638mm. The motors are coupled in permanent series pairs which operate in series/parallel for traction and in a figure-of-eight circuit in rheostatic braking. The traction equipment on each car consists of 2 air/oil operated camshafts which switch in and out sections of two resistor banks, also used to dissipate heat during rheostatic braking. The camshafts are supplemented by electro-pneumatic contactors. Except for the motors and absence of field weakening, the equipment is very similar to that supplied by GEC to London Transport for the 1972 Tube Stock.

The service braking system is electrically controlled: an electronic pulsed signal is sent down a train wire – the longer the pulse (or 'mark' as it is known) compared with the time between pulses (or 'space'), the greater the brake demanded. The cars are fitted with load-weigh cells and the output from these together with the demand called for is processed on each car to produce a blend of rheostatic and electro-pneumatic friction tread brake. This arrangement means that more heavily laden cars brake proportionately harder than more lightly loaded cars. There is a pneumatic brake pipe for emergency functions, such as deadman handle operation (manual driving mode only), tripcock operation, certain overspeed conditions, divided train and, originally, passenger emergency valve operation. The parking brake is spring applied and requires air pressure to hold it off. The control of this is train-lined, so that operation of the buttons in the leading cab operates the parking brake on each car throughout the train. The air brake equipment was supplied by Davies & Metcalfe.

Surrounded by large potted plants, and with awnings over the passenger doors, Car 101, still on a low-loader, was displayed in George Square, Glasgow, from 12th to 25th June 1977 to give the public their first sight of the new trains. The chromium surrounds on the small tell-tale lights were unique to this car at this time. *Ian Maclean*

The cars met the Railway Inspectorate's requirements for operation of one-man trains in single track tunnels. With no other staff member on the train, it was not acceptable to have the train controlled by a manual controller incorporating a deadman's handle or equivalent device. In the event of the driver becoming incapacited it is in the best interests of both the driver and the passengers that the train reaches the next station as soon as possible (including stopping at and restarting from intermediate signals if necessary), so the cars are arranged for automatic driving between stations. Driver involvement is confined to opening and closing passenger doors, initiating movement by pressing two 'Auto Start' buttons and sounding the whistle (now replaced by a horn) on approach to stations – similar to the duties on the Victoria Line of London Underground.

Unlike the Victoria Line, however, the system does not depend on coded track circuits, but has passive transponders set out along the track. (For signalling purposes some of these transponders have to be switchable, as will be seen later.) A transmitter on the leading car radiates radio energy downwards towards the track and when the car passes over a transponder, the signal is re-transmitted back in coded form, and is picked up by an aerial at the rear of the same car. A device known as an interrogator decodes the signal and passes it on to the Automatic Train Operation equipment in the leading cab. The system is designed to accept ten codes from the track, but only nine are used. When a train is standing at the stopping mark in a station platform, the aerial at the rear of the leading car is over a transponder in the anti-suicide pit. When the signal turns to green the transponder loop is switched on, allowing it to give the appropriate coded signal – Start Permit – and a blue indicator inscribed 'Auto Ready' illuminates on the driver's console. When the driver has completed the interlock circuit by closing the train doors and the cab droplight window, he or she presses the two 'Auto Start' buttons simultaneously and the 'Auto Ready' indication is replaced by a white 'N' indication (No speed limit). Provided all other conditions are met, the train will accelerate up to the normal governed speed (54 kph).

By arrangement with haulage contractor Pickfords, Car 107 was kept on its low-loader at the end of its delivery journey from Metro-Cammell in Birmingham so that it could be exhibited at a Strathclyde Public Transport Day on Sunday 16th April 1978 at GGPTE's Larkfield Bus Works. Here 107 is seen on the previous day in a procession of some of the exhibits against a backdrop of Charing Cross Mansions, while Idris Scott, the GEC Commissioning Engineer, and now the Underground Depot Engineering Superintendent, looks out for adverse signals. *Pickfords*

In a normal section with no intermediate signals or speed restrictions, the next transponder encountered is the 'B1' (First Braking), situated 150 metres from the stopping mark. On recognition of this signal, the train starts to compare its speed with a profile programmed into one of the ATO circuit boards and also starts an automatic count-down in terms of distance. Both of these originate from gear case probes sensing the passing of gear teeth. When the actual speed crosses the braking curve, brakes are applied, giving preference to rheostatic. At 37.5 metres from the stopping mark, a 'B2' (Second Braking) transponder is passed and corrects any error in the braking. In normal circumstances, this tends to ease off the brakes to produce a smoother stop.

On the approach to intermediate signals, there are switched 'B1' and 'B2' transponders at the same distances as for stations, but these are only active when the signal is at red. Near each intermediate signal there is a 'Restart' transponder loop which is switched on when the signal is at green. On receipt of the 'N' signal from the Restart loop a train which has been stopped at the signal will move off without the driver having to press the Auto Start buttons and run up to normal speed.

There are three levels of speed restriction built into the control system – 15kph, 25kph and 35kph. These are recognised as 'S1', 'S2' and 'S3' codes respectively, transmitted to the train from transponders in the track. Before a train will accept one of these, the memory has to be 'scrubbed' clean, so each speed restriction transponder is preceded (by about 2 metres) by a 'scrub' transponder. If a valid signal is not received within 5 seconds after a 'scrub', or if an 'S1', 'S2' or 'S3' signal is recognised before a 'scrub', the Auto Emergency Pilot Valve de-energises and the brake pipe is vented. Depending on the geographical location, trains may pass over an 'N' transponder after a speed restriction, which allows normal speed running to resume. There is also an Emergency Brake signal which could be given by B1 transponders on station approaches. This was activated by the Station Master pressing an Emergency Button on his panel or by the System Controller, but this was altered during the 1996 Centenary Resignalling Project. The track-to-train system was designed by Plessey and the train-borne ATO equipment by GEC.

Only the passenger running lines are equipped for ATO operation. To allow for movement of trains to and from service and for shunting, a manual fore-and-aft power/brake handle is provided, positioned for use by the driver's right hand. Moving the handle forward from the 'off' position applies power and pulling it back gives an infinitely variable service brake, ultimately reaching 'Emergency'. The cab cannot be shut down without having the controller in 'Emergency' and the brake pipe practically exhausted. There is a deadman's 'T' piece on the top of the handle which is only operative in the manual mode. Towards the left of the desk there is a Master Selector Switch which has Off, Auto, Forward, Neutral and Reverse positions. This is unlocked by a Yale-type driver's control key which is trapped in the lock unless the cab is shut down. The power/brake handle and Master Selector are interlocked so that the handle cannot be pushed into a 'power' position in ATO, but is free to be moved into the braking range.

The tripcock is mounted directly to the right-hand side of the leading bogie frame. It is reset by means of a Bowden cable attached to a treadle located in a cupboard set into the back partition of the cab. The door of this cupboard is opened by the driver's Yale-type control key, so the tripcock cannot be reset unless the cab is shut down. Once the tripcock has been operated, the driver cannot exceed 25kph (if he attempts to, he is auto-tripped) until he reaches the approach to the next station, where there is a key exchange box on the tunnel wall. The driver must then shut down his cab and use his key to open a lock on the box. This releases another key which he then uses to remove the speed restriction by turning a key switch on the offside cab console. After this he reverses the procedure to recover his control key. Originally the speed limit imposed was 15kph, but after representations to the Railway Inspectorate, followed by demonstrations, it was agreed to raise the limit to 25kph.

Variable height shoegear was designed because it was not possible to improve on the 1935 live rail position and it was desired to lower its height in the depot yard and on pointwork.

Shoes on their bottom stop would foul the tunnel segments in the cast-iron sections so shoe arms are attached to a cross-shaft so that the shoe which is on the live rail holds the opposite one at a similar height. The original arrangement was prone to various types of failure, including short fatigue life: the measures taken to overcome this are described in Chapter 9.

The 600 Volt shore supply socket is arranged so that with the plug inserted, shoes and motor circuits are isolated. This means that only the auxiliaries – motor alternator, compressor, etc, can be activated. As described on p.147, a Trackmobile is used to push cars out of the building.

The inter-car couplers are of the Wedglock type and are provided at both ends of each car. They are practically identical to those used on the London Underground 1972 Tube Stock, and incorporate two brake pipe and one main reservoir pipe port on the face plate. There are two 38-way contact blocks, one on either side, behind opening covers (colloquially known as 'Dutch Oven' covers). This design of coupler was first used on the 1935 Experimental Tube Stock in London, and on all London Underground passenger stocks since. Its unique feature is its small height requirement, having the contact blocks at the sides rather than above or below as most other types of automatic coupler do. The projecting tongue of each coupler is wedged against an inclined surface by an air operated wedge on the mating coupler. When the wedges are retracted the couplers part under the action of the buffer springs (provided the brakes on one of the cars are released!) Air to and from the coupler wedges is controlled from Westinghouse coupling units incorporating Brake Pipe and Main Reservoir Pipe isolating cocks. The Westinghouse units are located in the cab partition for the front coupler and under a seat at the trailing end for the coupler at that end.

The auxiliary supply is provided from a motor alternator set, one rectified output from which floats across the 50 Volt battery output. Another rectified supply is used for the air compressor motor and a third supply, at 850 Hz, is used for the main saloon lighting. The motor alternator is the GEC MG3007 machine used extensively on London Underground – particularly the 1962, 1967, 1972 Tube Stocks and A62 Surface Stock – though the rectifier/control unit was purpose-designed.

About the time the first cars were delivered to Broomloan Depot, half the transformer and mercury arc rectifier equipment was moved from Benalder Street sub-station and installed in the paint shop of the new Workshop building to allow energisation of the test track.

The first new car to be delivered was No. 103 on 12th January 1978, and commissioning work started immediately in the cleaning bay next to the paint shop which had been handed over to Metro-Cammell for the purpose. On 19th January, Andrew McKay, ever looking for good publicity, organised an opening ceremony and press event in the new Workshop building which was attended by about 30 people. He was most insistent that the press should see Car 103 moving and, since this could not be done under its own power, the car had to be pushed up and down No. 6 Road by one of the Clayton battery locomotives. Remarks were made about oranges and lemons (since the locomotives are painted yellow), and the next day's newspapers used the term 'Clockwork Orange' for the first time. Car 103 was the first to run on the test track on 26th January 1978.[2]

Signalling and System Control Room

The signalling system was arranged to be automatically operated by the passage of the trains (as indeed had the 1935 scheme) from Govan round the north side and as far as Ibrox on the Outer Circle, and the equivalent on the Inner Circle. The section between Ibrox and Govan includes the turn-out chambers with, as can be seen from Figure 8·2, two cross-overs and two turn-outs, with access to the depot via the ramps and a pair of headshunts (shown on Figure 8·1), where reversal is necessary. The signalled 'routes' (as they are called in railway signalling) from Govan round to Ibrox and vice versa were arranged for automatic operation or for push-button route setting by the System Controller: the routes between the headshunts and the turn-out chambers and between the headshunts and the depot yard were set up only by push-buttons.

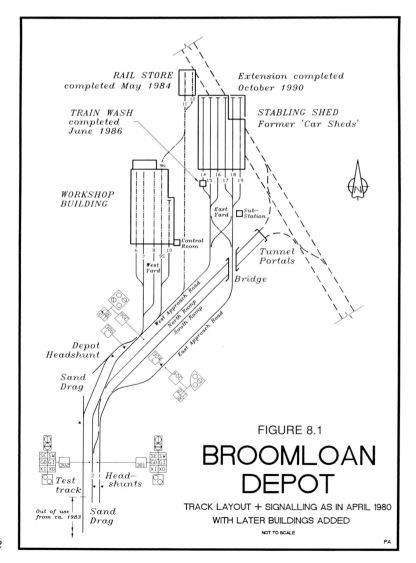

FIGURE 8.1

BROOMLOAN DEPOT

TRACK LAYOUT + SIGNALLING AS IN APRIL 1980
WITH LATER BUILDINGS ADDED

NOT TO SCALE

PA

A considerable degree of flexibility was built into the routes available to the System Controller. Normally trains enter the system from the headshunts to Govan (Outer) and Ibrox (Inner) platforms, and leave the system from Govan (Inner) and Ibrox (Outer) platforms. Trains can return to Depot under the authority of a shunt signal (307 on Figure 8·2) from Govan (Outer) and from the Inner Circle intermediate signal (102) under control of 308 shunt signal. Conversely trains can be put into service to Govan (Inner) platform and towards Ibrox on the Outer Circle, in both cases originally up to an illuminated 'Limit of Shunt' sign. (The shunt signals have since been renumbered.

An early decision was to retain the principle of trainstops and tripcocks as the basic safety device. The pneumatically operated London Transport design was not favoured, as it would have involved a compressed air distribution system, so one designed by

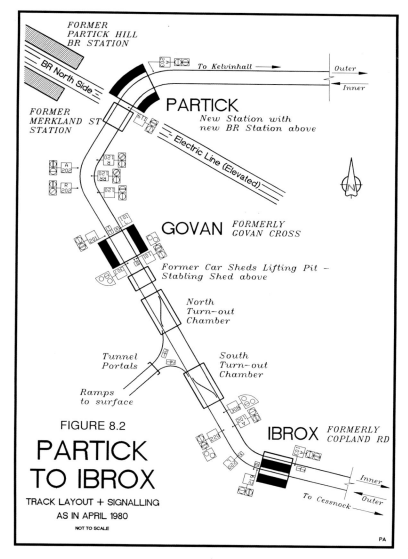

FIGURE 8.2

PARTICK
TO IBROX

TRACK LAYOUT + SIGNALLING
AS IN APRIL 1980

NOT TO SCALE

143

British Rail for the Liverpool Loop and the Great Northern electrification to Moorgate was adopted; this machine is operated by a hydraulic power pack. Since the track resistance tests had given satisfactory results, train detection by track circuits was decided upon. Jointless high frequency track circuits were considered, but they had not seen widespread use on d.c. traction systems at that time, so it was decided to 'play safe' and adopt the well-tried capacitor-fed 50Hz system, with double rail track circuits, except in the area with points, where single-rail track circuits were adopted. A disadvantage of this type of track circuit is that it requires impedance bonds to carry the traction return current across the insulated block joints. The impedance bonds then available (the Westinghouse P3 type) were basically large copper coils which allowed the traction return to pass, but blocked the a.c. track circuit signal, and were housed in substantial oil filled cast iron boxes located between the rails. Since these items were costly it was decided to minimise the number of track circuits, but to give the System Controller a better idea of the location of trains the indications were arranged in three sections, controlled by a track treadle (which, as in the 1935 scheme, returned the signal to danger) and a light beam, known as a platform occupancy detector.

The signals are, like the majority of the 1935 signals, 2-aspect, green-over-red. To obtain the specified 2-minute headway it was necessary to install five intermediate signals in the sections with the longest journey times. These sections were (on the Outer Circle) Govan to Partick, Hillhead to Kelvinbridge, St Georges Cross to Cowcaddens, Cowcaddens to Buchanan Street and Ibrox to Govan, and the equivalent sections on the Inner Circle. In some cases, because of curvature, the intermediate signals could not be seen at the point where brakes needed to be applied if the signal was at red: in these cases repeater signals (green-over-amber) were provided. In three instances the repeater signal passed out of the Driver's view before the intermediate signal was visible, so in these cases a 'repeater repeater' signal was provided. Position-light subsidiary and shunt signals were used for movements from the system to the headshunts, but main signals were provided in the headshunts for movements to Govan (Outer) and towards Ibrox on the Inner, because the next signal seen in these cases was a proper running signal.

The signal overlaps (the distance between the trainstop and the block joint) had been calculated on the basis of a train being tripped at a speed of 54 K/hr for station signals and up to 90 K/hr for intermediates, achieving 0.15g deceleration and coming to rest before reaching the block joint with a margin of about 30% to spare. On level track this worked out at about 110 metres for station signals, but was increased to up to 160 metres on the steeper and longer down gradients. Although the maximum speed which could be safely obtained in test running was 65 K/hr, it was discovered that because of rail conditions and other factors the expected braking rate could not be obtained reliably in practice. Since moving the block joints would have been extremely disruptive, and would probably have resulted in further delay to the re-opening, it was decided that double block working should be adopted as a temporary measure. In this case, when the rear of a train passed the third block joint past a signal it cleared to green, as shown in Figure 8.3.

Point machines were of a newly designed Westinghouse electro-hydraulic type. Tyne & Wear Metro and the Hong Kong Mass Transit Railway are the main other operators to have adopted the design. The main contractor for the signalling system was M. L. Engineering of Plymouth.

A System Control Room was set up at the south east corner of the new Workshop building: this position being considered the best for security. The Room is on the first floor, and originally had a adjoining Yard Master's Room with a panoramic view of the yard area. The largest display in the Control Room was the signalling mimic panel,

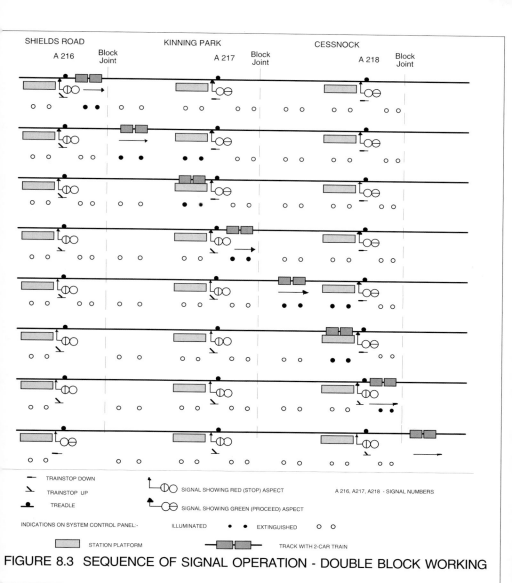

FIGURE 8.3 SEQUENCE OF SIGNAL OPERATION - DOUBLE BLOCK WORKING

which showed the state of occupancy of each track circuit and its sub-divisions, and the aspect of each stop and shunt signal. Adjacent to the representation of each station was a CCTV monitor showing platform views of that station. In front of the panel was the System Controller's desk, which incorporated a small control panel for setting routes to and from the depot, radio and public address equipment, internal and external telephones and banks of alarm indications from each station. Traction current switching is also performed by the System Controller, and a panel for that purpose was provided to the left of the room. A further panel monitored the pumping equipment.

Depot Facilities

The original idea was to modernise and adapt the existing Car Sheds building as the maintenance facility for the new rolling stock, and to build a new simple structure as a Stabling Shed. (The latter, as opposed to open storage sidings, was justified on the basis of security, and less likelihood of vandalism, as well as weather protection.) On further investigation it became apparent that maintaining the existing rolling stock for the second Circle to be converted in part of the building, whilst the first Circle and the other part of the Sheds were being converted, and vice versa whilst the second Circle was being converted, presented difficulties with no clear solution. Because of this it was decided a new purpose-designed building should be created on the adjacent former Govan Goods Yard site, and the existing Car Sheds building adapted as the Stabling Shed. This had implications for the track layout and ramped access, but the solution finally arrived at was very satisfactory, and, apart from relatively minor alteration, has stood the test of time.

As first built the maintenance section of the building was in four main parts:-

1. The bogie repair area and machine shop;

2. The lifting bay, including the stores at its eastern end;

3. The short-term (pitted) rolling stock maintenance area;

4. The long-term rolling stock maintenance and bench areas.

One of the issues which had to be settled early on was the method of lifting the cars off their bogies for maintenance. After considerable discussion a proposal for synchronised jacks was rejected, and an electric overhead crane running at right angles to the tracks was selected. The crane was built by Butters, and has a 25 tonne Safe Working Load, half being taken by each of two crabs. An ingenious swivelling beam was provided which enabled suspended cars to be turned, so the device acted as a crane, a traverser and a turntable. In the short-term maintenance area, rather than having side pits it was decided to have a sunken floor with elevated platforms for access to the interior of the vehicles. Initially plans were drawn up on the basis of two pitted roads, but this was later increased to three. These are known as Nos. 8, 9 and 10 Roads, of which 8 and 9 extend northwards into the lifting bay, and 9 is further extended through a battery locomotive charging bay, capable of holding two locomotives, and out into the car park area at the north of the building. Nos. 6 and 7 Roads extended the full length of the long-term maintenance bay, but were truncated by the new stores described below.

The main drawback with the new building was that the area allowed for the stores was far too small for the range of items it was necessary to carry, not just for the rolling stock, but for all the other equipment involved in the modernised Underground. After an extension had been built using the loading bank, a section of the bench area had been taken over and some long-term spares transferred to the former Seaward Street Sub-station, the problem was finally addressed in 1994–95 with the relocation of the Stores in the former bogie repair and part of the machine shop areas. (See Chapter 9).

As will be seen from Figure 8·4, at the north end of the building there is an office and amenity block, on the ground floor of which there are locker rooms, an office (originally occupied by the Timekeeper), main 'bothy' (mess room), first aid room, showers, toilets and switchroom for the incoming electrical supply to the Depot site. On the upper floor are offices (some of which were originally training rooms), a meeting room, reception area etc.

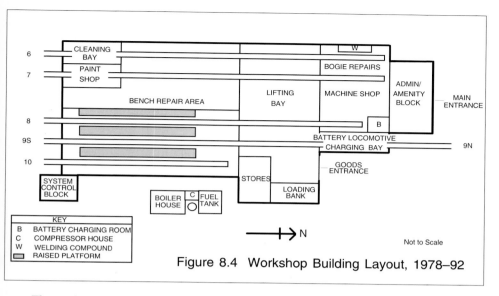

Figure 8.4 Workshop Building Layout, 1978–92

The architects were William Holford & Partners and the main contractor was Fairclough. At a 'topping out' ceremony a time capsule was buried in the floor of the machine shop area, and a brass plaque placed on the adjacent roof support column. The capsule contained a copy of the archive film made in 1974, a collection of long service badges, and a copy of that day's Glasgow Herald.

Much discussion took place on how to move vehicles about in the workshop building, since the London Underground and Southern Region system of overhead trolley jumpers, described on page 66, was not favoured on safety grounds, largely because of the prominent nature of the shoegear design. Capstan operation, which as we have seen was used in the old Car Sheds, was not favoured either: haulage chains close to the rails of the pitted roads were briefly considered, as was building the roads on a gradient, so cars could roll out under gravity. In the end a Trackmobile vehicle was selected, but adapted from diesel to battery operation – the first of its type so dealt with, and still believed to be unique. The machine is a small tractor-type vehicle with both road and rail wheels (in this case in parallel configuration) which can partially couple to the Wedglock couplers of vehicles and push them out until the shoes at the far end reach the live rail outside the shed door. Once back on flush track it can retract its rail wheels, and manoeuvre itself as required on road wheels. The machine was manufactured under licence from the American principals (the Whiting Corporation) by NNM of the Netherlands, and was delivered to Broomloan on 17th April 1978, after a brief public appearance at the Strathclyde Transport Day described at the end of this Chapter. The Trackmobile has proved very successful, and apart from a spell for refurbishment in 1994, it has not left the premises since delivery. It is regarded as an item of plant, so has not been allocated a fleet number.

In January and February 1978 the PTE vacated the old Car Sheds building, taking the machine tools they intended to keep (two lathes, a shaping machine, radial and pillar drills, etc), the two converted cable wagons, the original battery locomotive, and sundry other items large and small, and moved into the new Workshop building. The shed was handed over to Balfour Beatty for conversion to a Stabling Shed under the Depot Yard contract in March 1978.[2]

From Car Sheds to Stabling Shed

The braced uprights supporting the girders for the crane run provide the link between these three scenes. In the top view of the Sheds in 1896 only four coaches can be seen, one on the right with its front end raised, possibly for attention to its gripper bogie. The centre photograph shows the Sheds on 3rd April 1977, with the pit on the right and the lifting frame on the left, and the crane above it. Only half the floor space was required to accommodate cars, for most of the fleet was always in the tunnels, running during the day and parked at night. As part of the 1977-1980 modernisation, the pit was decked over, the windows bricked up, the crane removed, a new roof provided and six new tracks installed, each with a live rail and platform access to train interiors. The building is heated during low temperature periods to prevent the air brake systems on the cars freezing. *Glasgow Museum of Transport Collection (Top) /Ian Maclean (Middle and Bottom)*

After maintenance, Cars 117 and 123 are pushed out on No. 10 Road by the Trackmobile, which has road as well as rail capability. It was built by Noord Nederlandse Machinefabrik at Winschoten in Holland, and was unique in 1978 when it was delivered by being battery powered, all previous Trackmobiles of this size having been diesel-powered. *Ian Maclean*

The lifting pit was decked over, the inspection pits were filled in, and two tracks were laid in each of the three bays, with a platform between each pair of tracks. Live rails, covered by wooden protection boards, were provided for the full length of the tracks. The former industrial buildings acquired about 1965 and part of the original office block were demolished (see Figure 5·1) and a new gable wall built across the south end of the building with six electrically powered up-and-over doors. Because virtually the entire fleet was to be housed in the building a fire alarm system was installed incorporating a sprinkler system, and gas fired heaters were installed with a view to keeping the air temperature above 0°C in winter. A separate contract was let for re-roofing the building, removal of the crane and fitting new lighting. At one stage the unrefurbished building was used for the storage of new rolling stock either awaiting commissioning, or cars which had already been commissioned.

The six roads were numbered 14 to 19 inclusive reading from west to east, and when the method of cleaning the car exteriors had been decided No.19 Road was adapted to have a platform on each side with screen walls and no live rail. The method of cleaning adopted was to brush on detergent with long brushes by hand, then hose it off and polish the windows. Consideration was given to pushing the cars out using the original battery locomotive, and a Wedglock coupler was fitted at one end for the purpose, but no satisfactory way of releasing the spring-applied brake from that locomotive could be devised, so the Clayton locomotives were used instead, but even so it could take 20 to 30 minutes to build up sufficient air to release the parking brake; before the re-opening it was realised this was unsatisfactory, but it took until April 1982 for a scheme acceptable to the Railway Inspectorate to be devised and implemented. A short section of live rail was installed, and an interlocking arrangement between the isolating switch and the water cock was arranged, so that flashing lights and audible alarms operate whilst the live rail is energised.

Whilst reviewing the design of the rolling stock specification it was realised that a test track facility for testing and commissioning the new cars would be highly desirable, although this had not been included in the original proposals. Since most of the site of the former Govan Goods Station had been earmarked for the Stabling Shed and Depot approach, and the trackbed of the branch which had led to it was unobstructed, it was relatively simple for the PTE to acquire that strip of land, and to create a useful 500-metre long test track.

On 3rd July 1978 work proceeds on converting the Car Sheds into the Stabling Shed for the new rolling stock. The contract with Balfour Beatty included building platforms and laying track inside, and building a new gable wall at the south end as well as laying out the new trackwork in what will become the East Yard. A later contract with Norwest Holst included re-roofing the building with its raised transverse section which had accommodated the now redundant car lifting crane. To the left is the new workshop, and on the right is the tenement block which at that time housed Govan Fire Station and some of the firemen and their families. *Balfour Beatty*

The West Yard on 23rd May 1980 with Inner Circle train Route No. 14 on the south ramp from the tunnels, having reversed at Signal 308 between Govan and Ibrox. A single car stands on the depot headshunt, a battery locomotive is propelling a two-car train on No. 8 road and two two-car trains stand on Nos. 9S and 10 roads. On the right the east approach road leads towards the bridge over the ramps, while to the north-east the spire of Glasgow University and the multi-storey buildings of the Queen Mother's Hospital and the Royal Hospital for Sick Children dominate the skyline. *Ian Maclean*

In the Workshop Building Nos 8, 9 and 10 roads constitute the short-term maintenance area and have the running rails at ground level above a sunken floor and platforms for entry to car interiors and cabs. On 15th April 1990 a three-car train on No. 8 road is about to be pushed out by the Trackmobile, whilst a two-car train stands on No. 10 road. *Ian Maclean*

Car 104 in 6 road of the works building is slung ready for transfer to the yellow-painted accommodation bogies already positioned in 7 road. In the foreground is the wheel and bogie park, with spare trailer car bogie frames prominent, distinguishable by their wide wheel arches and brake calliper support beams. Car 104 has had the fairings removed below the outer door pockets following Car 131's visit to Hunslet-Barclay described in Chapter 9. *Ian Maclean*

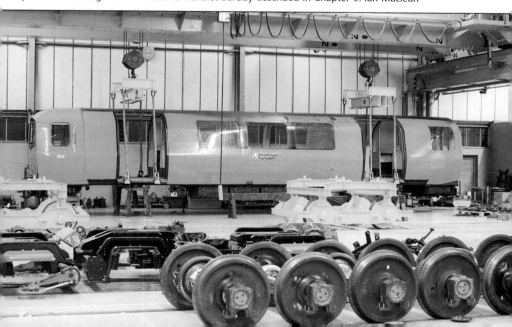

Re-railing Contract

One of the largest tasks of the Modernisation was the complete "gutting" of the tunnels and the formation of a completely new concrete-based track. The main objective was to produce a track system which was less labour-intensive to maintain; prior to modernisation, track maintenance, litter collection and platform washing occupied about 60 people on night shift while in 1996 there were about 30 on night shift and six station cleaners on day shift. It was considered impractical to fit a slip-form paving machine into the 11ft diameter tunnels, so a variation on the trial length was adopted using small pre-cast concrete blocks as rail support units set in concrete at 1·1m intervals, but every fourth support is a pre-cast concrete sleeper with relatively slim waist. The in-situ concrete was shuttered to provide a central drainage channel with the sleepers bridging it. Also unlike the trial length, cast-iron baseplates were provided. These had two eccentric nylon bushes for gauge adjustment and electrical insulation and although the design has been improved since, the principle remains the same. The baseplates are held down by studs screwed into the blocks and sleepers. The drainage channel between the rails is not filled with ballast but is bridged with pre-cast concrete slabs to form a convenient passenger emergency exit route; like the slabs used on the trial length of track, these ones are perforated to provide a measure of sound-deadening.

Insulating pads are placed under the baseplates and rubber rail pads in a recess in the baseplates. The baseplates were designed to cant the BS80A section rail in at an angle of 1 in 20 and the rails were fixed to the baseplates by 401A Pandrol clips without further insulation. (The new design of baseplate uses Pandrol 'e' clips, and has further insulation between the clip and the rail.) The original rail was rolled at Glengarnock Steel Works to BS11 quality in 40ft lengths. It was continuously welded by the Thermit process, though there were mechanical joints at signalling block joints.

At places where the radius of curvature is less than 200m, check rails are fitted to the inside rail of the curve. This represents about 10% of the route length. Up to 6mm gauge widening is installed on the sharper curves.

The live rail is generally, but not invariably, supported on steel brackets fitted to one end of the pre-cast sleepers. Porcelain insulators are bolted to the tops of the brackets, and the live rail, known as Westinghouse rubbing strip, slots into channel shaped caps at the top of the insulators. The normal height of the top of the live rail is 307mm above running rail level, and it was cadwelded into lengths up to 300 metres or so, with the ends bent down to form ramps at each end. It changes sides fairly frequently. So-called 'commutated sections' were cut into the live rail on the approach to stations: the shoes had to be supported at the 'tunnel' height, yet electrical isolation was necessary. The way this works is shown in Figure 8·5

Two turn-out chambers were formed between the Car Sheds pit and Copland Road, each containing a cross-over between the Inner and Outer Circles and a turn-out leading to one of the ramped tracks to the surface. There were thus six sets of points in the chambers, for which swing-nose crossings were specified. Those provided were of the continental cast-steel type, with a crossing angle of 1 in 5·224, and manufactured by Edgar Allen. The nominal radius of the curved stock rail was 50 metres.

The main contractor for the tunnel work was Taylor Woodrow Construction (Scotland) Limited, working principally from a base at Bridge Street Station, though access points were also formed at Beith Street (Partick) and at Kelvinbridge for transfer of ready-mix concrete. Within a few days of closure Taylor Woodrow, who had occupied the vacant ground to the north, south and east of Bridge Street station, had removed the glass pitched roof over the platform and formed an access point for craning-in plant and materials.

To provide mobility for materials, Taylor Woodrow acquired two diesel locomotives and two Clayton battery locomotives built (to order No. BO 186) to a gauge of 3ft as part of a larger batch of trolley/battery locomotives for use on the construction works of the aborted 1970s Channel Tunnel project. Originally the Clayton locomotives had outside frames, but these were too close together to achieve gauge conversion to 4ft by simply pushing the wheels further apart, and they were too far apart to put the wheels outside the frames, so the idea of leaving the wheels inside the frames on one side and putting them outside on the other side emerged. The wheels on the outside were boxed-in tram-locomotive style, but nonetheless they presented a lop-sided appearance, particularly from head on. Unlike the later PTE-owned locomotives (of which more below) these ones were contactor controlled. They were allocated Taylor Woodrow asset numbers TE4A002 and TE4A003, and spent most of their time based at Bridge Street, hauling an assortment of 4-wheel wagons formed on the frames of former passenger car bogies. For some reason these locomotives were named 'Roger' and 'Claus', but in which order is not certain.

Included in the re-railing contract was the provision of pumping equipment. Successful trials had been carried out in the early 1970s with submersible pumps, so this was the system adopted. Sumps were created at some 23 locations, and pairs of pumps with associated control panels were installed. In general the sumps were formed in the Outer Circle tunnel with pipes leading into them from the Inner Circle, but at certain points in the cast-iron lined sections separate sumps had to be formed. To form one of the sumps near Kinning Park it was necessary to freeze the ground with liquid nitrogen to prevent water-bearing sand and silt entering the tunnel.

The pumps are of two different ratings, depending on the flow of water and the height through which the water is to be lifted to reach the public drains. In each sump, under normal circumstances one pump is the 'duty pump', and the other is on 'stand-by' in case the duty pump fails or cannot control the water level for some other reason. An indication is transmitted to the System Control Room if a stand-by pump is called upon, if the water level rises above a pre-determined level or if the electricity supply to the local pump control panel fails.

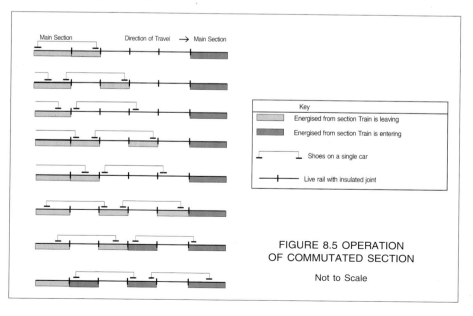

Key

▨	Energised from section Train is leaving
▩	Energised from section Train is entering
⊥	Shoes on a single car
──┼──	Live rail with insulated joint

FIGURE 8.5 OPERATION
OF COMMUTATED SECTION

Not to Scale

Stations

A key aspect of the Modernisation was to improve interchange between modes of transport as part of the PTE's co-ordination rôle. For that reason new British Rail platforms were built on the embankment south of Dumbarton Road at the point where the railway crosses the Underground tunnels, and a new combined BR and Underground station entrance and concourse were constructed virtually where the old Merkland Street entrance had been. Partick Hill station was then closed. In view of the expected interchange traffic, it was decided that the Underground should have two platforms, and providing access to them through the BR embankment would have been difficult had the original platform site been retained. In view of this a new platform chamber was built to the east of the embankment. The combined station was named Partick. The other point at which interchange between British Rail and the Underground could be improved was between Queen Street and Buchanan Street, and a pair of passenger conveyors[3] was provided between a new entrance to the Underground station adjacent to the Dundas Street entrance to Queen Street and the Underground station concourse.

Bus interchange arrangements were provided at St Enoch (improved stances) and Govan (new bus station to replace street stances). At many other places buses passed close to Underground stations, but no special facilities were warranted. A new bus interchange was brought into use at Partick on 3rd May 1982,[4] close to the entrance to the combined BR and Underground station. All westbound bus services on Dumbarton Road were diverted into the new facility, but eastbound services were unchanged.

Partick station replaced Merkland Street (Underground) and Partick Hill (British Rail), and provides interchange between the two railways and westbound (only) Dumbarton Road bus services. Here in May 1986 an SPTE Atlantean and an Ailsa idle at their stances alongside a Central single decker, while two BR Class 303/311 'Blue Trains', one in BR livery and one in SPTE orange and black, arrive and depart above. The station entrance and concourse are almost exactly on the site of the former Merkland Street station entrance, but the new Underground platform chamber sits beneath the car park, which is for shoppers and not for Park and Ride. The opportunity to distinguish between the stations by naming them Partick (Low Level) and Partick (High Level) was not taken. *Ian Maclean*

Despite the name signs, this is neither St Enoch nor Bridge Street, but a mock-up which was built in the PTE's Benalder Street sub-station premises to display architectural features proposed or agreed for the rebuilding of the stations. Metro-Cammell's three-quarter length mock-up car body completes the scene, but the roof ventilators above the windows (similar to those on contemporary London Underground tube stock) and the arm-rests in the seat backs were not perpetuated, and the saloon ceiling and lighting design was altered to increase the number of hand grabs and give better headroom. *John Laing plc*

When the system re-opened in 1980 a car park with about 150 spaces was provided on redundant ground to the east of Shields Road station: this facility had barrier controlled entry and exits. The hardstandings of the former Corporation-run car park at Kelvinbridge remained, but no agreement was reached on manning, maintenance, or revenue matters, so it was free and uncontrolled. The waste ground round Bridge Street station became an even less official car park. An extension, with about 150 spaces, was opened to the Shields Road car park in July 1985, and the following month the ground round Bridge Street, having been landscaped and converted into another 150-space car park with entry and exit barriers, was opened. The Bridge Street facility was rather slow to 'catch on' with the public,[5] but is now one of the most popular. The Kelvinbridge area was resurfaced, lined out, and barrier equipment installed to make it into a recognised 'Park and Ride' from August 1988. A further 140-space extension to the Shields Road car park was opened by Councillor Waugh, Chairman of Strathclyde Regional Council Highways and Transportation Committee, on 17th July 1991[6] using an area developed as overflow car parking for the 1988 Garden Festival. Both these extensions are eastwards, and the remote end of the second extension is nearly half way to West Street station! Various schemes were developed for converting some derelict industrial ground just north of West Street station itself into a further car park. The possibility of creating a ramp to reach the level of the former Cook Street Railway Depot was ruled out on cost grounds, so a modest 60-space car park was created immediately adjoining the station building: this was opened on 29th February 1988. All these car parks now have CCTV surveillance from the local station.

At some stage after the Modernisation started the Passenger Transport Authority reviewed Underground station names, and agreed that three stations should be re-named – Govan Cross became Govan, Partick Cross became Kelvinhall in an attempt to promote its use for travel to and from the Kelvin Hall, which was more than ¼ mile away, and to avoid confusion with the new Partick station. The rendering as "Kelvin-hall", however, makes confusion with Kelvinbridge more likely. Copland Road became Ibrox to advertise its proximity to Ibrox Park, home of Rangers Football Club.

As in the 1890s one of the main concerns was safety on the narrow island platforms. To achieve an improvement it was decided that at the busiest stations separate platforms should be provided for each circle; these were predicted to be Govan, Partick, Hillhead, Buchanan Street, St Enoch and (on football match days) Ibrox. The preferred option was for what became known as 'flank platforms' – that is outside both tracks and on the left in the normal direction of travel, but this was only found to be possible at Govan, Partick and St Enoch. Site constraints dictated that only one flank platform could be provided at Hillhead, Buchanan Street and Ibrox, and the island platform was retained for the other circle; in each case the flank platform serves the Outer Circle. Another far-sighted decision was to lengthen all station platforms to accept 3-car trains. Only Cowcaddens was long enough not to require some lengthening.

The platform surfaces are tiled, the main area being in shades of orange and brown and the edges cream, to assist partially-sighted people. The six stations with flank platforms have vertical walls to the chambers to which are fixed off-white ceramic tiles, with a row of wide tiles displaying the station name at intervals. Advertisement frames are fitted to these walls, with station lists giving the stations reached quicker from that platform. The chamber end walls (known as 'headwalls') have dark brown glazed tiles. The ceilings are of the suspended type, and incorporate metal slats, with light fitting diffusers flush with the underside of the slats.

Several of the nine stations which retained island platforms previously had glazed roof lights. At Bridge Street, on completion of the re-railing contract, the aperture where the roof had been was decked over. At Kelvinhall and Cessnock the roof structure was retained, but the glass was replaced by metal sheeting. Internally the platform chambers of all nine stations were panelled in a non-metallic flexible material of appropriate fire performance (since replaced in some stations as described in Chapter 9), having a cream finish on the inside, and curved to form an arch. In the centre of the arch and over the platform of each station there is a suspended slatted ceiling with concealed light fittings illuminating the arched panels, and recessed lights illuminating the platform directly. Curved advertisement frames are fitted to the panels and, as at the flank platform stations, station lists.

Although not covered in the original estimates the decision was made to incorporate anti-suicide pits between the rails adjacent to station platforms, as is standard practice in London Underground Tube stations. In some cases where the platform chamber structure was not being altered the depth of the pit was rather limited, but is better than the previous arrangement. Unfortunately measures were not taken to divert the drainage water coming from the channel in the tunnels on either side of the stations, and in some (e. g. Kelvinbridge) the pit has the appearance of an open drain.

At the instigation of the Fire Brigade, it became a condition of planning consent that all station platforms had an independent fire escape. In most cases new stairways had to be constructed leading to small brick buildings on the surface. At Kelvinbridge the former entrance stairway was used, and the normal entrance was created at the other end. Similarly, Bridge Street was 'turned round'.

At Govan and St Enoch completely separate fire escapes were provided for each platform, but at the other four flank platform stations the two passageways merged soon after leaving the platforms. At Buchanan Street, however, the passageway did not

Half the length of Cessnock's station chamber originally had vertical walls and a glass roof, but on 18th September 1979 the walls and daylight illumination are fast disappearing as new curved panelling is installed. An Outer Circle train on driver familiarisation passes through the building site. *G. Watson*

lead all the way to the surface, but emerged near the bottom landing of the Passenger Conveyors: this arrangement necessitated fire doors which would swing shut in the event of the fire alarm system being activated.

Consideration was given to catering for disabled people, and a preliminary plan was drawn up for lifts down to platform level at stations with flank platforms on the Outer Circle. After discussions with the Railway Inspectorate and other interested bodies, it was concluded that there were unacceptable safety risks to other passengers in having wheelchair-bound people in the trains, particularly in the event of tunnel detrainment in emergency. The end doors of the cars were too narrow for most wheelchairs, and could not readily be made wider. The proposal for lifts was dropped, but certain measures were taken to help people with other disabilities.

Escalators were provided at stations where a combination of the anticipated usage and depth warranted it. All the stations north of the Clyde except Kelvinhall were equipped with escalators for some or all of the distance between street and platform. South of the Clyde escalators were provided at Shields Road (street/concourse to intermediate level) and at Govan (street/concourse to platform level). At Buchanan Street a pair of passenger conveyors[3] some 60 metres long and angled at 1 in 12 were installed between the concourse and the Dundas Street entrance opposite Queen Street British Rail station, to which a connecting canopy was provided.

There are 28 escalators and two passenger conveyors. All these machines were built and installed by O&K Escalators of Keighley, West Yorkshire. The longest escalators are at Partick and Buchanan Street with rises of 8·35 and 8·2 metres respectively, and the shortest are at Shields Road with a rise of 3·63 metres.

The Railway Inspectorate had special requirements for escalators on railway premises which could be part of an escape route in the event of fire, and 26 of the machines came into that category. (The pair from concourse to Great Western Road at Kelvinbridge were the exceptions.) The inclined part of the machine could not be steeper than 30° (many escalators in shops etc are 35°), and there had to be at least three step widths at top and bottom before step forming started.

All the machines have fluted metallic treads and risers, and stainless steel balustrades and decking – there is no wood or other combustible material in their construction.

As originally built the north entrances of Buchanan Street and St Enoch stations each had a pair of escalators between the sub-surface concourse level and the street with their top landings in the open air. The Planning Authority considered putting a canopy of any kind over the entrance would spoil the vista down Buchanan Street, so, to avoid delaying the planning application, the Executive agreed to the arrangement. Certain steps were taken by O&K to prevent a build-up of ice or snow and to protect the machinery from water ingress, but these machines turned out to be by far the least reliable.

In due course the PTE was able to design a steel and glass canopy for the St Enoch entrance which minimised the visual impact in St Enoch Square and was acceptable to the Planning Department of the District Council. This canopy was constructed during the early months of 1986, and for a while replaced 'The Shell'[7] in Central Station as the 'in' place to meet friends.[8] The steelwork of the canopy was painted in Strathclyde Transport Red, and internal lighting was mainly by upward-directed fittings on the original dwarf walls.

A similar canopy was completed about a year later at Buchanan Street, this time with its roof arranged in steps to match the gradient of the street: this was officially opened by Councillor Malcolm Waugh, on 27th May 1987.[9]

Escalator step chain life and hand-rail drive problems have been significantly improved as a result of the canopies.

The original polycarbonate glazing panels and the arrangement of lighting diffusers over the upper flight escalators from concourse to Great Western Road at Kelvinbridge proved unsatisfactory, and by a combination of water penetration from outside and condensation from inside, the steelwork had started to deteriorate. The escalators were of the 'compact' type (the only ones on the Glasgow Underground, and similar to the Buchanan Street passenger conveyors) and did not have a separate machine room. Maintenance access at the top and from underneath was improved, the glazing was renewed with tinted glass, and lighting diffusers were improved between February and July 1992. The entrance was closed whilst this work was in progress.[10]

An attempt was made to create a 'house style' for the station buildings. All exposed brickwork, whether internal or external, is an attractive brown. Buildings which were completely new and separate from other structures generally had a raised 'lantern light' over the concourse – examples being Kelvinbridge, Cowcaddens, West Street and Shields Road. Bridge Street also made use of natural light, but in a different way. Buchanan Street and St Enoch have concourses below street level, reached by escalators or stairs, and the St Georges Cross entrance remains in the same place as it has been since the 1970/1 reconstruction (see Chapter 7), though the building is considerably altered. All stations had one or more self-illuminated 'U' signs prominently displayed, and individual neon signs for each letter of the station name over the entrances and at other strategic points, though this has since been modified.

All stations have booking offices with issuing windows at concourse level: the booking office is usually at one side of the concourse, though the one at St Enoch is an 'island' in the centre. Most stations have passenger-operated ticket issuing machines on the concourse, either in groups on 'island' sites or against a wall. At Ibrox a football match entrance/exit and concourse was created opening off Woodville Street, with arrangements to segregate flows of passengers when in use. This entrance has its own booking office and barriers.

Kiosks for the sale of newspapers, confectionery, cigarettes, etc were provided on the concourses at Govan, Partick, Hillhead, Cowcaddens, Buchanan Street, St Enoch and Ibrox. W. H. Smith, a company with long railway bookstall connections in England, took up a lease on all of these kiosks, evidently as part of a plan to develop in Scotland. All opened for business on 16th April 1980, but it was not very long before W. H. Smiths decided the margins did not reach the required levels, and after moves to hand the business over to another firm failed, the kiosks were closed on 30th November 1982.[11] The Govan, Partick, Cowcaddens and Buchanan Street kiosks have remained in virtually constant use by a variety of small family businesses, and the Ibrox and Hillhead ones were briefly reopened but did not last long. The St Enoch premises were developed as a Transcard Centre to replace a shop in St Vincent Street, and opened for business on Thursday 10th April 1986.[3] On 3rd October 1991 the Hillhead premises were reopened as a PTE Travel Information Centre,[12] primarily to assist the large numbers of students using the station; a range of Zonecards and other tickets not available from station booking offices are sold.

Areas intended as shop units were constructed on either side of the concourse at St Enoch, largely over the north end of the two flank platforms. Unfortunately the Fire Brigade requirements for fire precautions could not be satisfied, so the spaces had to be put to a variety of uses by the PTE. The Lost Property Office was moved to one of the spaces on 15th March 1982, as part of the planned withdrawal from 46 Bath Street. It stayed there until 30th November 1990,[13] when, because of difficulties in making the premises comply with the Sub-surface Railway Stations Regulations (of which more in Chapter 9), ScotRail agreed to take over the Lost Property function at Queen Street station.

At one stage it was intended that there should be an entrance from the St Enoch concourse into the basement of Arnott's, the department store then on the south side of Argyle Street, between St Enoch Square and Jamaica Street. This idea was finally rejected on security grounds. More successful has been a shop unit built into Partick station, but this is accessed from the street rather than the concourse.

In developing the design for Buchanan Street concourse the architects found they had a large expanse of wall with nothing of significance to put on it, so the idea was conceived to place a full-size representation of one of the old cars on it. As seen in Chapter 7, Car 41 had been repainted in the original livery, and still retained the trellis gates. This car was cut down to its original 4-wheel trailer length, and also cut in half longitudinally, and mounted on the wall, and forms an attractive display.

A fishmonger's business, McKechnie's, had occupied premises adjoining West Street station for many years. The site was required for the rebuilding of the station, so the business was temporarily transferred to a Portakabin on the Shields Road station site, and later a permanent new shop was incorporated into the Shields Road structure. Although attracting no passing trade, the business has a considerable local reputation.

Advertisement frames similar to those on the platform walls were installed at suitable points throughout the concourses and stairways leading down to the platforms. A number of these were arranged for back-illumination, and attracted a higher rental, and more have been added since. Large back-illuminated displays, known in the advertising industry as '12-sheet', were put up over the escalators at Partick (two sites), St Georges Cross, Cowcaddens and Shields Road, and over the passenger conveyors at Buchanan Street.

At Govan a Depot Office and canteen were built at first floor level over the concourse, and the building has become something of a landmark.

Station Facilities

Partly because the Station Master's 'base' had been moved from the platform to the concourse, and partly to give the System Controller a better overview than could be gained from the traditional-style signalling diagram, it was decided to install Closed Circuit Television (CCTV) in all the stations. At that time the best that could be done was a black-and-white system. There were cameras viewing every platform on the system and the concourses and escalators at selected points in the larger stations. The System Controller could view one platform at each station continuously and select the other, as required, at the six flank platform stations. In addition he could select two views from any camera on the system on separate monitors, one of which was usually arranged to cycle round all cameras on the system. On days when Rangers are playing at home, or there are other events likely to cause crowd control problems, the police often post an officer in the System Control Room to view these monitors. The Station Master had a small 5 inch monitor screen on his panel, from which he could select any camera on his own station, but not views from any other station. As will be seen in Chapter 9 this system has also been developed and up-dated. Public Address (PA) loudspeakers were installed throughout the stations. Messages can be broadcast over these from either the Station Master or the System Controller: originally the System Controller's messages had priority, but to comply with the Sub-Surface Railway Stations Regulations this had to be changed. The System Controller can broadcast to one station or combinations of stations, and can select all areas or staff areas only. There is no doubt this system has helped to keep rowdyism and vandalism at a low level.

The internal telephone system was replaced, and a new 200-line exchange was installed at the Depot. This allowed instruments to be provided widely throughout the Depot and stations (including platforms, though in locked cabinets to prevent public interference), at intermediate signals, and at pump control panels in the tunnels.

The System Control Room at Broomloan with a bank of closed circuit television monitors grouped around a mimic diagram of the railway. The Controllers' desk housed, from the left, the Tunnel Emergency Telephone System control panel, public address, security, telephone and radio panels and a route-setting "NX" (Entry-Exit) panel which was used to control train movements between the depot, the headshunts and the Circles. Major changes to the Control Room were made as part of the Centenary Resignalling Scheme. *Ian Maclean*

Ticketing

Relatively early in the development of the scheme it was decided that the system should operate on a flat-fare basis. Since there was never the intention to inspect tickets at the end of journeys, this meant that there was no need for the exit barriers to read or handle tickets. Even with the flat fare system a number of different types of ticket was required, including juvenile, concession and free (known as 'exchange') tickets for various categories of pass-holder. Westinghouse Brake and Signal Company won the contract to supply the equipment, which included their design of 'Rapid Mini Printer' in each booking office, including the match entrance at Ibrox. There were also passenger-operated machines on the concourses at the busier stations but these could only issue adult single-journey tickets; some of these machines were initially change-giving, but this feature proved unreliable, so was soon abandoned. All tickets issued from the booking offices and the concourse machines were from yellow roll stock of Edmondson width, but with a brown magnetic coating on the back. The date and type of ticket (adult or juvenile) was encoded on the back, and in the case of multi-journey tickets issued from outlets other than the Underground, the expiry date. The other outlets could not encode these tickets (which were on pre-cut card), so before the first journey they had to be presented to an Underground booking office for encoding on a validator, also supplied by Westinghouse.

Having acquired a ticket, a passenger had to put it into a slot on the entry barrier, which 'read' the magnetic code, and if valid, released the latch on the tripod gate and allowed one passenger through. In the case of single-journey tickets, it cancelled the magnetic code. The exit barriers had a similar tripod, but this would only move in the outward direction. For visual inspection purposes the tickets had the day and month of issue printed on them, but in the two digit 'year' space a number between 71 and 85 appeared; this was a code for the station of issue, 71 being Govan, and working clockwise round the system to 85 for Ibrox. In addition, each print block had a unique number which appeared in the text at the centre of the ticket. These blocks were often moved from machine to machine and station to station, however.

Battery Locomotives and Wagons

A bogie battery locomotive also capable of running off the third rail was envisaged when the Infrastructure Grant Application was drawn up, and indeed a specification was produced. Little interest for such a project could be generated amongst likely suppliers, so it was found more economic to buy two four-wheeled battery locomotives (in effect buying one bogie locomotive in two halves) and forgoing the option to run off the 600 Volt live rail.[14]

The two resultant locomotives were built by Clayton Equipment (their serial Nos. BO 0965A and BO 0965B) and delivered in November 1977. They incorporate two nose suspended axle hung traction motors of 48hp, and have 840mm diameter wheels, on a wheelbase of 1·75m, and a length over bufferbeams of 4.65m. Wedglock couplers, tripcocks, multiple unit control and thyristor motor control were other features. The locomotive brakes are of the direct-air type, but they are fitted with proportional valves to produce a variable pressure in the brake pipe for the control of coupled wagons: this equipment was supplied by Davies & Metcalfe. Each locomotive weighs about 14.8 tonnes, of which the 96-cell lead-acid battery contributes about 5·1 tonnes.[14, 15] The locomotives were painted yellow from the outset,[16] and were numbered L3 and L2 respectively by the PTE shortly after delivery. This was one of the few areas where the Grant Application estimates were higher than the actual.

When the locomotives were delivered acceptance tests and crew training of the ten drivers retained from the old system quickly followed.[2] Their first regular duty was moving cars between the Workshop building and the test track, across the site where Balfour Beatty were building the Depot access ramps, and laying track in the West Yard and headshunts – an area where, of course, there was no traction current available at that time.

Some of the cars and underframes were kept from the old system for possible further use. During the autumn and winter of 1977 the underframes from Cars 16 and 57 were adapted as cable carrying/laying wagons: this job was an integral part of the Modernisation programme as the cabling contract, unlike the re-railing contract, required the PTE to provide wagons, locomotives and drivers by early in January 1978. Considerable strengthening of the underframes was required to carry the anticipated load of cable drums, together with fixings for four pairs of cable drum jacks. The structural design work was done by Merz and McLellan, and mainly consisted of fitting a heavy girder along each side of each wagon spanning from bogie bolster to bogie bolster, and arranging for additional bogie swing since there were 50 metre radius curves in the depot area, compared with about 90 metre minimum radius in the tunnels.

Since, as we have already seen, the battery locomotives have Wedglock couplers standard with the passenger cars, it was necessary to fit similar equipment to each end of each wagon. New couplers cost about £850 each at that time. In an effort to save money an approach was made to the company scrapping London Transport 1938 Tube Stock, and they agreed to supply a total of 13 couplers at £50 each. These couplers were mechanically and pneumatically compatible and were suitable, since the electrical contact blocks were not required. When they arrived the face plates were tack welded together in pairs, the odd one having the greater part of a 14th coupler attached to it!

A considerable amount of the wagon conversion work involved the fitting of curved tracks for the radial bars peculiar to that particular version of the Wedglock coupler, together with sector bars, and spring buffers.

The main and auxiliary reservoirs had to be relocated on the underframe (previously they had been under seats) and were placed where the traction resistor grids and air compressor had been. A wooden deck was provided between the girders, and a caged area for man-carrying was built at one end at the contractor's request. A small cage was built at the other end to protect a look-out man during propelling moves. The conversion was a success as very little difficulty has been experienced with these wagons in service.[2]

On 20th May 1981 this five-car train resulted from the use of two-car set 116 and 111 and three-car set 106, 128 and 119 for disabled train push-out training. Retained but immobilised at the south end of the test track at that time were the pre-modernisation four-wheeled wagon ("The Tumbril") and the underframe of Motor Car 18.
Ian Maclean

Hire of Locomotives to Taylor Woodrow

By February 1978 Taylor Woodrow were falling behind their track renewal schedule. Although they had provided their own motive power they needed more if, in an effort to improve productivity, they opened up a new base for concreting the track bed at the old Merkland Street chamber with access from Beith Street, in addition to their original site at Bridge Street. They still intended delivering rails, sleepers, track blocks etc from Bridge Street. Since the cable-laying programme was being delayed by the lack of progress with the track, it was agreed to hire one of the new Clayton battery locomotives to Taylor Woodrow on condition PTE drivers were used. Locomotive L2, together with a battery charger and wagons adapted by Taylor Woodrow from old bogies, was lowered into the Merkland Street chamber by crane on 30th March, with crew training starting next day. Locomotive L2 had to be replaced by L3 on 19th April after developing a defective motor – thought to have been caused by a flash-over during so-called plug (electrical) braking. This braking arrangement was disconnected so that air braking was the only system available, and the locomotives have worked well since. By early May a concrete loading chute had been provided in what is now the roof of the platform access stairway at Kelvinbridge, and the locomotive was working from there. At the end of the hire period the locomotive was returned to the PTE on 18th July, but a further period of hire was negotiated, this time including PTE maintenance, and L2 went to Kelvinbridge on 2nd August, this time travelling through the tunnel, and returning the same way for maintenance on Saturdays, starting from 19th August. On one occasion about a month later L2 was found to have 2 pints of water in each motor, and it was decided to send the motors back to Clayton: they were not returned for four weeks, during which time only one locomotive was available as the PTE had not at that time purchased spare motors. Priority was given to cable train operation, but that was interrupted by a PTE Craftsmen's strike which lasted from 20th October until 17th November. During a further brief period of hire to Taylor Woodrow in January 1979, L2 developed bad flats, and the wheels had to be taken out and sent to Andrew Barclays in Kilmarnock for turning.[2]

The shortened No. 39 is positioned by one of Taylor Woodrow's Clayton battery locomotives (later to return to the Underground to become L4 or W5) for road haulage to the Transport Museum. On the pallets behind and to the right of the locomotive are Westinghouse P3 type impedance bonds, and beyond is 'Robertson's Compound' with the rail access gate out of view to the left. The west wall of the Stabling Shed is in the background. *J. K. Wright*

Cable train operation

Since the original traction feeding arrangement was to be retained, albeit with the station switchgear re-located, the ring main cable had to be renewed. The 1935 multicore cable used for signalling and communications purposes was also life-expired and had to be replaced. Early in 1978 Messrs Alex Robertson, the cabling contractors, set up a compound spanning the new 'Permanent Way Road' between the old and new buildings; this compound could accommodate the two cable-carrying wagons, and had storage for cable drums and site offices, etc.[2]

After several delays Robertsons started cable train trials from Broomloan on Monday 12th June 1978. Two days later a train loaded with 17 tonnes of cable was successfully stopped on the 1 in 30 down gradient of the Depot access ramp. The main difficulty encountered in the trials was the state of the track in the tunnels, with incomplete rail joints etc. Cable train running proper started a week later, from the North Turn-out Chamber southwards towards Ibrox on the Outer Circle. By a week after that Cessnock had been reached. In mid-August this work was interrupted by fumes, dust, etc produced by another contractor shot-blasting station chamber walls. On the evening of Wednesday 19th July there was the first derailment on the new system – locomotive L2 in the headshunts due to defective points.[2]

Strathclyde Transport Day

On Saturday 15th April 1978 a Strathclyde Transport event was held in Glasgow, with a procession of public transport vehicles – historic and modern – from Kelvingrove Park to the Bus Works at Butterbiggins Road, Eglinton Toll. In the procession were Underground Car 107, on delivery from Metro-Cammell, and an escalator on the lorry delivering it from O&K Escalators in Keighley. These exhibits and many more, including the Trackmobile, were on view at the Bus Works on Sunday 16th.[2]

Traction Current Distribution

For about ten years prior to modernisation the sub-stations at Benalder Street and Seaward Street had been operated remotely from Dalhousie Street sub-station, which was the only one to be manned. The control equipment was moved to Broomloan, and was arranged for operation by the System Controller from a panel in the System Control Room. The decision to close the system completely for modernisation meant that the Depot would be isolated from a 600 Volt dc supply source, so one of the two mercury arc rectifier sets from Benalder Street sub-station was moved and temporarily installed in the paint shop of the new Workshop building at Broomloan. As the modernisation progressed it was concluded that it would be necessary to return the transformer and rectifier 'borrowed' from Benalder Street. It was also realised that there would be limitations supplying the Depot and yards by the ring-main cable from Benalder Street and Seaward Street sub-stations, so it was decided to build a new sub-station with silicon rectifier equipment in the East Yard. This started to feed the yard area from 15th April 1981, and the temporary arrangement was retained as a back-up for the first three weeks. The mercury arc equipment was returned to Benalder Street in May 1981.[17]

Museum Pieces

As described in Chapter 7, Trailer Car 41 had been repainted in Glasgow District Subway livery in 1974 and ran thus until the closedown of the system. To enhance the appearance of the long blank west wall of the concourse at the rebuilt Buchanan Street Station, it was decided that a full size representation of one of the Subway cars should be positioned there. Car 41 was chosen, but it would be cut down to its original four-wheel length and also split in half longitudinally so that it could be mounted on the wall.

At about the same time the Glasgow Museum of Transport had a desire to show a short Subway Company trailer, and so Nos. 39 and 41 were brought together in the new works building at Broomloan, and the following engineering, carried out by Underground craftsmen, was devised.

The body of 41 was removed from its underframe and parts which were not required for display were scrapped. The underframe was then cut down to original short length and leaf springs (left over from scrapped Daimler buses), axles and wheels were rigged up. Next, No. 39's body was stripped and carefully examined, the joints where the 1902/1907 extension had been made were found and the extension was removed. The two ends were then placed, one at a time, on to No. 41's underframe and joined together. Finally, No. 39's underframe was adapted to take the shortened and split body of 41. The splendid results of all this ingenuity can be seen in Buchanan Street station and in the Transport Museum in the Kelvin Hall.

No. 41T in Buchanan Street concourse on 16th February 1991, alongside one of the soon to be replaced Crouzet passenger operated ticket machines. *Ian Maclean*

No. 39T on display at the Transport Museum in the Kelvin Hall, together (left) and motor car no. 1 and one end of trailer car no. 4 masquerading as a GEC-equipped motor car. *Ian Maclean*

Chapter 9

Inauguration, Re-opening and Consolidation, 1980–1996

Arrangements were made for Her Majesty the Queen accompanied by Prince Philip to re-open the Underground and the reconstructed Argyle Line during a full day visit to Strathclyde Region on 1st November 1979. This persuaded the Executive to strengthen its project management arrangements with the various consulting engineers and contractors involved; to this end London Transport International (the now-defunct consultancy arm of London Transport) was approached. They offered the services of London Underground's recently-retired Chief Signal Engineer, Mr Harry Haddoway, who started about March 1979 but regrettably became seriously ill some three weeks later, and died soon afterwards. He was replaced by London Underground's Engineer (New Works) from the Chief Civil Engineer's Department, Mr David Jobling. Shortly after this, in May 1979, the PTE Director General, Andrew McKay, died in a car accident on the M6 Motorway whilst on his way to Metro-Cammell in Birmingham for the official hand-over of the last of the new cars.

As the year wore on it became apparent the Royal event would precede the public opening by some weeks or even months, so, as far as the Underground was concerned, it became an 'inauguration'. The delay was caused by difficulties in commissioning the tunnel emergency telephone and the ATO systems, which had cut the driver training time in the tunnels to the bare minimum. After a ceremony at Strathclyde Region Headquarters, the Royal party was taken to Buchanan Street Underground station, meeting some of the people involved in the Modernisation on the concourse and platform there, and then travelled by the Outer Circle to St Enoch. At St Enoch more of the people involved were presented, the Queen unveiled a plaque, then walked to British Rail's new Argyle Street station and travelled by special train on the Argyle Line to Hamilton, where a formal lunch was provided by Strathclyde Regional Council.

The cars chosen for the short trip were 132 and 133, the last two delivered. This was because most of the cars had, during commissioning runs and driver training, developed cracks in the exterior paintwork corresponding to the panel joints, and in the worst cases the electrolytic barrier material between the steel frame and the aluminium panels had started to ooze through the cracks producing unsightly black lines. On many cars, too, the white band had become badly stained, and several had developed flatted wheels during driver training. Those selected had not completed their commissioning, and had not been into the tunnels, so were in pristine condition. Their paintwork was protected with copious quantities of car polish whilst they were put through their tunnel tests. They were the first cars to be adorned with the new 'Trans-Clyde' logos below the ⋘ symbols, but they had to be hand-painted, as no transfers were yet available.[1]

The train was examined by Special Branch police officers late the previous night at Broomloan Depot, and guarded by them until it was due to leave the depot. It carried special route number boards '1' at front and rear, with the figures in gold on a black background and two small Union Jack flags at each end. Once at Buchanan Street, the cars were given a final polish by car cleaners. The tunnels and stations were searched

Because the railway was not quite ready for public use, the Queen inaugurated, rather than opened, the modernised Underground on Thursday 1st November 1979 by travelling on a special train (Cars 132 and 133) between Buchanan Street and St Enoch. Here she and Prince Philip listen as Inspector (now Chief Operating Superintendent) John McDonnell explains the Automatic Train Operation system in the cab of 132. Driver James Cameron's arm can be seen just above the special route number board with its gold numeral '1'. *SPT*

by the police for anything suspicious. A contractor's employee placed a hoax bomb in one of the concourse ticket machines at Buchanan Street, which caused some excitement when the police found it, but apart from that the day's events went off as planned. The date coincided with Andrew McKay's successor, Alan Westwell, taking up his duties as Director General.

The occasion was the first time the new brown Underground uniforms had been seen in public. Brown had been selected because that had been the colour used by the Subway Company, and also because it blended with the predominantly brown/cream/orange colour schemes of the stations and rolling stock.

A considerable amount of fitting-out work remained to be done at the stations, but Buchanan Street and St Enoch were made to look complete, and the relevant escalators, at least, were commissioned in time. A tub with a shrub in it was arranged to catch one particularly persistent water drip at Buchanan Street!

Once the formal proceedings were over at St Enoch, staff training resumed, and continued for the next few months. Within a day or two Buchanan Street and St Enoch stations looked like building sites again!

Having missed several target dates for re-opening, the Executive decided not to announce another date until it was satisfied the new date could be met.

Commissioning of equipment and other preparations had reached a sufficiently advanced stage for shadow running to be implemented from Monday 10th March, using the initial public timetable which covered an operating day from 06:30 until 19:00 and called for six 2-car trains per Circle in the peaks, and four per Circle in the midday off-peak. Concurrent with this the Permanent Way Section started formal nightly line patrols, and an 'Authority to Switch on Traction Current' procedure was introduced between the Chief Permanent Way Foreman and the System Controller. One of the criteria was to achieve two weeks' shadow timetable running without serious difficulty. At first things were too erratic to consider a public opening, but with mounting media and local political criticism, there was pressure to open. Towards the end of March a press preview was organised: about the only adverse features reported were unfinished platform chamber lining and flooded anti-suicide pits at St Georges Cross. Also during March it was announced that the public opening would be on Wednesday 16th April, but because of remedial and other work still outstanding, the public service would be on a 6-day per week (Monday to Saturday) basis, finishing at about 19:00.

The first day's running was reasonably uneventful, and some 28,000 passengers sampled the new service. An unexpected peak appeared on the first day between noon and 14:00, when many city-centre office workers took a 20p ride round the Circle. Considerable numbers of children bought a 10p child's ticket and spent their after-school hours riding on the system and frequently transferring from train to train.

It is Wednesday 16th April 1980 and the first passenger train of the modernised Underground awaits its 06:30 departure from the Outer Circle platform at Govan. Norman Stirling, Director of Finance, Greater Glasgow Passenger Transport Executive, Miss Stirling, Hamish Taylor, Director of Planning and Development, GGPTE, Alan Westwell, Director General, GGPTE, and first passengers Ian and Colin Maclean look on as Councillor Malcolm Waugh, Vice Chairman of Strathclyde Regional Council's Highways and Transportation Committee, points out the newly-launched 'Trans-Clyde' brand name. *SPT*

One problem which had not emerged during trial running was that drivers had difficulty seeing the rear doors at certain stations, an aid for this having only been provided at one station. To ease this sudden crisis, bus inspectors were hurriedly drafted in to provide platform attendance at the trouble spots, and were prominent in their green uniforms. Within a matter of days mirrors were in place.

Between 30,000 and 35,000 passengers were recorded over the next few days, and over 40,000 were carried on each of the first two Saturdays. By early May the totals had moderated to about 28,000 passengers per day, and later in the summer, as was the case before and has been since, the numbers dropped.

There were incidents involving loss of shoegear at a rate of about one per month (described in greater detail later), and a number of flooding incidents, sometimes as a result of South of Scotland Electricity Board (SSEB) supply failures. The trainstops also gave trouble: one cause was the arm fouling a sheet metal cover over the return spring, but this was reasonably easy to remedy. Another problem was high resistance finger contacts: this was dealt with by chromium plating the contacts as had been done with the previous trainstops shortly before modernisation. The hydraulic power pack also gave some teething troubles.

Over the first few weeks there were about four occasions on which one or other Circle had to be suspended for periods of up to an hour, but in spite of that most initial public reaction was favourable.

The initial timetable had six trains on each Circle in the peaks (giving a 4-minute interval service) and four trains per Circle in the midday off-peak period. Experience showed the need for minor timetable adjustments by keeping the morning peak service running slightly longer. The Saturday service built up to five trains each way from noon.

After close of traffic on Friday 6th June 1980 one of the swing-nose crossings on the Outer Circle in the North Turn-out chamber 'lost detection' – it had not moved from its previous position, and became 'out-of-correspondence' with the associated point blades: as a result the signal protecting the points would not clear to green. An empty train en route from Ibrox to Govan stopped at the signal, and due to inexperience on the part of the relief System Controller, was given authority to pass the red signal without the reason for the signal remaining at red being established. The result was that all wheels of the leading car of the train (Car 104) became de-railed when it reached the points. The line was cleared in time for the next morning's service, however.

The entrance, concourse, escalators, ticket/control room and staff facilities at Hillhead had not been completed in time for the public opening, so a temporary booking office had been set up in a Portakabin which allowed access to the platforms by the emergency exit stairway. A temporary fire exit was provided through the building site of the new entrance using the permanent fixed stairway: it was to ease site work during this period that the stairway was positioned to one side of the escalators rather than in the more normal position between them. The new entrance and facilities opened for business on Monday 28th July.

From Monday 29th September 1980 the service was extended to run until about 22:45, a 3-train per circle (8-minute headway) service being provided from about 18:30. A week or so later the real turning point came – term started at both Glasgow and Strathclyde Universities, the upper flight escalators at Kelvinbridge went into service, and passenger journeys passed the 40,000 per day level; fortunately reliability greatly improved about the same time. An exhibition in the Kelvin Hall coinciding with the half-term holiday week in Strathclyde schools helped still further towards the end of October. Hillhead and Kelvinbridge became so busy in the morning peaks that passengers waiting for Outer Circle trains at St Georges Cross often could not board the first two or even three trains.

To ease these problems it was decided to make use of the lengthened platforms and increase a number of trains to 3-car length. As described in Chapter 8, 'double block' working was in force, so this, together with the staffing implications, made longer rather than more frequent trains the better option. Certain of the platform mirrors had to be adjusted to give drivers a clear view of the doors of the third car. Because of sub-station limitations it was found necessary to isolate the traction equipment on the middle cars: this adversely affected performance, particularly on the steep uphill gradients from under the Clyde, but did not render the 24-minute timetabled journey time unachievable. Shortly afterwards a way was devised which enabled the rheostatic brake to continue in operation, thereby reducing wheel tread and brake block wear. The first 3-car train went into public service on the Outer Circle on 4th November 1980: shortly afterwards up to four 3-car trains were running.

50,000 passengers in one day was exceeded for the first time since Modernisation on Saturday 13th December 1980 with St Enoch being particularly busy. In one week about this period the train lost mileage from all causes was only 0·01%.

A limited service was run on Christmas Day and Boxing Day 1980 and New Year's Day and 2nd January 1981, but on Christmas Day only 2,652 passengers were carried, and no-one at all booked at West Street! Services have not been provided on Christmas Day or New Year's Day since, except for a service starting about midday on 1st January 1983 because of an 'Old Firm' (Rangers vs Celtic) match at Ibrox. However only 5,847 passengers were carried.

On Monday 30th March 1981 a ceremony was performed to mark the 10,000,000th passenger.[1] As will be seen in Appendix 4 annual passenger figures rose steadily to about 13·76m by the 1986/7 Financial Year, but remained doggedly at between 13·5m and 13·6m until 1992/3, despite Sunday running, the Garden Festival and Glasgow's year as European City of Culture in 1990. Had it not been for these events, the figures would almost certainly have dropped. It was not until the effect of the arrival of the trailer cars showed up in the 1993/4 results that the annual figure started to rise again, but this was relatively short-lived. Pre-Christmas shopping in December also produces a marked seasonal peak.

The traffic pattern is heavily influenced by the University terms, particularly at Glasgow University, and to a lesser extent at Strathclyde University and Glasgow Caledonian University. Football traffic to and from Ibrox is another useful source of revenue, and to a lesser extent matches at Partick Thistle's Firhill ground.

Timetables and Fares

Although the need for a timetable may not be immediately obvious to the bulk of Underground passengers, without one it would be impossible to ensure drivers are available to relieve one another in an orderly way, and to organise efficient maintenance of rolling stock. In fact five main timetables are used:-

Timetable	First Trains	Peak Service ‡	Midday off-peak ‡	Evenings ‡	Last Trains
Mon to Fri (winter)	06:30	6	4	3	22:45
Saturday	06:30	4 *	5 †	3	22:45
Sunday	11:00	3	3	-	18:00
Mon to Fri (summer)	06:30	5	4	3	22:45
'Holiday Monday'	07:30	3	3	3	22:45
* from 09:20 † from 12 noon ‡ Trains per circle					

All trains return to the Depot on completion of their spell in service, but for trains remaining in service past the peaks drivers are relieved at Govan. All the timetables allow 24 minutes per 'journey' – i.e. one trip round the system – about 17 minutes of which are in motion, 5 minutes are allowed for all station stops, and 2 minutes for 'recovery time'. The two Monday to Friday services start with two trains leaving the Depot at 06:00, and going to the Inner and Outer Circle platforms at Govan, picking up the keys for the south side and north side stations respectively, and delivering them on their journeys to St Enoch. Meanwhile two more trains leave the Depot for Govan, so by 06:30 when the station doors are opened to the public two trains per Circle are in position to start service. The service builds up to the peak level by about 08:15. From about 09:15, two trains per Circle (winter) and one train per Circle (summer) return to the Depot, leaving a 6-minute service for the midday off-peak. Additional trains enter service for the evening peak from about 15:45, and from about 18:00 three trains per Circle are left in service, giving an 8-minute interval until about 22:30.

The relatively early finishing time at night was initially arranged to give adequate time for work outstanding from the Modernisation. After the stations are closed to the public various checks and procedures have to be gone through, and a staff train is run round the Outer Circle. Traction current cannot be switched off in the tunnels to allow track work to start until this train reaches the Depot at 23:30 at the earliest.

The flexibility offered by the ability to take trains easily into or out of service via the ramps is fully exploited for football specials when there are matches at Ibrox Stadium, for shoppers' specials in the run-up to Christmas, and for other events as deemed necessary.

Left Ibrox Station is situated close to Ibrox Stadium, home of Rangers Football Club, and handles large crowds at each event held there, football or otherwise. On such days the 'match entrance' and booking office in Woodville Street is used to supplement the main facility in Copland Road. The number of passengers allowed on to the platforms prior to the arrival of trains is controlled by Underground staff at the concourse entry barriers and at the foot of the staircases, backed up by two police constables. Here the arriving Route 4 has the almost undivided attention of the Outer Circle crowd, while an Inner Circle 'special' departs with a full load and leaves behind some city-bound fans who will have to wait fully four minutes for the next train. *Ian Maclean*

Pope John Paul II on his visit to Scotland held an open-air mass on Tuesday 1st June 1982 in Bellahouston Park, which is not far from Ibrox station. It was decided the best way to handle the expected number of passengers (possibly up to 80,000) was to run the normal service with one peak hour train on each Circle cancelled, and the resulting 5 trains per Circle formed as 3-car trains, with the remaining three cars of the fleet formed up as a spare train. 'Specials' were then to be run between the peaks and in the evening – effectively providing 5 trains per Circle all day. (To test the implications of this pattern of service on the traction current distribution system, a similar service was run on one Saturday in April.) It was anticipated returning passengers might not have been cleared from Ibrox by the time of the normal last trains, so contingency plans were made for keeping the Inner Circle running later if necessary.

Through-travel arrangements were made with British Rail via both Buchanan Street and Partick, but in the event did not approach the estimated figures, though returning passengers from Ibrox exceeded expectations. They started appearing at Ibrox at about 16:30, but the bulk presented themselves between 19:20 and 21:40, and were split into three queues; one to approach the Outer Circle platform via the fire escape for passengers with BR through tickets via Partick, the second to approach the Inner Circle platform via the main entrance for passengers with BR through tickets via Buchanan Street/Queen Street, and the third via the football match entrance in Woodville Street for people with Transcards or requiring to buy tickets.

Despite favourable weather – it was a day of bright sunshine and temperatures in the mid-80°s F all day – the passengers carried only reached some 69,500, but of these some 17,000 journeys originated at Ibrox. It would appear that about half the passengers were regulars, and the other half were people travelling to and from Bellahouston Park. It was not necessary to extend the service beyond the normal finishing time, nor to use the spare train.[2] It was not until 26th November 1994 that the daily maximum number of passengers carried equalled that of 1st June 1982.

Sunday services were run on the four Sundays before Christmas in 1986, on a one-shift basis from about 11:00 until 18:00, using 3 trains per Circle giving an 8-minute service.[3] Between 8,700 and 16,800 people used the service each day. A proposal to repeat the process in 1987 had to be abandoned because of a disagreement about overtime payments to station masters.[4]

A service was provided for the 22 Sundays of the 1988 Garden Festival, which was close to Shields Road station, from about 09:30 until 22:40, using 4 trains on each Circle. After the Garden Festival Sunday running continued, using the single-shift, 3 trains per Circle arrangement, and, except for some Sundays during the Festive Season, this has remained the standard arrangement ever since, though it has been augmented when justified by football or other special events.

To avoid delay to passengers returning from the Garden Festival, arrangements were made to sell combined entry and Underground tickets valid for the homeward journey at a discount price of £4·60: these were only on sale at Shields Road, and an extra ticket window was opened for the purpose. The price compared with £5·00 charged at the Festival entrance for entry only. It is estimated that the Garden Festival generated an extra 200,000 passenger journeys for the Underground, but as already mentioned, this had little effect on the annual total.

The various fare increases, from 20p adult flat fare in 1980 to 65p from 7th October 1996 exceeded the level of inflation over this period.[21] A 10p increase in May 1995 had a greater adverse effect on the numbers of passengers carried than earlier increases. The advent of new ticketing equipment permitted introduction of 'stored-journey' tickets, and other initiatives have included Heritage Trail tickets, which allow unlimited travel on the day of issue and suggest a number of walks from Underground stations to visit places of interest nearby.

Only very occasionally will single cars be taken on to the Circles for test and if so usually after the public service has finished. Here Car 114 pauses at Bridge Street at 23:00 on 7th May 1986, *en route* round the Inner Circle. *Ian Maclean*

Left Two of the experimental passenger-operated ticket machines installed in the 1930s; these were opposite the booking office at Hillhead station. *Glasgow Museum of Transport*

Right Crouzet self-serve ticket machines were introduced on the modernised Underground in December 1984, this one being in the concourse at St Enoch station. *Ian Maclean*

Floods

Structural damage was caused at St Enoch station on Saturday 10th January 1981, when a contractor working on a landscaping scheme in St Enoch Square burst a water main whilst excavating a tree planter pit, resulting in a large in-rush of water and sand which moved an internal brick facing wall adjacent to the down escalator to the Outer Circle platform. But for the escalator itself, the brick wall would probably have collapsed. The in-rush filled the sump on the Outer Circle north of the station with sand, and the Outer Circle track quickly flooded. Both Circles were suspended until the extent of the damage could be assessed. Once it was established that the main piles had not moved, the Inner Circle was resumed with a speed restriction to minimise vibration. The sump had to be cleared of sand, the wall demolished and rebuilt and the escalator stripped, thoroughly cleaned, rebuilt and re-commissioned.[1] Whilst the repair work was in progress on the Outer Circle platform the north end was closed.

During exceptionally heavy rain on the evening of Wednesday 18th September 1985 water flowing down the Depot access ramps exceeded the capacity of the pump discharge system and initially flooded the trackbed in the North Turn-out Chamber and caused a track circuit failure. Later the water spread along the Outer Circle tunnel to Govan station and exceeded the pumping capacity there too, and started to flow down the gradient towards the sump at the low point under the Clyde. The pumps there were also unable to cope, so some of the water flowed through the Clyde Man-hole into the Inner Circle which is lower at that point. Shortly afterwards an Inner Circle train with about 55 passengers on board ran past the low point, and came to rest on the Govan side of the flood. After the passengers had been de-trained to Govan, the train was eventually recovered by the two battery locomotives. In the early hours of the next morning water coming through the roof of the old Merkland Street chamber flowed down both tunnels and overwhelmed the pumps at Partick Station, resulting in flooding of the track there and frustrating the hope of re-opening at least the Outer Circle on time. Specialist pumping equipment was hired and taken to Partick, and the Inner Circle was re-opened about 19:00, followed by the Outer Circle some two hours later, Some 60mm of rain fell in the 24 hours to 04:00 on Thursday 19th September: in contrast when the system was flooded by heavy rain in September 1976 it took about three weeks to resume service, emphasising the improvement in the pumping and drainage arrangements during the modernisation.[5]

On the week-end of 10th and 11th December 1994 heavy and prolonged rain fell on Glasgow and the west of Scotland generally, causing widespread flooding in a number of areas, especially parts of Paisley. Just after close of traffic on Sunday evening 11th December, the River Kelvin overflowed its banks at Kelvinbridge, and considerable quantities of water entered both Underground tunnels, some of it through the joints in the cast iron segments, flooding the tracks, the Outer Circle being the worst affected. After the flood water subsided, safety checks had to be made on the tunnel structure, and it was Wednesday 14th December before the complete Inner Circle was re-opened for traffic, the Outer Circle following two days later: temporary speed restrictions were imposed in both cases. Meanwhile temporary shuttle services were run, from Ibrox to St Enoch (subsequently Buchanan Street) and from Govan to Kelvinhall, later extended to Hillhead. Three stations, Kelvinbridge, St Georges Cross and Cowcaddens, were closed on the Monday and Tuesday.[6]

Flood water from the Kelvinbridge area entered the disused Kelvingrove Tunnel of the former Glasgow Central Railway at the Eldon Street portal, flowed down to Exhibition station, then contributed to flooding of the Argyle line tunnel from Exhibition station to east of Argyle Street station, inundating two 314 3-car units in the process. It took some nine months to restore services on the Argyle Line.

Flooding around Kelvinbridge station on the morning of Monday 12th December 1994. While clearly showing the effect of the River Kelvin overflowing its east bank, the photograph, reproduced with kind permission of The Herald and Evening Times, also covers many railway features in the area.

1. Great Western Road on Great Western Bridge ("Kelvin Bridge") over the River Kelvin.
2. Shop frontage at 433 Great Western Road incorporating the site of the entrance to the Underground's former passenger lift to Kelvinbridge Station. The lift shaft descended through the tenement building to a level immediately above the subway tunnels, from where a passage led to the landing at the top of the stair to the platform.
3. The emergency exit from today's station at 76 South Woodside Road, at the foot of the "iron stair" from Great Western Road. This was the station entrance prior to the 1977-80 modernisation.
4. Covered escalator from Great Western Road leading directly into the station concourse.
5. Kelvinbridge Underground station.
6. Park and Ride car park, partially flooded in this view. This was formerly the site of British Railways' Kelvinbridge Goods and Mineral station.
7. Caledonian Mansions.
8. River Kelvin, in spate.
9. Footbridge, formerly the bridge carrying the Glasgow Central Railway from its tunnel under Great Western Road and Caledonian Mansions over the Kelvin and into *its* Kelvinbridge station; the platform ends were also carried by the bridge.
10. At this point the Glasgow Central Railway left the open air by passing under Eldon Street Bridge and immediately entering Kelvingrove Tunnel, which took it under Kelvingrove Park and on to the former Stobcross station (now Exhibition station). Most of the flood which submerged the Argyle Line at the time of this photograph came through the tunnel from here.

3 to 8 is the east-west line of the Underground tunnels
9 to 10 is the north-south line of the former Glasgow Central Railway, and was part of the route intended for the Strathclyde Tram.

For several days during the 1994 Kelvinbridge flooding described on page 174 shuttle services replaced the regular timetable. On 12th December Route 15 (Cars 114/203/122), running wrong-direction to St Enoch on the Outer Circle, arrives at Shields Road as the driver of Route 18 (Cars 102/205/133), running wrong-direction to Ibrox on the Inner, checks the platform before departing. In such situations automatic train operation is not available, and as required for extended manual control of normally ATO trains, each set has two drivers and displays a red hand lamp in a front window. *Ian Maclean*

Ramp access to the tunnels from the Depot means that trains on the modernised Underground have to cope with surface weather, and here on 9th February 1991 Route 15 (Cars 109/118/126) drifts into Headshunt 1, while Route 5 (Cars 115/132/131) awaits its departure signal in Headshunt 2. The backs of the signals controlling access to the tunnels are visible on either side of Route 5. The unoccupied track on the right is the test track. The housing scheme in the background dating from 1935 has since been demolished. *Ian Maclean*

Other Incidents

Most of the early shoegear/live rail incidents resulted in damage to the cars' shoe-gear, and the breakage of one or two live rail insulators at most. The first major exception to this pattern was during the morning of Wednesday 16th December 1987, when an Inner Circle train in the Kelvinbridge to Hillhead section dislodged the live rail outwards and put a strain on the porcelain insulators which progressively broke until a length of about 200 metres of live rail was lying on the trackbed, and some 50 insulators were broken. Repairs took all day and most of the following night, as the rail had to be cut into manageable lengths to manhandle back on to the new insulators.[4]

There were three incidents in quick succession on 18th, 23rd and 24th February 1988 in which a shoe went down the inside of the live rail approaching Cowcaddens on the Inner Circle, all of which caused considerable disruption. These were caused by the live rail, which is on the inside of the right hand curve at that point, being 'wide to gauge'. After the second incident a 15kph speed restriction was imposed; coincidentally, the first two incidents involved the same train – Cars 130 and 116.

The potentially worst incident in traffic hours since Modernisation took place on Wednesday 27th October 1993 in the Kelvinbridge to Hillhead (Inner Circle) section. At 11:15 an Inner Circle train was brought to a halt in the tunnel approximately 350 metres after leaving Kelvinbridge, having lost traction current. The driver could find nothing wrong with the train, but since current could not be restored, it was decided to de-train the passengers. An Inspector approaching from the rear found that for about 200 metres behind the train the drainage cover slabs were displaced and broken, so the passengers had to be taken the longer distance forward to Hillhead. It emerged that the leading pair of wheels of the third car (126) had become derailed as the train left a check-railed curve about 135 metres west of Kelvinbridge, but the car had remained coupled to the rest of the train and stayed upright and in-line, the passengers evidently being unaware anything was wrong.[7]

Whilst the investigations into this incident were going on, a speed restriction had to be imposed between Cowcaddens and Buchanan Street on the Outer Circle following temporary repairs to a broken rail. At approximately 13:45, smoke appeared at Cowcaddens station platform. Well-rehearsed emergency procedures were immediately brought into action to evacuate the station, and the smoke subsided once traction current was switched off from the Outer Circle as well. It transpired that one of the track feeder cables had been punctured and contaminated water had broken down its insulation. Seven passengers and four staff were treated for smoke inhalation at the Royal Infirmary. The Outer Circle service was re-instated at 16:00, and by midnight the defective Inner Circle train had been recovered and taken back to the Depot. Track repairs were sufficiently advanced for full services to resume the next morning, albeit with a temporary speed restriction in the affected area.[7]

Passenger Incidents

The bulk of passenger incidents have involved elderly or intoxicated people falling on escalators or stairways. There have been occasional incidents where someone's leg has gone down between a platform and a car, but none involving a moving train. There have also been occasional cases of intoxicated people falling off platforms on to the track, but on the vast majority of occasions approaching trains have been stopped. The first incident since the Modernisation where someone ended up under a train was at Kinning Park on 18th April 1988, when an elderly man with mental health problems climbed down onto the Outer Circle track and was standing in the anti-suicide pit when an incoming train hit him; he died of internal injuries after being removed to hospital. Up to the time of writing there have only been two or three similar incidents, none with fatal consequences, justifying the provision of the pits at Modernisation.

Name Change and Further Projects

A year after GGPTE was set up, Local Government in Scotland was reorganised and the Highways & Transportation Committee of Strathclyde Regional Council became the Passenger Transport Authority. The Regional Council decided to extend the remit of the Executive somewhat and to reflect that the name was changed to Strathclyde Passenger Transport Executive in December 1980.[1] Investment in the Underground has continued since completion of the modernisation, and some 20 major projects were completed or committed by the time the Regional Council was abolished on 31st March 1996. These, together with other more minor changes, are discussed later in this chapter. Details of the Chairmen and Vice Chairmen appear in Appendix 1, Part C. In 1986 as a result of the bus deregulation legislation, the PTE's bus operation was set up as a separate company, initially wholly-owned by Strathclyde Region. Alan Westwell, the PTE Director General, opted to become the Managing Director of the new company, and Stephen Lockley, from Strathclyde Region's Chief Executive's Department, became Director General. Details of the other directors appear in Appendix 1, Part B.

Passenger Rolling Stock

When the cars were delivered their exteriors were painted in an overall light orange livery, with a broad (about 150 mm) white band under the centre and trailing end saloon windows, and across the trailing end of the cars, omitting the communicating doors. The cab window surrounds and the upper part of the front door pillars were painted matt black to give the impression of a single wide windscreen. The only other embellishments were plain white Helvetica numerals for the fleet number, appearing under the driver's droplight, and the ⋘ logo appearing on the panel to the rear of the driver's droplight. Before entering service all the remaining cars received 'Trans-Clyde' transfers similar to the hand-painted version applied to 132 and 133.

It soon became apparent that the livery was unsatisfactory: the roofs of the cars became soiled with tunnel dust and stained by substances dripping into the tunnels. The latter caused unsightly streaks and runs, often across the white band. The problem of cracking paint at the panel joints was still present, and as a test Metro-Cammell repainted Car 114, but with the joints covered with plastic tape; this, although not ideal, helped to restore the overall flush appearance of the cars, and was adopted as standard on subsequent repaints.

In the summer of 1981, the PTE decided to adopt a darker shade of orange, with dark brown roofs and passenger door edgings (another area subject to unsightly soiling), and to eliminate the broad white band. The shades chosen were not British Standard colours, but were named 'Govan Orange' and 'Govan Brown' by the paint manufacturer. The matt black treatment of the cab front was retained, as were the white numerals. The 'Trans-Clyde' branding was also retained but the ⋘ symbol disappeared. Cars 102 and 123 were turned out in this livery in August 1981, and by the end of the year another 8 cars had been dealt with, and a further 10 were done in 1982, and 4 in 1983. By the summer of 1983 the livery (with black instead of brown) had been applied to the buses operated under two PTE contracts. In June 1983 the Highways & Transportation Committee decided that the new livery should be applied to all forms of passenger transport for which it was financially responsible. Essentially this meant ScotRail trains financed by the PTE under Section 20 of the 1968 Transport Act, and the PTE-owned bus fleet. The Director General, Alan Westwell, was keen on the use of matt black in bus liveries, and wanted to incorporate this into a revised version of the Underground scheme. The brown areas became black, and in addition the centre saloon windows were given a narrow black surround, and the two window pillars per side also became black. The 'Trans-Clyde' branding was discarded, and instead a 'Strathclyde Transport'

In a two-car set the motor cars are coupled back to back, and if a third motor car is added, its cab will always be at the outer end of the rake. Here one car has been detached, leaving the remaining two in a seldom-seen configuration. *Ian Maclean*

Only in exceptional circumstances, such as the "push-out" of a failed train from the tunnels by the following train, will cars couple as shown. On this occasion in March 1983, crew training was taking place on the now-abandoned test track. Car 117 is in the livery which succeeded that on Car 131. *Ian Maclean*

logo, incorporating the Strathclyde Regional Council stylised map of Scotland, was applied below the centre saloon windows on each side. Because it was politically unacceptable in the west of Scotland to call the main colour 'orange', the name of the colour became Strathclyde Transport Red! The first two cars in the new livery were Nos. 133 and 132, dealt with in July and August 1983 respectively, but the 'Strathclyde Transport' transfers were not available until mid-August, so both cars ran in service for a short time without branding. The first car to receive this treatment was also given a 'warning yellow' front, but this idea was abandoned before it entered service. The matt black was difficult to apply and became discoloured, so was quickly (and unofficially) replaced by gloss black, except for the cab front which remained, as it always had been, matt.

Most of the cars which received the 'Trans-Clyde' scheme wore three liveries during their first 4½ years in service. The last car in the original livery was 121, which went straight to the 'Strathclyde' style in November 1983, and the final car in 'Trans-Clyde' livery (brown roof and door edges) was Car 127 which last ran in that form on 10th April 1986.[8] The next change was not until 1994 when refurbished cars started to appear with black exterior fleet numbers.

In the West Yard on 27th July 1983 were, from the left, trailer cars 4, with trellis gates, and 32 with centre as well as end sliding doors, and modern cars 122 in original livery and 131 in the new darker orange. When the Glasgow Museum of Transport was about to move from its original location in the former Coplawhill Tramcar Overhaul Works in Albert Drive to the Kelvin Hall it became apparent that extra space in its new home could be found for an additional Underground exhibit, but not for a whole car. Trailer car No. 4 was transferred to the Albert Drive workshop in April 1985 where it was cut in two. The front portion was retained and rebuilt as a representation of a recently-converted motor car c.1938, resplendent in scarlet and cream with fully lined-out panels. An internal mirror convinces visitors that the car is twice as long inside as it is outside. *Ian Maclean*

The interior colour scheme remained unchanged until refurbishment in 1993–6, though the trailer cars which entered service in 1992 had different interior decor. The main interior change prior to refurbishment was an increase in the number of advertisement card frames, from 8 originally in the centre saloon, first to 12 still all in the centre saloon, then to 14 which included a pair in the trailing end saloon.

The original design of shoegear presented a number of problems. One of the components in the system which kept the shoe level as the arm moved from the high to the low position or vice versa (known in Underground parlance as the 'kidney piece' because of its shape) was re-designed changing the material from Tufnol to steel, and coincidentally changing its shape but not its nickname! The shoe retraction system was found to be more trouble than it was worth: shoes could become latched up if they encountered a particularly high portion of live rail, and when latched up to bring a car back to Depot after one of the all too frequent shoegear incidents often became unlatched! The latches, re-setting cylinders and associated pipework were progressively removed. A design fault was found in the bearing arrangement for the cross-shaft which could prevent the shoes dropping from the high to the low position, and resulted in a number of cars losing shoegear on the wooden protection board above the live rail under the island platform at Hillhead. The so-called bearing housings (in which the spindles attached to the shoe carriers moved), also machined from Tufnol, were found to be susceptible to breakage at a particular point, so were progressively 'beefed up'. The shoe carrier, basically a steel pressing with a steel spindle welded into one end, also required redesign. After about 7 years fatigue became the main failure mode, so most of the components were replaced to the respective latest designs, and the failure rate improved considerably, and remained at a manageable level. An improved version designed by Brecknell-Willis for use on the trailer cars was put on trial in August 1991 on Car 101, and produced no serious faults in its first year of operation. This system retained the cross-shaft arrangement, but used lighter components and eliminated the hydraulic damper. With only minor alterations it was adopted for the trailer cars, and subsequently it was fitted to the power cars on refurbishment (see photograph on page 188).

In common with contemporary London Transport and British Rail trains, the passenger alarm handle when operated applied the automatic air brake. There was one alarming incident when a passenger on a train crowded with spectators for a match at Ibrox pulled the handle and the train stopped on the approach to Govan on the Inner Circle. Before the driver could reset the handle some of the passengers left the train through the cab and climbed down on to the track before traction current was switched off: fortunately nobody was injured. That, together with incidents on other railways, made the PTE, after consultation with the Railway Inspectorate, alter the system so that pulling the handle sounded an audible alarm in the occupied driver's cab, but did not stop the train. With the very short inter-station distances there are few incidents which cannot wait for attention until the train arrives at the next station, where invariably it would be much easier to handle the problem. These alterations were completed in August 1986.

When first put into service the cars had a 15kph speed restriction automatically imposed on them after re-setting the tripcock, having passed a signal with raised trainstop. Since manual driving was obligatory in these circumstances it effectively meant that drivers had to keep speed down to a maximum of about 13kph. On occasions it was debatable whether tripping trains past a failed signal was preferable to suspension of the circle concerned. The PTE concluded that increasing the limit to a nominal 25kph (about 23kph actual maximum) would considerably ease matters. After a cab ride to satisfy himself that there was sufficient sighting distance ahead for a train to be stopped from this speed in emergency, Major Olver of the Railway Inspectorate agreed to the proposal, and the cars were altered by September 1985.[8]

An unexpected feature of the traction equipment on the power cars came to light in May 1986 when sub-station gaps were introduced in the North Turn-out chamber in connection with the Traction Power Supply Modernisation project described later in this Chapter. When trains on the Inner Circle reached the gap after leaving Govan they were still accelerating, and the loss of traction current as the 9 metre shoe span of the cars crossed the 14 metre gap caused the camshaft equipment to go back to the starting position, but there was nothing, whilst running in ATO, to indicate to the equipment that it should resume notching. The drivers quickly found that lowering the cab droplight and raising it again produced the desired effect, but fortunately a relatively simple wiring alteration in the equipment cases resolved the problem.

To increase patronage from the 13.7 million level it was realised almost all trains should be of 3-car length. There were insufficient cars to do this, so more were required. Experience had shown that 3-car trains could maintain time whilst running with the traction equipment on one motor car cut out, so it was concluded that the additional cars could be trailers, saving weight and having lower windage resistance than motor cars. It was decided that eight new cars were required.

Transmark (the consultancy wing of British Rail at that time) assisted the PTE in producing a 'performance type' specification. Mainly because there was a considerable amount of more prestigious railway rolling stock business on offer at the time, the established builders including Metro-Cammell, who had built the power cars, declined to tender. After a prolonged tendering period the order was finally given to a new company, Hunslet Transportation Projects Limited (TPL) in October 1989. Their offer was for cars similar in dimensions to the power cars, but they declined to tender for options in the specification for:-

cars 1 metre longer;
cars of similar length but 4-wheeled instead of with bogies;
use of bogies with steerable axles.

Since Hunslet TPL had no manufacturing capability, they sub-contracted the work, mainly to other companies within the Hunslet Group. The body shells and bogies were built by Hunslet Gyro Mining Transport Limited (GMT) at Leeds with some sub-assemblies being fabricated by Qualter Hall. The completed body shells and bogies were transported by road from Leeds to the Kilmarnock works of Hunslet-Barclay Ltd for exterior painting, fitting out and commissioning.

After some initial debate, the cars were designed to be as self-contained as possible, so they have shoegear to the revised design mentioned above, a 600V compressor, static converter (instead of motor alternator), Wedglock couplers at each end, and revised internal colour scheme. Otherwise the cars were made as visually similar to the power cars as possible, except, of course, that no driver's cab is provided, the space being used for an extra four seats. These cars followed the London Underground trend in having grooved rubberised floor covering, instead of the maple lagging used previously in both London and Glasgow. The interior panels are a deep cream shade, and the seat covering moquette is predominantly dark brown with a tan area and yellow, orange and black markings intended to indicate where passengers should sit to maximise capacity. The cars were delivered by road to Broomloan Depot between April and August 1992. They carry fleet numbers 201 to 208 inclusive, and have white numerals near both ends of the side panels.

The cars were built to a performance specification, and the problem arose as to how to check performance on a non-powered vehicle, when the performance which mattered was braking. The matter was resolved by taking two recently-overhauled motor cars out of normal service, 'calibrating' them by testing their brake performance at a number of

Above right The body shells were assembled and glazed at Hunslet GMT's Leeds works and transported by road to sister company Hunslet-Barclay at Kilmarnock for fitting out, painting and commissioning. On 15th January 1992 the shell of No.207 arrives at the new Assembly Shop after an overnight trip from Leeds. *Ian Maclean, by kind permission of Hunslet- Barclay Ltd*

Right Car 201, complete with standard gauge accommodation bogies, shows that the best way from the paint shop to the assembly area is by air. In the background are British Rail Class 155 'Sprinter' units, originally built by Leyland Bus, under conversion to Class 153 single cars by the fitting of second cabs to their non-driving ends. Also in the picture is one of Hunslet-Barclay's Class 20 locomotives, which are mainly used to haul contractors' weed-killing trains on the Railtrack system. *Ian Maclean, by kind permission of Hunslet-Barclay Ltd*

Top Combined training exercises simulating possible accidents on the Underground are held regularly for staff and the emergency services. In order to make the rescuers' tasks as difficult as possible, a five-car train was marshalled for 'Operation Mandarin' on 17th May 1992, and here Cars 117, 104, 123, 102 and 129, with four cabs facing south and one facing north, enter Headshunt 2 before reversing and heading off to the "disaster scene" at Shields Road. *Ian Maclean*

Above In order to speed up the bedding-in of the disc brakes on the last four of the new trailer cars it was decided to run them in pairs. Three power cars were required for the train to reach normal service speeds and braking rates, and here a five-car test train consisting of Nos. 125, 131, 207, 202 and 112 waits on 15th August 1992 for its midnight departure. *Ian Maclean*

locations, then running them with each trailer car in turn and checking that the brake performance was the same at the pre-determined locations. Before this could be done the brakes on the trailer cars had to be bedded-in, so the cars were taken out on test runs after traffic hours on weekend evenings and did two journeys on each Circle, stopping at every station. To reduce the number of nights, the last four trailer cars were done in pairs: to achieve this from realistic speeds a 5-car train consisting of 3 power cars and two trailers was formed up on each occasion – probably the longest through-controlled trains to have run on the Glasgow Underground up to that time, though a 5-car train without through control had been run in conjunction with a simulated emergency exercise in May 1992. The 'calibrated' power cars used were 112 and 131, and these were kept out of passenger service from 2nd May to 12th October 1992. The first five trailer cars entered service in October 1992, and the rest by early December.

The trailer cars quickly achieved their intended objective – to move the annual passenger journey figure upwards from the level of about 13.7 million per year at which it had been stuck since about 1986. Between October 1992 and mid-1994 the weekly figures were usually higher than the equivalent the previous year, and in the calendar year of 1994 some 14,644,771 passengers were recorded.[6] Despite up to four (and occasionally five) power cars being out of commission for refurbishment it was possible to run the vast majority of trains as 3-car, though it was necessary to revert to up to two 2-car trains when the winter service recommenced in late August 1995.

One of the advantages of having all 3-car trains is that intending passengers spread themselves out along the full length of the platforms, which contributes to more orderly alighting and boarding. The peak capacity has been increased by about 30% without a significant increase in staff costs.

Her Royal Highness the Princess Royal visited Hunslet-Barclay's works on 22nd June 1992 and inspected some of the trailers, including 204, which she boarded. She also met many company people, and in this photograph, left to right, are Jim Lyle, Hugh Dykes, Jim Park, Russell Wear (author of "Barclay 150", a history of the company), Lorna Craig, whose name appears on company Class 20 locomotive 20902, Richard Draper, Bob Gunn, Princess Anne, Joe Baxter (hidden) and Peter Kewney, Managing Director of the company. *Hunslet-Barclay Ltd*

Car 201 at Buchanan Street (Inner Circle) on 26th October 1992, the first day on which trailer cars were used in public service. *Ian Maclean*

The interior of Car 207, showing the cream-coloured décor and the mainly brown moquette which is exclusive to the eight trailers. *Ian Maclean*

Although, in general, the motor cars had performed well, certain areas began to cause concern after about 10 years in service, particularly corrosion in some parts of the body, mainly of the floor plates in the double doorway areas and of the steel framing below the windows in the centre saloon. To help draw up a specification for tackling the problem Car 131 was sent to Hunslet-Barclay in June 1991 and had various panels removed for investigation. The trailer car project had demonstrated that better materials were available for some applications, and the Fennell Report into the Kings Cross fire, the Hidden Report into the Clapham collision and the HSE report into the Cannon Street buffer stop collision indicated that some changes in material and structure were desirable. Jones Garrod were appointed as consultants for the project, a specification was produced, and tenders were returned in mid-September 1992. A contract was signed with ABB Transportation Ltd of Derby in March 1993, although a letter of intent had been sent some weeks earlier.

As a result of the exercise with Car 131 certain surface corrosion was found on the outsides of the solebars, so some of the bottom skirt fairings were removed from the whole fleet to allow initial treatment of the corroded members. These fairings were not replaced until refurbishment.

The first car (No. 107) was moved to Derby by road in January 1993, and was used for design finalisation and evaluation purposes: it was the first car to return in February 1994. The intention was to have no more than 4 cars out of service simultaneously, and to complete the whole 33-car fleet by December 1994, but the latter date proved unrealistic, and the completion date was progressively extended to December 1995. During the summer of 1995 the PTE agreed to release a further car to assist in accelerating the programme, and the last car left for Derby on 8th November 1995. An official handing-over ceremony for this car (No. 110) was held at Broomloan Depot on 9th January 1996.

No. 107 was the first car to be refurbished by ABB Transportation Ltd and these photos show progress and improvements.

Left At Litchurch Lane Works, Derby, on standard gauge accommodation bogies, the car is stripped to the bone while corrosion is cured and front-end strength is added.

Newly arrived in the inspection bay from the paint shop, with the masking paper being removed. The new cab shell incorporates round headlights with hinged access panels. *Ian Maclean by kind permission of ABB (2)*

Back home at Broomloan on 10th February 1994 and gleaming in its new coat, 107 shows off its re-equipped and brilliantly lit interior in 19 Road after a short run through the yards. *Ian Maclean*

New Brecknell Willis shoegear and 'umbrella guard' at the cab end of 107's leading bogie. *Ian Maclean*

The driving position in the cab, little changed from before but with a new cab shell incorporating a raised section in the dome to accommodate the aerial for the new radio system; its send/receive set with integral microphone and loudspeaker is mounted at head height between the windows. Beneath the side window is the master selector switch handle (automatic/forward/neutral/reverse), and the power/brake handle is in the 'Emergency' position in the slot in the foreground. *Ian Maclean*

The opportunity was taken to upgrade the cars in other ways. Internally they received rubberised flooring, new moquette (to yet a third design), new internal panelling (metal instead of plastic-faced hardboard), new lighting diffusers, improved advertisement frames, and modernised internal notices, the overall effect being much brighter. Externally a new phenolic resin cab skin was provided incorporating new, round, high intensity headlights, and a pronounced hump in the dome to accommodate the aerial for the new radio communications system. Orange external 'doors not closed' indicator lights were provided on the roof, and external 'platform close' buttons at the trailing end, but otherwise the cars do not look greatly different from previously. The door control circuit was completely re-designed, and, like the trailer cars, the door nosing rubbers now 'interlock' with each other rather than abut as previously. A new adjustable driver's seat was provided, and access to various items of equipment in the cab area improved, together with extra collision protection at both ends, which hopefully will never be put to the test. As noted already the only external livery change was to substitute black fleet numerals for the white ones previously used. Part way through the contract horns were substituted for whistles, and a door closing 'bleeper' system introduced. Cars already refurbished were retrofitted with these features by ABB staff at Broomloan.

Inside Car 124 before refurbishment, looking towards the communicating door to the next car.
Ian Maclean

The view towards the driver's cab in Car 102 on 24th September 1994, after refurbishment by ABB. Many improvements were incorporated, the most noticeable being lighter-coloured panelling, new seating with a more restful pattern of moquette and replacement of the maple wood flooring with grooved rubber matting.
Ian Maclean

The basic approach to rolling stock maintenance has remained similar from late 1979, when the PTE took over from Metro-Cammell, until the time of writing (September 1996). Maintenance personnel carry out the following checks and routines:-

Nightly test of safety devices on all trains to be offered for service the following morning; sweep and dust of car and cab interiors; 7-Daily examination over a pit, at which wearing parts such as brake blocks and collector shoes are changed, air reservoirs drained etc; 16-weekly (originally 9-weekly) shop inspection, which includes all of the 7-Daily, but also includes opening equipment case covers, visual inspection and minor rectification, check of door interlock settings etc; Programmed Lift, at which wheels are changed, traction motors checked and overhauled, bogies overhauled etc.

In addition to these routines, fault-finding and repairs and from time to time minor modifications are carried out.

Each car passes through the automatic car washing machine two or three times a week, and is given a manual exterior brush wash and interior clean every two weeks or so. This latter operation was made much more effective from 1994 when the three car cleaners were transferred from day shift to night shift.

During Programmed Lift a high proportion of the work is on the bogies, motors, wheelsets, etc, and this usually takes longer than the routine work on the car bodies etc. For that reason two complete car sets of bogies (i.e. four in all) were provided for the power cars, and one spare car set (two bogies) for the trailers. This means that cars rarely re-enter service after Programmed Lift on the same bogies as they had when they were taken out of service.

Consideration was given during the modernisation period to renovating the existing wheel lathe or purchasing a new one, but it was concluded that the expense could not be justified with the workload arising from a fleet of only 33 cars. Initially the only company with the equipment and expertise capable of turning the Underground's wheels was Andrew Barclay at Kilmarnock. For a while in the mid-1980s wheelsets were sent to Messrs Commercial Components in Irvine, but when units such as axleboxes, or indeed wheels themselves, had to be pressed off and on, Barclays remained the preferred contractor. (Another contractor managed to damage five axles beyond repair in the course of pressing off wheels, out of eight sent.)

Initially the cars on Programmed Lift were placed on stands when lifted off their bogies, but a pair of old trailer car bogies which had been retained for the purpose was adapted as accommodation bogies in September 1986. This meant that lifted cars could be moved along straight tracks inside the Workshop building, particularly into the heavy duty cleaning bay, where the undersides could be steam cleaned. In preparation for the arrival of the trailer cars another pair of bogies was converted in June 1992,[9] in both cases the work being contracted to Hunslet-Barclay.

Car exterior re-painting was generally done by supplementing the one Underground coach painter by personnel drafted in from the PTE's (later Strathclyde Buses Ltd's) Bus Works at Butterbiggins Road. This work was concentrated into the summer period when timetable requirements are reduced.

Another task which severely stretched the Underground's limited resources in the late 1980s and early 1990s was dealing with the problem of corroded floor plates in the doorway areas of the cars. This involved removal of a substantial area of maple floor lagging, cutting out the corroded plates, shaping and welding-in patches, applying anti-corrosive treatment, then relaying the floor. In the worst-affected cars the job also involved removal of the draught screens, and re-assembly at the end of the job. With only two bodymakers and one tinsmith, cars could be 'stopped' for considerable periods of time.

Service Fleet Developments

Wagon 57 was adapted again towards the end of 1980, when a large Ingersoll-Rand electrically driven air compressor was fitted to it, together with supports for a battery standard with those on the Clayton battery locomotives. This was to provide power to tools and equipment used for track maintenance such as rail saws, drills, grinders etc, without resorting to petrol or diesel-engined devices which were not favoured for tunnel use.

In 1983 the underframes from former motor car Nos. 2 and 20 were sent to Andrew Barclay for conversion to rail carrying wagons. These two were converted in a similar way to Nos. 16 and 57 so far as coupler arrangements and bogie swing were concerned, except that at one end of each wagon a British Rail-type buckeye coupler, together with separate main reservoir and brake pipe hoses, was fitted. The wagons are used as a pair, coupled together by the buckeyes, but only ever coupled to locomotives etc at the 'outer' ends, which have ex-London Transport 1938 Tube Stock Wedglock couplers. There is a roller track down the centre of each wagon for manoeuvring rails, and a 500 Kg retractable winch with chain blocks at the inner end of each wagon. Davies & Metcalfe distributors were fitted instead of the original Westinghouse triple valves, and shortly afterwards Wagons 16 and 57 were similarly converted. The bogies of RW2 and RW20, as they became, were fitted with modified brake levers etc. to accommodate the same non-metallic brake blocks as used on the new passenger cars. Further modified sets of brake levers were supplied to the PTE to convert Wagons 16 and 57 to the same arrangement.

As described in Chapter 8, Taylor Woodrow acquired two Clayton battery locomotives for use on their re-railing contract. At the end of that contract and after a period of hire to the PTE (when they were allocated numbers L4 and L5) Taylor Woodrow transported them to their headquarters at Southall, Middlesex, where they were put in 'open storage', and remained so for the next six years or so. In early 1987 the PTE was considering options for rail grinding, and an additional battery locomotive was an attractive proposition. After having the locomotives checked by a Clayton representative, the PTE acquired them in a derelict state for the price of £3,700, and they were delivered to Broomloan in March 1987.[10] Both locomotives were sent to Clayton on 6th September 1988, and were cannibalised to produce one (actually L4, formerly TE4A003) for use in conjunction with an Italian rail grinding machine which was about to be hired for a period. The locomotive retains a contactor/resistor control system and 1.61m wheel-base, and on its return was provided with a new Chloride battery standard with those on the other two locomotives and the compressor wagon. The completed locomotive and recovered parts from the other returned on 21st November. On completion of the grinding work, a scheme was developed for making L4 more operationally interchangeable with the original two locomotives and this work was awarded to Hunslet-Barclay (as Andrew Barclay became in January 1989); the locomotive was despatched from Broomloan on 6th October 1989.[10] Tests on its return revealed that the air compressor had insufficient capacity, and one standard with those on L2 and L3 was fitted by the PTE, which involved enlarging the compressor enclosure. The 1977 conversion from 3ft gauge to 4ft gauge still gives the locomotive a lop-sided appearance, although the provision of platforms on either side of the battery container disguises this somewhat. This locomotive, like L2 and L3, has always been in a yellow livery.

In the late 1980s thought was given to procuring a further wagon, and after considering various options it was decided to convert the remaining ex-Taylor Woodrow battery locomotive frame into a 4-wheel wagon, a job contracted to Hunslet-Barclay. This vehicle retains a cab as the look-out position for propelling moves, and is now known as W5 (photo overleaf).

Top Locomotives L2 and L3 lead Wagons 57 and 16 past the top of the tunnel access ramps and into Headshunt 2. There the train will reverse and the wagons will be propelled down a ramp and on to the work site. *Ian Maclean*

Centre The configuration of the rail-laying train is illustrated by L3, rail wagons RW2 and RW20 and L2. The wagons are always used as a pair, and each has a buckeye coupler and a support frame for a block and tackle at its inner end. Down the centre of each wagon is a roller track on to which the new rail is positioned and its weight taken by the chain tackle. The rail is laid on the track bed as the two wagons are uncoupled and driven apart by their respective locomotives. Old rail is lifted from the location by a reversal of the procedure. The System Control Room is located in the upper floor of the building above L3. *Ian Maclean*

Above When Taylor Woodrow regauged their two battery locomotives from 3ft to 4ft to work on the rebuilding of the Underground, the right hand wheels (looking forward over the battery) had to be placed outside the main frames and the left hand wheels inside, as shown in this view of locomotive L4 and wagon W5 standing in Headshunt 2 on 17th May 1992. Both vehicles now have tripcocks and Wedglock couplers at both ends. The photograph on page 163 shows one of the pair in 1978 condition. *Ian Maclean*

Traction Power Supply Modernisation

The three mercury arc rectifier sub-stations had been considered to have 5–10 years of useful service left, so they were not included in the Modernisation, other than having the remote control gear moved to the System Control Room. During 1982, however, a scheme was developed for the replacement of the three original sub-stations with four new ones, and in addition to fit a second rectifier set in Broomloan sub-station, which to some extent acted as a prototype. London Transport International were appointed as consulting engineers, and Strathclyde Regional Council's Department of Architectural and Related Services was appointed as architects.

The incoming supplies were at 6.6KV or 11KV, depending on the voltage of the SSEB network in the area of each sub-station, although it was the intention to make all supplies 11KV in due course. Two transformers were provided at each site, which reduced the voltage to about 600: in the case of those in the 6.6KV areas they were capable of adjustment to 11KV. The equipment is based on silicon rectifiers, and each sub-station has two 1MW sets, one fed from each of the transformers. The rectified supplies are connected to a 600 Volt d.c. bus-bar through remote-controlled circuit-breakers as shown in Figure 9.1. The bus-bar is split in the middle, the two halves being connected via a 'bus-coupler' circuit-breaker, which is normally 'open'. Each half of the bus-bar has the 'live' side of another three circuit breakers connected to it: a supply to the live rail on the Inner Circle, a supply to the live rail on the Outer Circle (both known as track feeders) and a supply to a ring-main circuit breaker. The equipment is arranged to 'double end feed' sections of live rail as is normal practice on London Underground, rather than have a single feed near the centre of each section: this is to reduce voltage drop in the live rails, and thereby obtain more consistent performance from the trains. The tunnel emergency telephone system is arranged to open the appropriate track feeder circuit-breakers at the two substations feeding the section concerned.

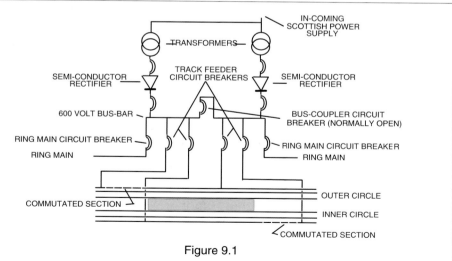

Figure 9.1
ARRANGEMENT AT BYRES ROAD, DUNDASVALE, EGLINTON STREET
AND CORNWALL STREET SUB-STATIONS
(BROOMLOAN SUB-STATION DIFFERENT BECAUSE OF DEPOT SUPPLY)

In discussions with the Railway Inspectorate the view was that the sub-stations should have names different from the passenger stations, thus the four new sub-stations are:-

Byres Road: above Hillhead station.
Dundasvale: alongside Cowcaddens station;
Eglinton Street: between Bridge Street station entrance and the kerb line of Eglinton Street;
Cornwall Street: adjacent to Kinning Park station.

The site of the Byres Road installation was the most difficult to settle, various options being considered before the site above the station was finally decided upon. Part of the difficulty was that the site just north of the station and the 'air space' above the station had been sold to a property developer, and the site had already been developed. The PTE then had to buy back the space above the station! In the cases of Dundasvale and Eglinton Street the transformers were housed on the roof of the brick-built sub-stations and enclosed in non-structural cladding. Tenders were invited in the early summer of 1983, and the contract was placed with Taylor Woodrow (Scotland) Limited, who sub-contracted the electrical work to Messrs James Scott, a Glasgow firm.

Dundasvale was the first of the new sub-stations to be brought into use from Monday 25th March 1985,[5] and was initially a direct replacement for Dalhousie Street.

Over the weekend of 10th/11th May 1986 Byres Road, Eglinton Street and Cornwall Street sub-stations were brought into use together with the second set of equipment at Broomloan, and Seaward Street and Benalder Street were taken out of use.[8] For the first week the new sub-stations fed the system via the ring-main cable and the 1935-vintage BT-H switchgear in each station (except St Enoch where more modern switchgear had been installed), but over the next weekend they were re-arranged to the double-end feed configuration.[8] The old switchgear was taken out of use (the panel from Shields Road going to the Glasgow Museum of Transport) and a new Tunnel Emergency Telephone System brought into use.[8] After a further week or so Dundasvale sub-station was taken out of use for remedial work,[8] and finally brought back into service over the weekend of 18th/19th October 1986.[11] As part of the scheme a new Traction Control Supervisory Panel was installed in the System Control Room, and the control desk itself was extended to accommodate a mimic panel to indicate use of the Tunnel Emergency Telephone System.

The new arrangements meant that commutated sections of live rail were not required at the entry to every station. The dividing point between the Cornwall Street to Broomloan and Broomloan to Byres Road sections was in the North Turn-out chamber, where, uniquely, it was possible to form physical gaps 14 metres long between the two sections in each circle. Commutated sections were retained for their original purpose at Hillhead, Cowcaddens, Bridge Street and Kinning Park. Largely for fault-finding purposes, mid-section isolating links were provided close to the stations nearest the mid-point between sub-stations.

Stations

Developments since Modernisation in Park-and-Ride car parks, bus interchange facilities, canopies over escalators, kiosks and use of the spaces adjoining the concourse at St Enoch have been described in Chapter 8.

To enter into the spirit of the 1988 Garden Festival floral displays were installed at most stations. Because of the hostile environment for most types of colourful plants (strong draughts, lack of natural lighting etc) and the difficulties anticipated in watering genuine plants, good quality artificial ones in wooden troughs were provided instead.

Sites included the headwalls over the street-to-concourse escalators at Buchanan Street and St Enoch, and on the walls near the barriers at Hillhead and Buchanan Street; this produced some ridicule in the press, but it was short-lived when it was pointed out genuine plants would be provided outside Kelvinbridge, Shields Road and Cessnock stations.[4] The 'plants' were gradually pilfered from the more accessible sites, and attempts at cleaning the remaining ones reduced their fire-resistant properties, so the last of them were removed about 1994.

Following the Fennell report into the Kings Cross fire on London Underground in November 1987, new statutory regulations under the Fire Protection Act came into force. These are known as the Sub-surface Railway Stations Regulations. The fact that the stations had been completely refurbished to modern standards, including separate fire exits from the platforms, and that the escalators had no wood or other combustible materials in their construction, minimised the improvements required, but nonetheless the following had to be carried out:-

- Fire Alarm Call points installed on all platforms for passenger or staff use;

- linear heat detectors installed under all escalators (except upper flight at Kelvinbridge, which is not considered to be in a prime escape route) and passenger conveyors;

- a dry-pipe sprinkler system under the lower flight escalators at St Enoch;

- a pre-recorded evacuation message to be broadcast over the station public address system, which required up-grading of the P. A. system to Fire Alarm standards;

- Provision of padlocked boxes at station entrances for Fire Brigade use, containing plans of the station;

- sealing of cable ducts etc. to prevent smoke dissipation;

- improvements in ventilation and smoke extraction arrangements for staff areas;

- improvements to the internal telephone system so that emergency calls to the national network could be made from all telephones including those on platform headwalls, which had new unlockable doors fitted to their cabinets;

- improved fire evacuation training for all station staff (ongoing).

Before these measures were implemented it had been decided to make the whole Underground non-smoking – not just the trains as previously – and notices were posted to that effect at station entrances.

Arrangements were put in hand for simulated emergency exercises at roughly 2-year intervals and are described later in this chapter.

The platform chamber lining panels at the nine island platform stations had a vegetable fibre content, which after prolonged exposure to water drips on the back produced unsightly blisters on the visible surface. After prolonged attempts to find a substitute material which met the fire performance requirements, and following the Kings Cross fire, it was decided to use vitreous enamelled steel; this was not easy, because the panels had to be accurately curved and shaped to avoid subsequent cutting which would have damaged the enamelling. The first station so treated was St Georges Cross between January and March 1992,[12] and the panels were in shades of buff and brown. In the spring of 1993 Kelvinhall and Kelvinbridge stations were similarly treated, but finished in lime green and light blue respectively.[7] Early in 1996 tenders were invited for similar work at Cessnock and Cowcaddens, the former being complete by July and the latter by the end of August.

The station premises at Cessnock are partly under a listed building in Walmer Crescent, and partly under property at No. 1 Cessnock Street. At the time of modernisation both were unoccupied. No. 1 Cessnock Street was refurbished, and the flats sold to owner occupiers: this solved the problem of the property not being weather proof, but from time to time defective plumbing etc. caused problems. The Walmer Crescent property was developed as bed-sitters, with similar results, but during the early hours of Monday 29th January 1990 the building was gutted by fire, and the ticket office was badly affected by water. The station was closed for a week, but was then reopened using the original ticket office with temporary lighting etc. From Tuesday 6th March a temporary ticket office was set up on the concourse whilst permanent repairs, including a waterproof membrane above the ceiling, were carried out.[3] Before this work was complete there was another plumbing incident in No. 1 Cessnock Street, causing water penetration into the switchroom and concourse, and partial collapse of the dampa ceiling on the concourse. The original ticket office was brought back into use, and the temporary one removed, on 23rd June 1991.[13]

Advertising at stations is a valuable source of revenue, and was originally managed by WHS Advertising; their interest passed to Primesight in the mid-1980s who remain the PTE's contractor at the time of writing. Over the years there has been a gradual increase in the number of illuminated advertisement frames, mostly on concourses and stairways, and a powered 'Tri-wonder' sign was installed on Buchanan Street concourse. A2-size frames (approximately 420mm by 570mm) were installed on walls adjacent to escalators and the passenger conveyors in 1990, but unlike those in London do not primarily advertise swimwear and lingerie! Refrigerated chocolate vending machines were installed on both platforms at St Enoch in March 1996, by which time National Lottery scratch card machines had been set up in the Travel Centres at Hillhead and St Enoch.

The neon signs outside the stations, both the station names formed of individual letters and the 'U' signs, were deteriorating through weather and vandalism, and had become difficult and expensive to maintain. In 1993 it was decided to replace these, and a scheme was devised for individual enamelled steel letters to be mounted on polished stainless steel backgrounds with separate external illumination. The new signs were manufactured by Burnham Signs and installed during the spring of 1994. There was a delay in obtaining planning permission for the external light fittings, but the whole installation had been completed by about June 1995. The station interior signs, including those listing stations served from each platform, were replaced during the early summer of 1996.

Ticketing Equipment

Towards the end of 1984 four French-made Crouzet automatic ticket and change-giving machines were installed at Hillhead (two), St Enoch and Buchanan Street (one each).[13] These machines were virtually identical to 34 installed on the ScotRail (as the Scottish Region of BR now called itself) North Electric line between Partick and Airdrie. Both groups were capable of selling through tickets between the two systems. The tickets were of Edmondson width, and had a single narrow oxide strip on the back for magnetic encoding. The Crouzet machines at unstaffed ScotRail stations suffered considerable vandalism, and in preparation for the Garden Festival in 1988 four from the ScotRail pool were re-allocated to the Underground, and installed at Buchanan Street, St Enoch and Shields Road.[12] A small number of portable Crouzet machines was acquired for use when booking office machines were defective, and occasionally to provide additional booking capacity at St Enoch. The tickets from these did not show a station of origin, and used pre-cut stock.

By this time trouble was being experienced in maintaining the original ticket machines. In addition there was difficulty in sourcing the Edmondson-width oxide-backed roll stock, and there were quality problems with the oxide-backed board required for Transcards and staff passes. Late in 1989 a contract was awarded to Westinghouse Cubic to design and install new Booking Office Machines (known thereafter as BOMs), concourse ticket and change-giving machines (known as SPOMs – standing for Strathclyde Passenger Operated Machines), to modify the entry barriers to accept credit-card width tickets, to re-design the swing gates, and to overhaul the exit barriers. The scheme proposed, and accepted, was based on equipment supplied to London Underground, and incorporated a central computer in the Depot Office at Govan and local computers at each station, programmed with fare information: this was to improve the accountancy and statistics gathering operations. From the public viewpoint, the project started with the installation of new swing gates and the overhaul of the exit barriers. Starting with Ibrox, from Saturday 15th June 1991, and Govan, from 21st June, the new credit-card sized tickets went on sale. There was a four week delay before the next station, Kelvinbridge, was brought into use on 29th July, but thereafter stations were converted regularly, finishing with West Street on 15th August.[13] The SPOMs, unlike their London Underground equivalents, were arranged with front access for servicing, which gave greater flexibility in concourse layout.

Closed Circuit Television

By the early 1990s the original black-and-white television monitors and cameras were obsolete, and it was becoming difficult to obtain spares, particularly for the 5-inch monitors on the Station Masters' panels. Over the years technology had advanced so that colour cameras capable of operating at the lighting levels achieved in the stations were available. The opportunity was taken to review the whole CCTV requirement, and a new colour system was introduced in 1992/3. Cameras and monitors were provided at most station platforms (instead of just Bridge Street (Inner Circle), and Ibrox (Outer Circle), and most of the mirrors were replaced by cameras and monitors. In the System Control Room an additional bank of monitors was provided to view the non-platform areas of stations. As a separate exercise CCTV surveillance cameras were installed in all the station Park-and-Ride car parks, and to view Govan and Partick Bus Stations.

Platform mirrors were replaced by closed circuit colour television monitors at most stations in 1992. For Ibrox Outer Circle platform the monitor is mounted on the false headwall inside the tunnel mouth, but here driver Margaret McBride, who seldom watches television, personally checks for clear doors before departure.
Ian Maclean

Depot

During the modernisation a palisade fence had been built at PTE expense on Housing Department land at the top of the original railway-built retaining wall behind the houses of the Moor Park housing scheme (known locally as 'Wine Alley'), and because the adjacent headshunts and test track were electrified, a chain link fence was erected round the Depot site boundary including the full length of the test track. The residents of the housing scheme resented the presence of the test track and headshunts as they severed a short-cut to the Helen Street area, and they systematically undermined the palisade fence and cut their way through the chain-link fences. Attempts were made to improve the chain-link fence by supplementing it with weld-mesh material, but a compromise was achieved only after an additional palisade fence had been constructed as far as, and then across, the ends of the headshunts. Double gates are provided where this fence crosses the test track, but vandalism in the area beyond has led to the rest virtually being abandoned. The early stages of driver training are now carried out in the stabling shed and yard, and later stages first on non-passenger trains in the evening off-peak, and then on passenger trains with a 'teacher driver'. Emergency procedure training and final testing of trainee drivers is done on the system during non-traffic hours.

In the early 1980s traditional railway-style cast-iron 'trespass' notices were put up round the Depot perimeter, together with similar DANGER 600 VOLT RAILS notices. Other than on preserved railways, these were probably the last new notices of their kind to be put up in the country.

During the modernisation period it had been decided that provision of a Rail Store building could be deferred. There had been some debate as to what was required; the thinking was that rails would only require to be replaced relatively slowly, and that with minimum orders of about 250 tonnes, several years' supply would be delivered at each order. To prevent corrosion before use it was considered the rail stack should have a roof and a means of transferring new rails from the delivery lorry to the stack, and from the stack to rail-carrying wagons, was necessary. The design evolved into a 2-road shed capable of accommodating all four works wagons, spanned by a 2-tonne overhead electric crane, with a rail stack area, and lock-up rooms to act as Thermit Welding material stores (which needed to be heated) and tool and equipment stores. It was sited towards the north end of the Broomloan site, close to the gatehouse. The contract for the building was won by Messrs Henry Boot, and work started in snowy conditions in January 1984. The building, which cost about £150,000, was handed over to the PTE in April, and shortly afterwards 200 tonnes of 1% chrome rail were delivered[14] – but not before a Chartered Institute of Transport meeting had been held in it!

It had been hoped that hand washing of the cars once a week or so would be adequate (as it had been prior to Modernisation), but this turned out to be too optimistic. As a result plans were drawn up to install a mechanical wash, and after briefly considering siting it on the East Approach Road, it was decided to position it on the approach to No. 14 Road, just south of the Stabling Shed. Because space was limited the whole equipment was specified to be accommodated in one unit. Messrs Smith Brothers & Webb won the contract, and the machine, which has one set of side and roof brushes, was installed during the summer of 1986.

As part of the trailer car project the Stabling Shed was extended into the North Yard, and Nos. 18 and 19 Roads were extended to the same length as Nos. 14 to 17 Roads. Broomloan Cottage and the former Parish Hall building had been demolished by that time, but the land ownership could not be established, and marginally insufficient ground was available to make the extension rectangular in plan: in consequence the east wall is stepped-in part way along its length, and No. 19 Road tapers towards

No. 18 at the north end. Messrs Ewing Construction won the contract to build the extension, which was completed in October 1990, well before the first trailer cars were delivered. No. 19 Road was allocated to Hunslet TPL for commissioning work on the trailer cars, though in the event they had to use No. 18 Road as well.

During the summer of 1992 a large prefabricated cabin was installed in part of the machine shop, and the Maintenance Supervisors moved into it: the newly formed Maintenance Planning Section was also accommodated in it. One of the Section's first tasks was to select a computerised Maintenance Planning system, and from 1993 the system was installed and data loaded into it. The system issues job cards for maintenance, repair and modification work, checks progress and keeps records of work done on each piece of equipment.

Shortly afterwards steps were taken to solve the chronic shortage of space in the stores. The other section of the machine shop and bogie overhaul area were earmarked for a two-storey stores facility. This meant the machine shop and bogie repair area (including its overhead crane) had to be re-located. The new store, including a new delivery entrance in the west wall of the building, was opened in 1994. The 'UndergrounD' sign formerly on the north wall of St Enoch station has found a new home above the store counter.

Leakage through the tunnel structures stains the car exteriors very quickly if cleaning is delayed unduly, and to ease the load of the car washers, who are based in No.19 Road of the Stabling Shed, a mechanical wash was installed on No.14 Road at the approach to the shed in June 1986.
Ian Maclean

Tunnels

In the early hours of 29th August 1981 a Permanent Way employee on nightly track patrol noticed cracks in the track bed concrete of the Outer Circle between the former lifting pit and Govan station. On further investigation it was discovered that considerable quantities of fine sand had entered the tunnel, evidently leaving a void in the ground, and that the base of the tunnel had subsided. Arrangements were made to introduce a shuttle service on the Outer Circle, and to impose a temporary speed restriction on the Inner Circle in the area concerned; however by 31st August it was decided it would be safer to suspend services in this area on the Inner Circle as well, so shuttle services were introduced there too. Repair work was put in hand, and substantial quantities of cement grout were pumped into the ground round the tunnels, and the track in the Outer Circle was re-levelled. An 8-minute Outer Circle service was resumed on 24th September, and a similar 8-minute frequency Inner Circle service started on 25th September. Normal running resumed on 29th September.[15]

It was deduced that if the ground round the tunnel could be kept dry, sand would not enter through the inevitable small cracks in the brick and concrete construction; it was water in-flow which carried the sand with it. As a consequence a ground de-watering system was installed, initially with temporary pumps between the tracks in the Govan platform chamber. Later on a pair of permanent pumps was installed between the tracks in the former lifting pit. A power supply for the pumps was run along the tunnel from the switchroom at Govan station, and gauges were put on some the cracks in the affected part of the tunnel. Well-point, vacuum monitoring and crack monitoring equipment was installed in Govan switchroom to simplify checking of the equipment.

About the middle of 1994, after 12 years of constant use, the de-watering system was in need of refurbishment. Temporary pumps were again installed in the Govan platform chamber, and a contract was let to Messrs Andrew Sykes for new permanent pumps to be installed in the former lifting pit: the new permanent pumps were brought into use in January 1995.[6]

During landscaping of St Enoch Square in January 1981 contractors hit underground cables which had formerly supplied the premises under the station approach arches, and blew fuses in the local SSEB sub-station supplying St Enoch Underground station. The result was that the three sets of submersible pumps fed from St Enoch failed; the normal inflow of water is such that failure of the supply to one of these sets results in the Outer Circle tunnel north of the station becoming flooded within 20 minutes. It was clear an independent electrical supply was required, and after brief consideration of stand-by generators, it was decided that a pump supplied from the 600 Volt dc traction ring main cable was the best solution. Submersible d.c. pumps were impractical, so a suction pump was provided at platform level, to draw water from the low point. As a second phase, similar pumps were installed at Buchanan Street and Shields Road.

Problems with a leaking sewer above the tunnel between St Georges Cross and Kelvinbridge in January 1983 revealed a 'low point' in the tunnel between Kelvinbridge station and the Kelvin crossing, so an additional sump was formed there with three of the larger capacity submersible pumps in it. Unusually the sump was on the Inner Circle instead of the Outer as with the others, and is known as Sump 17A.

Ground investigation works prior to the construction of the Royal Concert Hall, which straddles the Underground tunnels between Cowcaddens and Buchanan Street stations, revealed that strengthening work should be carried out. The work, which was contracted to Ewing Construction, included bricking-up four cross-passages, grouting the centre wall and fitting steel 'walings' formed from old running rail to the centre wall, and was carried out in 1989.[16]

About 1991 problems of sand and water ingress in the masonry-constructed part of the Shields Road to Kinning Park section increased, and Messrs Ove Arup were appointed as consultants to advise on the action necessary to safeguard the tunnels. They advised grouting, and a contract was let for about a third of the length to Messrs Balvac, Whitley & Moran in October 1991, the work being carried out between November 1991 and 31st March 1992. Further contracts were let to the same contractor for the remainder of the section in October 1992 and December 1993, the whole job being completed in July 1994.

Early in 1990 it was decided to strengthen the tunnel lining in the section through rock between Cowcaddens and Buchanan Street, close to the point where preliminary work for the Buchanan Centre was about to start. This commercial project was delayed by the general economic situation so the contract was not let until about October 1992. This problem was different in nature to the one at Kinning Park, and the work was entrusted to a local firm, GB Maintenance.

Track

A problem which manifested itself early on was de-bonding of the support blocks and sleepers from the track base concrete. In some cases this may have been due to unsuitable shimming before placing of the base concrete, in others inadequate compaction of the base concrete, and in yet others water seepage into the tunnel during the curing process. Taylor Woodrow carried out a programme of grouting up such blocks before the end of the warranty period, but numerous contracts have been let over the years in an attempt to control the problem. In many cases 'repaired' blocks have failed again within a relatively short time.

The first rails to be changed were on Sunday 28th March 1982 when a set of dished rails near the top of the North Ramp was changed:[17] this was treated as a training exercise, and used rails left over from the Modernisation. Five lengths of 1% chrome rail were laid on the Outer Circle between Cessnock and Ibrox on Sundays in April and October 1985, but the first main effort was on the Outer Circle just after Hillhead, where wet tunnel conditions seemed to encourage rail corrugation,[18] and about 80 metres of track had become very noisy; nine pairs of rails were changed between June 1985 and March 1986. Between September 1986 and May 1987 some 440 metres of the Inner Circle track between Buchanan Street and Cowcaddens was relaid with 1% chrome wear resistant rails to reduce the noise from the original rails which had become badly corrugated. In August 1987 a start was made on 450 metres of the Outer Circle between Cowcaddens and Buchanan Street.[11] Much of this work was done on Sundays, when new rails which had previously been delivered to site were exchanged for worn rails and connected with temporary fishplates.[11] The old rails were collected from site and the new rails Thermit welded as soon as possible during the next week. The temporary fishplates produced the "clickety-click" sound characteristic of jointed track, and seldom heard these days other than on preserved railways. It was hoped that the wear resistant rail would also be resistant to corrugation, but after a period in use no difference could be detected. Rail relaying has been a feature of the system since 1986: metal loss on the rails in many places is more because of corrosion in the humid tunnel conditions than wear. The Buchanan Street to Cowcaddens Inner Circle section had to be relaid again in 1996.

A short section of the Outer Circle track between Shields Road and Kinning Park – at the crest of the gradient after the tunnels dip below the former General Terminus Quay branch, and corresponding to a change from cast-iron segments to masonry construction – was of non-standard design following the Modernisation. Because of clearance problems the track had to be set very low in the tunnel, which brought the foot of the rail very close to the segment flanges: to gain adequate support for the track the rails were set, tramway style, in flush concrete over a 14 to 15 metre length. A fractured rail was found in this section on nightly patrol at the beginning of April 1985, and because of the track design in that area the rail could not be readily replaced, so temporary repairs were carried out, and the permanent speed restriction reduced from the previous 35kph to 15kph.[5]

The opportunity was taken during the Glasgow Fair holiday to rebuild this section of track to a more satisfactory design and to effect permanent repairs. The contract was let to Messrs Henry Boot who had performed very well in the construction of the Permanent Way Rail Store building. The job was programmed for the full two weeks of the Fair, but was in fact completed in time to resume traffic on Friday 26th July. It was found possible to reduce the length of non-standard track, and the 6 metre length which remained was reconstructed as a concrete base up to rail head level with two troughs in it to take the rails. These were placed on a continuous resilient pad, and secured into place using a material known as 'Corkelast'. Meanwhile an augmented service was run on the Inner Circle and shuttle trains ran all day between Govan and Partick and from Tuesday 16th to Thursday 25th July inclusive in the peaks only between Hillhead and Buchanan Street on the Outer Circle.[5]

Rail changing as a means of dealing with corrugation was resorted to because no suitable machine could be found to grind the rails *in situ*, but because the changing took so long, and was so expensive in materials and labour, efforts were redoubled to find a machine. When a diesel powered machine owned by an Italian company (Rotra-Metro of Padua) was demonstrated on London Underground, a delegation from Glasgow went to see it in action, with the result that a 30-shift trial contract (which included the services of an operator) was arranged.[16] The machine was adapted from standard to 1220mm gauge: a limitation was that it could only grind one rail at a time, and needed 6 to 8 'passes' to achieve a satisfactory result. This was the first diesel-powered machine to be used in the tunnels since reopening after Modernisation, and stringent measures were taken to control and monitor the exhaust. Work began on 4th November 1988, and the machine operated under its own power to and from work sites near Broomloan until L4 was ready, after its return from Clayton, to haul/propel the grinder to more distant sites from 16th December. The grinder produced an immediate reduction in the noise level in the trains, and introduced a characteristic 'whistling' sound from the rails which persisted for some months. Because of its success the contract was extended by 60 shifts. The grinder returned home to Italy just before Easter 1989,[15] but on its last shift was involved in an alarming incident, when it ran from Buchanan Street (Outer Circle) to the low point under the Clyde between St Enoch and Bridge Street with nobody on it. Fortunately nobody was on the track, so no harm was done.

The grinder was brought back for a further 40 shifts between 22nd January and 21st March 1991,[13] and efforts were concentrated on the north side where the noise from rail corrugation seemed to be worst. Once again L4, now in improved form, worked with the grinder, as it did on a contract from Wednesday night 10th February to Sunday night 21st March 1993.[19]

About 1990 approaches were made by Pandrol UK Ltd and a plastics company with which they were working to see if the Underground would be prepared to stage a trial of plastic base-plates. The existing equivalents were cast-iron, and had also been designed by Pandrol. Advantages were seen to be lighter weight and better electrical resistance. A trial of some 20 plates was arranged for one rail near the top of the North Ramp, and organised in such a way that the original base plates could be reinstated very quickly if need be. No problems were encountered, so the next stage was to do both rails on the straight section of the South Ramp at the tunnel portal. Once again

Early in the morning of 6th March 1993, during its third visit to the Underground, the Rotra rail grinder works through Cowcaddens station, having been propelled to the start of its duties by battery locomotive L4, seen behind. *Ian Maclean*

no particular difficulties were encountered, although some of the baseplates were slighly damaged during installation. A need arose to realign the Inner Circle track on the approach to Partick, so the opportunity was taken to install a further batch of plastic baseplates there; this was done in March 1993.[19] These fairly quickly showed signs of distress, so they were removed after a few months.

Fibre-Optic Cable

Following Modernisation the various indications and CCTV signals were transmitted from the stations and sub-stations via multi-core cables to the System Control Room. When the new ticketing equipment was installed, the integrity of the cable routes caused problems, so in anticipation of other applications it was decided to install a pair of fibre optic cables round the tunnels, and to link one of them to the PTE Head Office at Consort House, West George Street, close to Buchanan Street station. These cables are routed via the Outer Circle tunnel, but only one is used for PTE purposes; the other is leased to British Telecom, and so is a source of revenue for the Underground. Since installation the cable has been used for computer links from the Underground to Consort House, for the colour CCTV system, and other communication and indication links as well as the fare collection equipment.

Signalling

Whenever the opportunity presented itself the signalling overlaps were increased with a view to eventually achieving the original aim of single block working. The first site chosen was West Street on the Outer Circle, followed by Buchanan Street (Inner) and Bridge Street (Inner). It then became possible to operate single block between West Street and Buchanan Street. Maintenance of the intermediate signals was awkward, and the Inner Circle one between Buchanan Street and Cowcaddens was removed in November 1993.

As described in Chapter 8 six cast-steel swing-nose crossings were provided for the two crossovers and the two turn-outs in the Turn-out Chambers, and as seen earlier in this Chapter one of them was an indirect cause of a derailment. More significant, however, was the difficulty in maintaining the correct action of the drive, detection and lock rods between the point motor and the lugs projecting down from the 'sharp' end of the nose. It was all too easy, whilst trying to adjust the rod length and ensure the lock nuts were tight, to lock up the spherical bearing: this had the effect of causing the rod to bend, and eventually break at the weakest point – at the screw thread. This usually resulted in loss of detection, which in turn prevented clearance of signals for routes over the swing-nose crossing concerned. When, in addition, wear was detected on parts of the swing-noses, it was decided to replace them with flange-running crossings of the type used in Broomloan Yard. It was not known if this would have a noticeable effect on ride, and noise, but to gain experience it was decided to do one normally passed by trains in the trailing direction first, and that at 502 Points was changed in August 1989.[16] Since there were no ill effects, one more was done about 1990, and the rest by the end of 1994.

An incident occurred at Govan at the end of the morning peak in which the driver of an Outer Circle train which was about to be taken to the Depot under the control of the shunt signal provided for the purpose, moved off without checking the signal, and was 'tripped' on the trainstop. It so happened that the System Controller was also taking an Inner Circle train out, and had the route set for it. The front wheels of the Inner Circle train just reached the next track circuit, which had the effect of 'route locking' the whole turn-out area, with points set for the Depot from the Inner Circle. The Outer Circle driver said he had heard a trainstop drive down, and saw that the 'Depot' sign was illuminated, so assumed he was intended to go; he had not, however, checked the signal as he should have done. As a result of this the 'Depot' signs at Govan and Ibrox, which were not fully incorporated into the signalling system, and were intended more for passenger information, were removed on and from 31st May 1994.

About 1993 concerns began to mount on the condition of the insulation of much of the wiring used in the signalling system. The cable and wire used in the Modernisation had been to the then-current Railway Industry Standards, but the type of insulation used became brittle after 10–15 years, a condition which had been noted on several installations of similar age on British Rail. An embargo was put on any form of signalling modification, including the elimination of further intermediate signals, and consideration given to how to deal with the problem. Rewiring the system on a like-for-like basis was discussed, but was considered to be impractical without lengthy closures. Since the capacitor-fed track circuits had proved difficult to keep in adjustment in the wet conditions in some parts of the tunnel, and because of the difficulty in moving block joints, it was considered that high frequency 'Traction Immune' jointless track circuits should be adopted. Brief reconsideration was given to an axle-counting signalling system, which had been rejected at the time of the modernisation, but was not pursued. It was also recognised that the Underground relay interlocking system was one of the last of its type to be installed, before Solid State Interlocking (SSI) became the norm on British

Rail. With this system computer logic is used, and the method of control is significantly different. This, too, could be installed alongside the existing system, and changed over relatively quickly. The adoption of SSI then led to thoughts of improving the System Control Room, particularly the ergonomics. Various incidents in the Depot area led to the inclusion of a signalling system for the yard. Because it is not expensive to programme additional routes into the computer of an SSI system, it was decided to provide for more flexible working in the Govan to Ibrox areas, in effect making the Partick – Govan – Ibrox section bi-directionally signalled, and to allow for use of the crossovers between the Circles without having to go to the headshunts.

Acer, now Hyder, were appointed as consulting engineers, and they produced a detailed technical specification, which went out for tender late in 1993. No acceptable offers were returned, so some adjustments were made to the specification, and it was put out to tender again in May 1994. ABB Signalling, based in Plymouth (successors to ML Engineering who installed the Modernisation signalling, and which became ADtranz from 1st February 1996) were awarded the contract for what had become known as the 'Centenary Signalling Scheme' in December 1994. Installation work started in February 1996.

The SSI system they offered was based on an American system of Vital Processor Interlocking (VPI) which had not been used in the United Kingdom before. Similar equipment was being supplied for the East London Line signalling on London Underground, but because of delays to that project caused by the Thames Tunnel refurbishment, the Glasgow installation became the one requiring Railway Inspectorate approval under the Transport & Works Act procedures.

Although a new large mimic panel was provided, the main signalling controls were transferred to VDU workstations, operated by computer keyboard and mouse. The opportunity was taken to transfer the sub-station remote control and other indications to the same workstations. Associated with the yard signalling was a Depot Entry system for the pitted roads in the Workshop building, incorporating flashing warning lights and an audible warning inside the building when trains are being moved in and out.

The new equipment was brought into use over four weekends – 17th/18th August, 24th/25th August, 31st August/1st September and 5th/6th October. On the last of these weekends the control workstations were transferred to a temporary Control Room, to allow redundant equipment to be removed from the original one and new desks and equipment installed. Public service was stopped early on the four Saturdays, and no service was provided on the Sundays. The first week-ends involved feeding the existing track relays from the larger number of new TI track circuits. The Yard signals and bi-directional working facilities were brought into use on Monday 7th October. The original control room was brought back into use a week later.

Simulated Emergency Exercises

In the summer and autumn of 1987, Strathclyde Fire Brigade gave some thought to organising a simulated emergency exercise in the Underground involving themselves, the Police, Scottish Ambulance Service etc, but were have difficulties justifying the cost. The Kings Cross fire gave added emphasis to the idea, and the first exercise was held on Sunday afternoon 27th March 1988 (just before Sunday services started for the Garden Festival) at Govan.[4] Similar exercises were held at St Enoch on Sunday 18th March 1990,[3] and at Shields Road on Sunday 17th May 1992, the latter during normal traffic hours, when the operation of a substitute shuttle service from Govan to St Enoch via the north loop was bedevilled by shoegear problems,[12] largely caused by live rail ramps for 'wrong direction' movements being out of gauge.

Simulated emergencies involving Underground, Fire, Ambulance and Police personnel are held regularly on the route, and here 'Exercise Right Lines II' is well under way at Kelvinbridge on Sunday evening, 29th October 1995. Umpires, in the blue waistcoats, mark up their score cards as a fireman jumps down to assist an ambulance man tending one of the 'casualties'; Depot Engineering Superintendent Idris Scott and Driver Joyce Johnston stand by in the cab of Car 110. Traction current has been shut off at the scene, and a short-circuiting bar (right foreground) connects the third rail to a running rail, to ensure that it will stay 'dead' if power is accidentally switched on. *Reproduced Courtesy of The Herald and Evening Times*

In 1994 there was an exercise at the Fire Brigade's request one Sunday evening in the Kinning Park to Cessnock section. The fifth exercise, one involving all services, was at Kelvinbridge in October 1995, and another at Fire Brigade instigation on Sunday evening 31st March 1996, in the turn-out chamber area, involving access through the Depot Yard. These exercises have proved valuable, and many lessons have been learned.

Track Walking and Permanent Way

The main routine work for the Permanent Way Section is a patrol of the whole system each night before traffic runs the next day. When no service was provided on Sundays, or when no service is planned on public holidays over the Festive Season, the line is not walked the previous night. Under normal circumstances three pairs of men are each detailed to patrol approximately one third of the system. These patrols first noticed the crack in the tunnel caused by the subsidence at Govan in 1981, and the broken rail at Shields Road in 1985. Rail relaying has been an almost continuous process since 1986, particularly in the masonry sections on the north side of the Clyde, and the West Street to Kinning Park area.

Immediately after Modernisation maintenance of escalators and fare collection equipment was contracted to the respective suppliers. In June 1982 the PTE took over all escalator maintenance except handrail replacement, which requires special skills for the jointing process, and has been contracted out. About the same time fare collection equipment maintenance was taken over, and contract maintenance ceased.[20]

Contract station cleaning has been a feature since re-opening. Each day a contractor sends staff into two stations before they open to the public, and having swept up litter from the previous evening, they use the first trains to travel to other stations for the same purpose. For many years platform cleaning was carried out by the Permanent Way squad on night shift, but a more thorough dust and clean of the platform chamber walls, and all ceilings etc at roughly 6-monthly intervals is now contracted out. Particularly since the Kings Cross incident 'de-fluffing' of escalators has been done by contract at approximately yearly intervals.

Staffing

The number of drivers was increased about the time that running was extended to 22:40 to the present total of 45. Originally they were all on the same 'cycle', which involved occasional weeks on night shift driving battery locomotives for maintenance trains. In May 1992 a group of 12 drivers was put on a separate cycle, and they now do a week of night shift every six weeks, and so they are much more familiar with the locomotives and wagons. About 40% of them are women.

There are some 63 Station Masters, two 'steady' ones allocated to each station, and the others used for meal and holiday reliefs, or as 'spares' to cover unexpected sickness or absence. Originally tickets were sold by 'Booking Office Assistants', but following the Kings Cross fire, they were trained in station emergency evacuation, and so have been redesignated 'Station Assistants': there are 65 of them.

The number of Line Inspectors and Depot Inspectors (who administer the daily signing-on of Drivers, Station Masters and Station Assistants) has gradually risen to eight and five respectively. There are four System Controllers, and four Assistant Controllers, who usually act as Yard Masters, supervising shunting in the Depot yard. The Line Inspectors also 'cover' the posts of Yard Master and occasionally System Controller, though this is more often done by Assistant Controllers. Line Inspectors also deliver most of the Traffic Staff training, though the Training Assistant prepares the courses and presents some of the training.

Signal Linesmen and Car Examiners (12 of each) were dual-skilled from 1979, and more recently the escalator and fare collection craftsmen have also become dual-skilled. Electricians, fitters, bodymakers, a turner, a coach painter, welder/tinsmiths and store-men complete the skilled staff. In addition there are labourer/drivers, handymen, cleaners, and night shift Permanent Way labourers. These are supervised by three day shift supervisors, four supervisors on rotating shifts and three night shift Permanent Way supervisors. Together with administrative, professional and technical staff there were 325 employees involved full-time on the Underground in March 1996.

Productivity deals for maintenance employees, involving increased flexibility, and for drivers were agreed in 1996. The former, in particular, helped gear the staffing arrangements to the increasing use of electronics, and to the need to demonstrate competence required by recent safety legislation.

Safety and Quality

The privatisation of British Rail affected the Underground to the extent that it had to comply with the plethora of new railway safety legislation. A key element of this was drafting a safety case for submission to the Health & Safety Executive, to which the Railway Inspectorate was transferred from December 1990. The document was approved in February 1996. Amongst other things, the safety case sets out the intended management style, including references to ensuring employee competence, and the planned Quality Assurance system. Demonstrating competence hinges on encouraging employees to submit themselves to a process of assessment advocated by the Rail Industry Training Council (a body set up in 1991) in line with the principles of National/Scottish Vocational Qualifications. Initially voluntary, this may in due course become a condition of service. In the meantime the internal training courses for all traffic staff and others involved in maintenance are being reviewed. In the broader sense competence includes social behaviour and attitudes, so to show 'due diligence' as required by the Railway Safety Critical Work Regulations, a system of random breath and urine testing for alcohol and certain illegal drugs was started in February 1996. With regard to Quality Assurance, work is progressing on gaining accreditation under the ISO 9000 Standard (previously, and perhaps better, known as BS5750).

Car No.109 with newly-affixed SPT logo under centre main window and centenary logo on the interior draught screen. *Ian Maclean*

Car No. 122 in 8 Road on 4th October 1996 after being repainted by Hunslet-Barclay in a version of the Glasgow District Subway livery to commemorate the Underground's Centenary.

Centenary

To mark the Centenary of the railway a special logo was commissioned, and appears opposite. Two power cars, 122 and 127, were repainted during the summer of 1996 in a livery loosely based on that of the Glasgow District Subway, and all other cars had the Centenary logo posted on one window of each pair of passenger doors. In June 1996 Car 55, retained from the old system, was taken off site for renovation and returned in October in the 1935 livery, though retaining its solid doors. Unfortunately it is not possible to take it into the tunnels for clearance reasons, so this was mainly a cosmetic restoration. Also as part of the Centenary, works of art of various kinds were commissioned by the Executive for display on St Enoch concourse and at Partick.

Plans for the Second Century

SPT had until May 1996 two schemes in hand which would impact on the Underground – the CrossRail line and the StrathClyde Tram – but the latter scheme was rejected by the Commissioners at the public inquiry in May 1996, and will not be re-submitted.

Plans for the CrossRail scheme to connect the Paisley and Cathcart Circle lines to the Queen Street Low Level line at High Street station, using existing bridges and viaducts, were deposited in Parliament in March 1995. This scheme includes high level platforms at West Street with stairways or escalators to the present Underground station. The timescale for this scheme will be influenced by the funding arrangements stipulated by the Scottish Office. Other rail development schemes are unlikely to have much, if any, effect on the Underground.

On 11th June 1996, Car No.55 left the Underground for the first time since it was delivered there in 1901. Its destination was Heritage Engineering Limited of New Lanark, where it was to be restored to allow it to be used as a mobile exhibit at a planned Open Day in 1997 to commemorate the Centenary of the Underground. *Ian Maclean*

Chapter 10

Suggested Extensions

Several motions were passed by the Corporation and its Committees at various stages between about 1920 and 1947 suggesting extensions to the Underground.

Following Corporation meetings in January and December 1937,[1] proposals were made for a line from Robroyston in the north east of the city via Foresthall, Springburn tram terminus, Sighthill and Pinkston to join the existing route at Buchanan Street and follow it to just beyond Bridge Street where it would have continued southwards to Newlands and Kings Park. It is likely this portion would have run under Eglinton Street, Victoria Road and Queens Park, but how much of the rest of the route was intended to be in tunnel is not clear. No doubt the growing concerns of war prevented work starting on this ambitious project.

By 1944 a scheme had been developed for an Eastern Circle, duplicating the existing route between Buchanan Street and Bridge Street, with stations at Kennedy Street, Blochairn, Dinart Street, Carntyne, Rigby Street, Belvidere Hospital, Dalmarnock, Richmond Park and Hutcheson Square.[2, 3]

By 1948 it was realised that any new lines should be built in conjunction with developments on the newly-nationalised British Railways, and taking into account the City Engineer's First Planning Report, which amongst other things referred to local transport needs, and also foresaw the abolition of the extensive tramway network. It was also proposed at this time to combine the British Railways stations at Queen Street and Buchanan Street into a new 'North Station', and Central and St Enoch stations into a new 'South Station', close to the present Bridge Street Underground station.

In his report on the proposals to the Municipal Transport Committee in May 1948, E.R.L. Fitzpayne envisaged electrification (probably on the outside 3rd rail principle) of 'selected' railway lines. These were:-

1. The Central Low Level line from Rutherglen and Tollcross to Maryhill via both Partick West and Kelvinbridge and from Maryhill via Possilpark, Stobhill, Riddrie and Carntyne back to Rutherglen.

2. The Queen Street Low Level lines from Dennistoun and Bridgeton Cross to Hyndland, Whiteinch and Maryhill via Anniesland.

3. The Cathcart Circle line from Central (High Level) and its branches to Whitecraigs and Kirkhill, extended over existing freight lines to Tollcross.

Like the 1944 proposals, a new electric railway, partly in the open and partly in tunnel, would have followed the Underground tunnels from north of Buchanan Street to near Bridge Street, probably in twin tunnels at a lower level than the existing Underground. Part of the object of the new line was to connect the new North and South stations. At the northern end the line would have taken a somewhat wider sweep than the 1944 proposals, and would have followed the line of Alexandra Parade, made use of the wide central reservation of the Edinburgh Road from Cumbernauld Road to Queenslie, then turning south and finally west passing through Mount Vernon to join the 'selected' railway route, namely the Central Low Level. South of the South station the line would have proceeded southward and westward under the Tradeston Gas Works to Pollokshields, then following the route of St Andrews Drive, Haggs Road, Pollokshaws Road and Barrhead Road to Barrhead. To serve the Paisley area a junction would have been provided near Shields Road, from where the line would join Paisley Road West at Ibrox, and continue to Paisley. Another route would have used the Glasgow Central Railway tunnel from Kelvinbridge to Botanic Gardens, then carried on along Great Western Road to Duntocher.[4] The vehicles intended for this system were more like single deck Continental trams than trains. They would have been bogie vehicles about 45 feet long, and coupled into 2-car units with a corridor connection between the two cars. Each car would have had seats for 48 passengers and standing room for a further 34.

A report by Sir William Halcrow & Partners in April 1954 tentatively suggested, but did not recommend, Underground routes somewhat similar to Fitzpayne's 1948 ideas, except that south of the river a single route would have gone to Castlemilk. This scheme would also have made use of the Glasgow Central Railway route between Glasgow Cross and Anderston, and projected a line to Drumchapel, with Underground interchange at Partick Cross. It would have made use of the central reservation on Great Western Road from Kelvinside to Blairdardie.[5]

Electrification of the Queen Street Low Level line and the Cathcart Circle were among the first group of schemes proposed under the British Railways Modernisation Plan of 1955, and the public funding of those schemes effectively thwarted any idea of Underground extensions. By then the decision had been taken to replace the remaining trams with buses, so the Underground was left to carry on with its important role largely unchanged.

A later variation on the Halcrow scheme envisaged a triangular junction with Kelvinbridge, Hillhead and Botanic Gardens as its three corners, with a line heading off towards Maryhill from Botanic Gardens.

In the late 1980s thoughts once again turned briefly to Underground extensions. On this occasion the motivation was the fact that the original 'Blue Train' (303) electrical multiple units, which had just been refurbished, would not last long into the new century, and the thought that direct replacement might not be the best option. A wide-ranging study was carried out which included three schemes for Underground extensions.[6] The most ambitious was for an extension from the Ibrox area to Glasgow Airport, the second was for an extension from Kelvinbridge and Hillhead, using the former Glasgow Central Railway trackbed to Maryhill and Ruchill, then heading off to serve a new housing area at Summerston. The third was for a single track loop leaving the Outer Circle near Bridge Street, rising up to the viaduct which formerly formed the route into St Enoch main line station, crossing the river on the existing bridge, and following the viaduct past Glasgow Cross, and shortly afterwards entering the central reservation of the proposed East Flank Motorway. The line (and motorway) would have gone into tunnel near the Royal Infirmary, and the line would have rejoined the Outer Circle between Cowcaddens and Buchanan Street. Trains would have gone round this loop anti-clockwise. All these schemes were rejected on cost, and, particularly in the case of the Airport extension, the small size of the vehicles.

Enthusiasts, too, have offered their ideas for expansion of the railway. In 1971 Scottish Transport carried an article describing how British Rail electric trains from the Paisley to Glasgow line could use the trackbed of the former Princes Dock branch, the outer bores of the disused Harbour Tunnel at Finnieston and short lengths of new tunnel at each end, to join the Queen Street Low Level line just west of Charing Cross station. Since the proposed link would cross over the Underground tunnels just east of Copland Road, a rebuilt joint station was envisaged at that point. (The 1990s CrossRail scheme would provide a similar south-north link without the need for expensive tunnelling.)

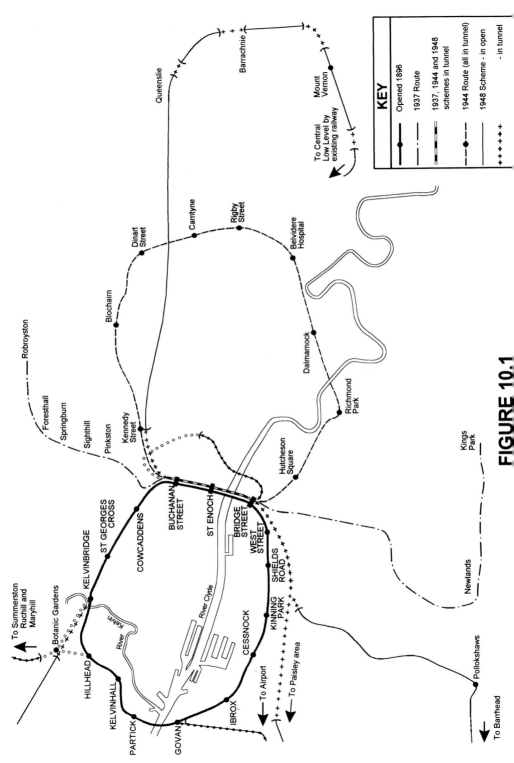

FIGURE 10.1

KEY

	Opened 1896
	1937 Route
	1937, 1944 and 1948 schemes in tunnel
	1944 Route (all in tunnel)
	1948 Scheme - in open
	- in tunnel

In 1973 the Scottish Rapid Transit Group put forward a plan entitled *New Life for the Subway*. This proposed extensions to provide more through traffic mainly by using abandoned railway trackbeds in the north of the city. The rolling stock envisaged would have had both third rail and overhead line current collection equipment, the latter being more suitable, in the Group's opinion, for further light rail extensions. The route proposed would have been the so-called 'Northern Circle', leaving the present route at Kelvinbridge and using the former Glasgow Central Railway tunnel to Kirklee, and then on by Maryhill, Ruchill, Milton, Barmulloch and Sighthill to rejoin the Underground tunnels between Buchanan Street and Cowcaddens.

After the Modernisation some thought was given to extending the test track under Edmiston Drive to form an interchange with the Paisley to Glasgow line on the site of the former Ibrox station: an alternative was to curve westwards and make the interchange at the existing Cardonald station. To keep the options open the PTE purchased the land south of Edmiston Drive, but subsequently sold it again. It is difficult to see how operation of the branch could have been satisfactorily integrated into the Circle services.

Your authors would like to see the system extended so that more intensive use could be made of the tunnels, which are operating at nowhere near their potential capacity. As seen earlier, the question of non-standard track gauge has usually been the stated reason for not carrying out extensions in the past, but when one considers what has been run on 3ft 6in gauge railways in southern Africa and elsewhere, it is not in itself a sustainable argument. Inability to inter-run with main line suburban trains is also largely irrelevant, as 'light rail' and 'heavy rail' systems usually operate on segregated tracks in any case. The small loading gauge is a more persuasive argument, but even there modern developments might lead to a design making better use of the available cross-section by, for example, lowering car floors. The basic operating simplicity of the system would not be seriously compromised by making an outer loop from, say, Cessnock/Ibrox to Partick via Hillington, Renfrew and Yoker with at least a pedestrian link to Glasgow Airport. The Clyde crossing could be by bascule bridge to save the cost of tunnelling, and would replace the Renfrew Ferry which has been run under Underground management since April 1995.

Running into the open air could, however, affect another Underground feature of long standing – the smell. Legend has it that parents would bring children with whooping cough into the system as the smell was supposed to have beneficial effects. For years the smell was attributed to Archangel Tar, with which it was alleged the cables were lubricated. The smell was still there some 40 years after removal of the cables, so another explanation was sought when the Museum of Transport was preparing to set up the Subway Gallery at Albert Drive, and consideration was being given to reproducing the smell. A bio-chemist from Glasgow University visited the tunnels one night in 1977 in an attempt to identify it: armed with a rack of corked test tubes, each containing a different organism, he sniffed the tunnel atmosphere, then each tube in turn. Unromantically he reckoned the nearest match was an organism associated with wet mud, but no attempt was made to reproduce it at Albert Drive, nor after the Museum's move to the Kelvin Hall. Even more elusive than the smell are ghosts. Over the years accounts of sightings or spine-chilling cold draughts have been recounted, but usually only when the press or other authors asked! The current stories seem to concern the Hillhead and Shields Road areas.

Whatever the future may bring, the Underground is, at the dawn of its second century, in a good position to play any part required of it. To enable it to stay in this position it is hoped the new Passenger Transport Authority will respond to its financial needs as well as Strathclyde Regional Council did over the previous 21 years.

Chapter 11

And Finally . . .

The Underground has always had a special place in Glaswegians' hearts. They are intensely proud of their little railway, and treat it as they would an old friend – with amusement, ridicule and irrepressible Glasgow humour. As your authors have watched the 'new' Underground develop, they have come across many happenings and anecdotes which seem to convey its atmosphere. In no particular order of importance, they offer the following gallimaufry.

As seen in Chapter 9, for the first six months of the modernised Underground the service finished at 7pm. On Friday 1st August 1980 Rangers were to play Arsenal in an evening friendly at Ibrox Stadium. An Inner train running late arrived at Govan at 6.55 pm, and the driver was instructed to detrain his passengers and proceed to the Depot. He suggested that "riot" would not be a strong enough word to describe the reaction of the 'Gers supporters packing his train. The Controller then gave him permission to carry on to Ibrox, empty the train and return wrong-direction to the Sheds. Inside the train the hymn singing, the stamping of feet and the pounding of fists on the car ceilings had reached a crescendo, but an adverse signal prevented departure. The driver switched on his microphone and addressed the faithful. "There's a red signal up ahead, but as soon as it changes to blue, we'll leave." An even louder roar greeted this, and within the minute a trainload of happy Bluenoses was off to Ibrox. (For non-Glaswegians, a true Rangers supporter will not acknowledge the existence of any shade of green, and particularly not Celtic FC green.)

It was nearly Christmas, and the lady and gentleman on an Inner Circle train at St Enoch were obviously well pleased with their purchase of a child's rocking horse, which was resting on her lap. A parcel most difficult to wrap – and of course wrapping is the universal sign that goods have been paid for – Lewis's assistant had compromised and tied a bag over the horse's head. A nice wee man sitting opposite leaned over and said to the lady, "Does yer horse no' like the Subway?"

A boy on roller skates arrived at high speed at the ticket window at Ibrox and offered coins for his fare. "You cannae travel on the Subway on skates," said the Booking Office Assistant firmly. "OK, missus", said the lad, rescued his money and departed equally fast. A minute later he was back. "Kin Ah git oan if Ah take ma skates aff?" "Of course," said the BOA. Whereupon, he removed the skates with their integral shoes, paid his fare and ran downstairs to the platform in his stocking soles, ticket in one hand and shoegear in the other.

The months of July and August 1985 saw day after day of rain in Glasgow – the wettest summer for almost a hundred years. It affected everybody, especially the lady who stepped from a train at Cessnock, instinctively put up her umbrella and walked along the platform, up the stairs and out into the street, blissfully unaware of the merriment she was causing.

The Glasgow Subway Poems

In 1982 the Scottish Arts Council proposed that poems should occupy vacant poster sites on the Underground, and the Passenger Transport Executive of the day initially agreed. The first offering, a series of four by Glasgow poet Edwin Morgan, was offbeat and humorous and concerned "Subway Animals" – piranhas, budgie, cat and giraffe.

Subsequent events were described by local journalist and author Cliff Hanley in one of his books. "The Morgan works were judged unsuitable by the Transport Executive, whose spokesman said, among other things, 'There is no guard on Underground trains, no smoking or drinking is allowed and The Subway Piranha, it was felt, was wide open for parody. We must take this opportunity to assure our passengers that, as far as we know, there are no piranha fish in the Underground.'

"Readers of the Glasgow Herald (now The Herald) rushed to the poet's defence in letters to the editor, both in prose and poetry . . ." and the paper's leader column, under a headline "Hands off Piranhas", remarked that it was not every municipal subway which had occasion to ban a giraffe, a busking cat, a tankful of piranhas and a budgie.

The quartet have been read in the London Underground and, in French, in the Paris Metro, but not, so far, in Glasgow! A few years later and the spokesman could have pointed out that the Underground would always get the better of animal intruders; a train hit and killed a fox near West Street on (unlucky for it) 13th August 1996.

The Low Down on Christmas
One of the railway's senior managers is a keen cyclist, and knowing that the trains would not be running and the traction power would be off, he devised something completely different for the afternoon of Christmas Day 1994 – along with two companions, he cycled round the Outer Circle! Interviewed afterwards, he said that the weather had been no problem, but the actual run was not something he would ever want to do again – even line-walking would be easier!

A familiar sight on the system every Christmas has been John Hennessy substituting for Santa Claus. In his driving days he merely wore the outfit while at the controls, usually of Route 10, an Outer Circle Christmas Shoppers' Special, but after he transferred to the maintenance staff, he collected "Cash for Kids" on the trains, and his activities resulted one year in this cartoon:-

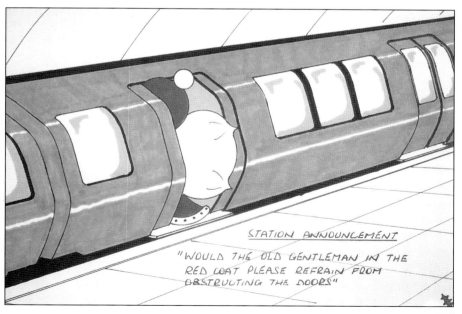

The Glasgow Underground Song

It is perhaps not generally known that Cliff Hanley had a hand in the railway's own song, which he and Ian Gourley wrote in 1952. This catchy piece will forever be linked in older Glaswegians' minds with two of Scotland's funniest comedians, Jack Milroy and Ricky Fulton, who often used it in their portrayals of Francie and Josie, two Glasgow Teddy Boys of the time. To this day, Scottish radio and television stations use parts of this song as background whenever they feature the Underground:-

They tell me that Majorca is a dandy place to be
Or Switzerland or Italy or even gay Paree
There's many lovely beauty spots on the Clyde of Firth
But I would rather always travel doon below the earth,
There's . . .

There's names that ring with magic that can thrill you through and through
They seem to call you back with an enchantment ever new
Those places faraway are like a song that's sweetly sung
You roll them round your mouth and feel them sliding aff your tongue,
There's . . .

I never liked the stoory winds, the showers and the snaw,
The sun can get too burny and the sleet's no nice at a'
But I don't mind the climate now as on my way I go
The *dolce vita's* waiting there a hundred feet below.
There's . . .

Fashion on the Subway

An unusual event took place on Thursday 28th August 1975, when a special train was chartered by Fraser's store in Buchanan Street to stage a fashion show! Car 18 was lowered on to the Outer Circle about 09:30, and ran one trip solo, then Car 41 was lowered and coupled to it. In this formation it followed Route No. 7, and picked up the models at St Enoch at about 11:15. The 'audience' came aboard at St Enoch for two 'sittings' (or shoogles) at 11:45 and 12:50. The front car was blacked out and used as a changing room, and the audience was carried in Car 41, which was decorated with curtains and tassels etc for the occasion. Passengers booked for the experience at Fraser's store and on payment of 1d (old penny) received a king sized ticket (115mm × 240mm) printed as a facsimile of an old Geographical ticket, but of a type never used on the Subway.

Dancing on the Subway

One of the contributors to Glasgow's year as European City of Culture in 1990 was Glasgow Independent Dance, a group of professional dancers and teachers. On four of the Sunday evenings in September, they staged two performances of "Dancing Underground – an incredible journey under the city by way of Glasgow's Underground. Performers will merge with the audience as they travel on the Tube and platforms normally used to the silent shuffling of impatient feet will become stages for bustling, lively performances."

A three-car train was used on each occasion, with the leading car's windows blacked out, as it was the artistes' dressing room. The other two cars were for the audience, who had pre-booked, and had dimmed lighting within coloured shades, additional loudspeakers for recorded music strung from the roof grab handles and printed dance routines in place of the normal card advertisements. The theme was described on the journey from St Enoch to Ibrox and the set pieces were performed there and at Govan, Hillhead, Buchanan St and finally at St Enoch, the train non-stopping at the intermediate stations.

"The Subway"

For its first forty years, it was simply "the Subway"; for years after electrification, Glasgow Corporation tried to have it called "the Underground" and some incomers refer to it as "the Tube". In the 1960s and 70s, the largely imported staff earned it the title of "The Donegal and Pakistan Light Railway" and Cliff Hanley once named it "the world's largest model railway."

In 1962, Anthony Burgess wrote a controversial book entitled "A Clockwork Orange", and from it, in 1971, Stanley Kubrick made an equally controversial film with the same name. In January 1978, newly delivered Car 103 and a Clayton locomotive were inspected by journalists. After remarks about "oranges and lemons", since the car was in the new orange livery and the locomotive was painted yellow, an official commented that when the system reopened, the trains would run like clockwork. The next day's newspapers used the term "The Clockwork Orange" for the first time and, unfortunately, the name has stuck. (In 1983, when the railway ran into several operational problems, one of the local papers headlined it as "The Clockwork Lemon".) Anthony Burgess died in 1993 but, alas, not one of the newspaper obituaries mentioned the railway's connection with his book – but then the trains did not fly black flags either.

The Passenger Transport Executive has variously advertised it as "the Magic Circle", "the Magic Roundabout" and "the Underground Movement", one wag has suggested that with so many females on the payroll, it could perhaps be "the GWR" – Glasgow's Women's Railway – but to most Glaswegians, it will always be "the Subway".

Appendix 1

Part A **Directors of Glasgow District Subway Company and Glasgow Subway Railway Company, 1890–1923**

Name	Occupation	Period of Office	Remarks
Henry Robert Baird	of Duriss	Nominated in 1890 Act. Stood down by 1905	Chairman by March 1898.
William Weir	of Kildonan, Ironmaster	Nominated in 1890 Act. Stood down c.1913	
James Parker-Smith	of Jordanhill (M.P.)	Nominated in 1890 Act. Stood down c.1919	
Sir William McOnie		Nominated in 1890 Act. Stood down by 1905	
William Laird	Ironmaster	Nominated in 1890 Act. Stood down by 1905	
Alexander Simpson	Civil Engineer, Glasgow		Chairman by 1905 until c.1921
James Laird	Writer to the Signet, Glasgow	By 1905. Stood down c.1909	
Andrew K.McCosh	Ironmaster of Coatbridge	By 1905. Stood down c.1916	
W.S.Wilson	Civil Engineer, Glasgow	By 1905. Stood down c.1922	
Robert Simpson	Civil Engineer, Glasgow	c.1915–1923	
J.N.Murdoch	Accountant, Glasgow	c.1917–1923	
William Whitelaw	of Corstorphine, later Kirknewton, Ratho, and Kirknewton	c.1917–1923	Chairman c.1921
W.W.McCosh	Ironmaster, Glasgow	c.1921–1923	
William James Baird	of Elie, Fife	c.1922–1923	

Part B **Directors of Greater Glasgow P.T.E. and Strathclyde P.T.E.**

Ronald B. Cox	Director General	1973–76
William Murray	Director of Operations	1973–77
Andrew F. McKay	Director of Planning	1973–76
	Director General	1976–79
W. Norman Stirling	Director of Finance	1973–80
	Director of Finance and Personnel Services	1980–86
Joseph Coyle	Director of Industrial Relations	1973–80
Hamish M. Taylor	Director of Planning & Development	1976–80
	Director of Technical Services & Development	1986–date
Neil Townend	Director of Operations	1977–79
Alan R. Westwell	Director General	1979–86
Keith W. Moody	Director of Operations	1981–85
Stephen R. Lockley	Director	1985–86
	Director General	1986–date
John McNamee	Director of Finance and Personnel Services	1986–date
Malcolm C. Reed	Non-Executive Director	1995–date
Aidan O'Donnell	Non-Executive Director	1995–date
Iain Wylie	Clerk and Legal Adviser to PTA/PTE	1996–date

Part C Chairmen and Vice Chairmen of Greater Glasgow PTA, Strathclyde Regional Council, Highways and Transportation Committee, and Strathclyde Passenger Transport Authority

Cllr. Thomas McLaren	Chairman GGPTA	October 1973–May 1975
Cllr. Joseph K Russell	Vice Chairman GGPTA	October 1973–May 1975
Cllr. Thomas Fulton	Chairman H&T Cttee	May 1975–May 1978
Cllr. John Reid	Vice Chairman H&T Cttee	May 1975–May 1978
	Chairman H&T Cttee	May 1978–May 1982
Cllr Malcolm Waugh	Vice Chairman H&T Cttee	May 1978–May 1982
	Chairman H&T Cttee	May 1982–May 1994
Cllr. James D Cannell	Vice Chairman H&T Cttee	May 1982–October 1984
Cllr. John Fitch	Vice Chairman H&T Cttee	October 1984–May 1986
Cllr. Kenneth J Murray	Vice Chairman H&T Cttee	May 1986–June 1987
Cllr. Duncan Mills	Vice Chairman H&T Cttee	June 1987–May 1990
Cllr. Charles Gordon	Vice Chairman H&T Cttee	May 1990–May 1994
	Chairman H&T Cttee	May 1994–March 1996
Cllr. James Gibson	Vice Chairman H&T Cttee	May 1992–May 1994
Cllr. Walter McLellan	Joint Vice Chairman H&T Cttee	May 1994–March 1996
Cllr Anne Maggs	Joint Vice Chairman H&T Cttee	May 1994–March 1996
Cllr. Charles Gordon	Chairman SPTA	April 1996 to date
Cllr. Harry McGuigan	Joint Vice Chairman SPTA	April 1996 to date
Cllr. Eric Ross	Joint Vice Chairman SPTA	April 1996 to date

Source: Internal Memorandum from Mr H.M.Taylor, dated 20 May 1996

Appendix 2

Principal Shareholders as at 6/12/1890

Shareholder	£10 shares held
James Douglas Baird, 168 West George Street, Glasgow	10,000
William Allan Coats, Thread Manufacturer, Skelmorlie Castle, Skelmorlie	5,000
William Laird, Ironmaster, 168 West George Street, Glasgow	2,000
The Hon. John Muir, Lord Provost of Glasgow, Merchant, 22 West Nile Street	2,000
Alexander Simpson, Civil Engineer, Eversley, Ayton Road, Pollokshields, Glasgow	4,000
William Weir of Kildonan, Ironmaster, 168 West George Street, Glasgow	10,000
Alexander Baird of Urie, 168 West George Street, Glasgow	2,500
Edward William David Baird, lieutenant, 10th Royal Hussars, 168 West George Street, Glasgow	5,000
Henry Robert Baird of Durris, 168 West George Street, Glasgow	3,500
William Baird of Elie, 168 West George Street	7,500
	51,500

Source – Public Record Office File MT6 534/12

Appendix 3

Tunnel Construction Contracts

The various contractors built lengths of single tunnel as follows:-

Mr. George Talbot	1,343 yards
Mr. David Shanks	495 yards
Messrs Charles Brand & Son	2,119 yards
Messrs John Patterson & Sons Ltd	1,227 yards
Messrs Hugh Kennedy & Sons	2,559 yards
Messrs Watt & Wilson	1,322 yards
Messrs James Smith & Co.	817 yards
Messrs Robert M'Alpine & Sons	1,645 yards
	11,527 yards

Source: 'Glasgow District Subway – Its Construction and Equipment, 1905'

Known details of contracts let are as follows:-

Contract No.	Tender Return Date	Section	Length	Successful Contractor
5	1/5/91	Summertown Road, Govan to near Merkland Street, Partick	657 yards of covered way. 876 yards of iron tunnel	Charles Brand and Son.
2	12/1/92	Coburg Street to Shields Road	558 yards, partly brickwork and partly iron	Messrs John Patterson and Son.
3	12/1/92	Ditto	658 yards of covered way	Messrs John Patterson and Son.
12	12/1/92	St George's Church to St George's Cross.	760 yards in rock	Robert M'Alpine
13	12/1/92	Ditto	880 yards in rock	Robert M'Alpine

Source: The Contract Journal and Specification Record, 15/4/91, 20/5/91, 27/5/91, 23/12/91 and 27/1/92.

It is believed Charles Brand and Son received the first contract let, for St George's Church to Coburg Street, but gave up the contract. Hugh Kennedy and Sons had a contract in the Kelvinbridge area.

Appendix 4

Passengers Carried – Company Period

Year to 31st January	Passengers Carried	Year to 31st December	Passengers Carried
1898	9,628,392	1912	12,934,659
1899	12,445,201	1913	14,574,334
1900	13,655,563	1914	14,115,096
1901	13,839,816	1915	14,761,053
1902	14,638,584	1916	15,923,953
1903	16,370,410	1917	17,948,170
1904	16,698,414	1918	20,970,950
1905	16,308,435	1919	14,783,518
1906	16,038,012	1920	11,011,448
1907	16,309,767	1921	11,379,227
1908	17,206,790		
1909	15,786,981		
1910	15,068,622		
1911	15,124,707		

Source: Notes by General Manager, Tramways Department 21/2/22.

Passengers Carried – Public Ownership Period

Year to 31st May	Passengers Carried	Total Receipts £	Year to 31st May	Passengers Carried	Total Receipts £
1924 (10 months)	11,964,627	72,516	1960	28,012,004	447,141
			1961	27,046,778	437,304
1925	20,008,445	99,122	1962	26,912,753	428,684
1926	19,730,794	96,702	1963	26,033,914	426,571
1927	18,478,569	94,911	1964	26,111,613	422,340
1928	20,595,269	99,703	1965	24,984,645	474,089
1929	20,399,537	96,758	1966	22,874,687	541,382
1930	19,969,185	93,150	1967	22,053,618	520,906
1931	17,817,658	81,883	1966	22,874,687	541,382
1932	15,846,627	73,001	1967	22,053,618	520,906
1933	14,317,817	67,435	1968	21,306,218	563,198
1934	14,036,184	65,829	1969	19,173,906	588,543
1935	14,412,591	67,265	1970	17,729,054	671,507
1936	17,885,519	85,493	1971	16,561,661	722,644
1937	21,597,582	104,334	1972	15,261,711	781,983
1938	23,997,292	116,357	1973	13,924,309	841,143
1939	25,813,930	129,820	1974 ‡	13,212,314	
1940	26,748,007	134,170	1975 §	12,227,381	
1941*	17,074,108	99,822	1976 **	10,054,778	
1942	28,510,679	177,004	1977 †	7,367,053	
1943	31,270,730	193,900	1978 †	310,118	Closed 21/5/77
1944	33,704,711	208,051	1981 †	9,827,927	11½ months
1945	34,210,160	209,020	1982 †	10,890,809	
1946	35,002,655	218,268	1983 †	12,120,650	
1947	36,582,135	229,477	1984 †	12,446,839	
1948	37,186788	230,397	1985 †	12,693,629	
1949	37,343,652	231,402	1986 †	13,148,407	
1950	37,290,437	231,405	1987 †	13,759,081	
1951	36,669,098	233,612	1988 †	13,588,533	
1952	37,113,261	245,485	1989 †	13,579,664	
1953	35,971,340	301,449	1990 †	13,501,648	
1954	33,620,696	311,505	1991 †	13,571,648	
1955	34,370,813	318,392	1992 †	13,560,035	
1956	34,481,190	343,572	1993 †	13,500,055	
1957	33,479,192	382,594	1994 †	14,030,105	
1958	32,672,347	370,564	1995 †	14,656,268	
1959	31,633,630	356,842	1996 †	14,285,464	

* Underground damaged by bombing   † Year to 31st March.   ‡ 1/6/73 to 15/5/74
§ 16/5/74 to 15/5/75   ** 16/5/76 to 31/3/77

Sources: GCT Annual Report of Accounts; GCT and GGPTE Annual Reports, 1948–78;
A Report on the Future Development of Passenger Transport in Glasgow by E.R.L. Fitzpayne,
May 1948; Scottish Transport Nos. 38 to 49 Scottish Transport No.36

Appendix 5

Details of Original Rolling Stock

No.	Date in service	Builder	Type as built	Converted to Electric Traction Date	Type	Solid Doors	RB axle-boxes	Fluor. Lighting	Last Day in Service	Disposal	Remarks
1	1896	Oldbury	G	30/10/35	(MH)	19/05/64	1/06/56	7/10/68		8/06/77	To Glasgow Transport Museum
2	1896	Oldbury	G	9/03/35	(MH)	13/02/65	6/10/54	-	19/07/76 Col.	-	Converted to Rail Wagon, 1983
3	1896	Oldbury	G	23/02/35	(MH)	-	20/06/55	-	23/10/67	?	Converted to camshaft control for 3-car train
4	1896	Oldbury	G	1/12/36	(T)	-	10/09/58	-		1987	To Glasgow Transport Museum
5	1896	Oldbury	G	21/04/36	(T)	?	7/04/59	-	21/05/77	30/05/77 AY	
6	1896	Oldbury	G	2/03/35 2/07/38	(T) (GP)	2/11/63	17/10/56	24/12/68	21/05/77	1/06/77 B	MV motors fitted 12/08/76
7	1896	Oldbury	G	3/07/36	(T)	-	18/5/57	-		21/11/77	Purchased by Sir Wm McAlpine - to NRM
8	1896	Oldbury	G	3/03/36	(T)	-	15/07/57	-	21/05/77	30/05/77 AY	
9	1896	Oldbury	G	28/12/35	(T)	/39	31/01/55	15/07/70	21/05/77	30/05/77 AY	
10	1896	Oldbury	G	29/01/36	(T)	-	4/02/57	-		08/06/77	Purchased privately to Arran - disintegrated Conv to GEC Motors 22/11/75
11	1896	Oldbury	G	19/01/35	(MH)	30/11/61	31/08/56	31/05/67	21/05/77	U/F Retained	
12	1896	Oldbury	G	12/03/35	(MH)	21/01/58	21/01/58	3/03/67	21/05/77	2/06/77 AY	
13	1896	Oldbury	G	9/09/35	(T)	10/05/66	27/01/61	10/05/66	10/12/75	5/05/77 TW	Used as store at Bridge Street. Vestibule Doors Removed.
14	1896	Oldbury	G	20/05/38	(GP)	by '63	21/06/57	26/05/69		1/06/77 B	MV Motors 7/06/76
15	1896	Oldbury	G	02/02/35	(MH)	by '63	9/05/49	-		1/06/77 B	
16	1896	Oldbury	G	21/02/36	(MH)	by '63	17/02/53	-	31/05/76 Col.	-	Converted to Cable wagon 1977/8
17	1896	Oldbury	G	5/07/35 4/11/38	(T) (GP)	15/01/51	15/04/54	21/03/68	21/05/77	1/06/77 B	Non-standard fluoro' lighting diffusers. Non-standard centre saloon partitions.
18	1896	Oldbury	G	28/04/38	(GP)	?/06/63	29/01/52	?/09/68		U/F Retained	Non-standard centre saloon partitions
19	1896	Oldbury	G	15/10/36	(T)	by '63	3/07/52	-	21/05/77	30/05/77 AY	Vestibule doors removed
20	1896	Oldbury	G	30/03/36	(MH)	by '63	6/08/53	-	21/05/77	-	Converted to Rail Wagon 1983
21	1897	Oldbury	G	27/09/35	(MH)	16/11/60	15/06/56	-		1/06/77 B	
22	1897	Oldbury	G	10/02/37	(T)	by '63	3/06/57	-		12/05/77 TW	Fluorescent lighting trial from 19/04/46. Vestibule Doors Removed.
23	1897	Oldbury	G	1/12/35	(MH)	18/04/61	2/10/53	20/01/71	21/05/77	2/06/77 AY	
24	1897	Oldbury	G	16/02/35	(MH)	by '61	22/12/53	11/05/70	21/05/77	2/06/77 AY	
25	1897	Oldbury	G	26/01/35	(MH)	by 03/62	9/05/52	-		2/06/77 AY	Vestibule Doors Removed.
26	1897	Oldbury	G	17/12/36	(T)	9/12/66	19/10/52	-		12/05/77 TW	
27	1897	Oldbury	G	18/10/35	(MH)	16/10/62	1/11/58	-	21/05/77	2/06/77 AY	Vestibule Doors Removed.
28	1897	Oldbury	G	31/08/35 31/12/38	(T) (GP)	?/10/65	3/07/53	-	W/E 22/06/68	?	
29	1897	Oldbury	G	18/11/35	(MH)	by 6/62	30/06/59	-	21/05/77	25/05/77 TW	GEC Motors 29/07/75 to 23/07/76
30	1897	Oldbury	G	7/08/35 15/07/38	(T) (GP)	2/09/64	13/07/56	22/08/69		1/06/77 B	MV Motors ? to 24/05/77

No.	Date in service	Builder	Type as built	Converted to Electric Traction		Solid Doors	RB axle-boxes	Fluor. Lighting	Last Day in Service	Disposal	Remarks
				Date	Type						
31	1898	HN	ST	23/08/38	(LT)	-	16/03/60	c 1969	c.12/6/68	?	Vestibule Doors Removed. Broken up at Broomloan.
32	1898	HN	ST	6/12/38	(LT)	c 1957	19/02/58	-	-	11/07/90	
33	1898	HN	ST	2/12/38	(LT)	-	-	-	-	By 1914	
34	1898	HN	ST	12/03/38	(LT)	-	16/02/54	-	-	1/06/77	To Bridge Inn Ratho
35	1898	HN	ST	25/04/38	(LT)	by '63	28/8/53	-	-	30/05/77 AY	Vestibule Doors Removed.
36	1898	HN	ST	10/11/36	(LT)	-	29/04/53	18/6/64	c 16/4/69	?	
37	1898	HN	ST	14/08/36	(LT)	by '63	1/10/54	/68	-	25/05/77TW	Vestibule Doors Removed.
38	1898	HN	ST	3/06/38	(LT)	-	10/07/57	03/70	21/05/77	30/05/77 AY	Vestibule Doors Removed.
39	1898	HN	ST	-	-	-	12/12/52	-	21/05/77	21/05/79	To Glasgow Transport Museum.
40	1898	HN	ST	-	-	-	-	-	-	By 1914	
41	1898	HN	ST	19/08/37	(LT)	-	2/10/57	-	-	Buch St.	Displayed at Buchanan St. station.
42	1898	HN	ST	25/03/37	(LT)	-	25/04/58	12/69	19/07/76 Col	Broken up 8/76	
43	1898	HN	ST	8/04/38	(LT)	-	21/04/59	-	21/05/77	2/06/77 AY	
44	1898	HN	ST	17/05/37	(LT)	-	8/05/52	-	c 9/03/70	?	
45	1898	HN	ST	17/06/36	(LT)	14/12/67	17/10/58	-	31/05/76 Col	Broken up 8/76	
46	1898	HN	ST	-	-	-	-	-	-	By 1914	
47	1898	HN	ST	-	-	-	-	-	-	By 1914	
48	1898	HN	ST	-	-	-	-	-	-	By 1914	
49	1898	HN	ST	-	-	-	-	-	-	By 1914	
50	1898	HN	ST	-	-	-	-	-	-	By 1914	
51	1898	HN	ST	-	-	-	-	-	-	By 1914	
52	1898	HN	ST	26/04/38	(LT)	Pre 1961	18/04/52*	-	-	2/06/77 AY	
53	1898	HN	ST	-	-	-	-	-	-	By 1914	
54	1898	HN	ST	-	-	-	-	-	-	By 1914	
55	1901		G	12/11/35	(MH)	4/02/60	1/11/55	-	21/05/77	Retained	Fluorescent lighting trial 19/4/46
56	1901		G	30/09/36	(MH)	by '63	19/03/56	-	12/01/68	?	Converted to camshaft control for 3-car train
57	1901		G	17/12/35	(MH)	by '63	6/03/57	-	21/05/77	-	Converted to Cable wagon 1977/8
58	1901		G	22/05/36	(MH)	by '63	18/07/52	8/01/68	31/05/76 Col	-	
59	c.1913		G	27/06/35	(MH)	?/07/65	20/10/61	-	11/09/74 Col	Broken up 11/75	
60	c.1913		G	03/33	(MP)	by '63	13/04/53	-	W/E 19/4/69	Broken up 6/69	

Key:

AY = Arnott Young, Dalmuir
B = North of England Open Air Museum
Col = collision
G = Gripper car
GP = GEC equipment and Pickerings underframe.

HN = Hurst, Nelson & Co., Motherwell.
LT = Bogie Trailer (Long 44 seat saloon)
MH = MV equipment and Hurst, Nelson underframe)
MP = MV equipment and Pickerings underframe.
NRM = National Railway Museum, York

RB = Roller bearing
ST = 4-wheel trailer (24 seats)
T = Bogie Trailer (Short 42 seat saloon)
TW = Taylor Woodrow
* Also quoted as 21/05/54

Appendix 6

Details of Present Rolling Stock
Part A – Metro-Cammell Power Cars

No.	Date delivered	Date in service	Trans-Clyde Livery	Strath-clyde Livery	Refurbishment		
					To Derby	From Derby	In Service
101	27/1/78	16/4/80	10/9/82	12/9/85	27/7/95	27/9/95	4/10/95
102	9/6/78	16/4/80	14/8/81	10/7/84	6/5/93	25/3/94	12/4/94
103	12/1/78	16/4/80	18/9/82	13/5/85	1/6/95	3/8/95	8/8/95
104	24/2/78	16/4/80	3/11/81	4/4/85	3/8/95	5/10/95	11/10/95
105	9/3/78	16/4/80	28/9/81	20/8/84	5/10/95	23/11/95	30/11/95
106	16/3/78	16/4/80	28/9/81	3/10/84	13/10/94	5/1/95	15/1/95
107	17/4/78	16/4/80	6/10/81	1/9/84	14/1/93	10/2/94	3/3/94
108	21/4/78	17/4/80	28/9/81	16/7/84	15/2/95	6/4/95	9/4/95
109	2/5/78	18/4/80	10/9/81	8/8/84	26/10/95	7/12/95	19/12/95
110	19/6/78	16/4/80	21/10/81	16/9/84	7/11/95	21/12/95	21/1/96
111	30/6/78	16/4/80	27/8/82	16/7/85	20/12/94	2/3/95	15/3/95
112	3/7/78	16/4/80	12/7/82	10/8/85	5/1/95	15/3/95	19/3/95
113	14/7/78	16/4/80	2/9/82	21/8/85	2/3/95	27/4/95	29/4/95
114	21/7/78	16/4/80	6/5/83	9/5/86	7/9/95	7/11/95	10/11/95
115	16/8/78	16/4/80	16/7/82	5/6/86	5/5/94	14/9/94	17/9/94
116	29/8/78	16/4/80	30/6/82	21/6/85	27/4/95	22/6/95	27/6/95
117	11/9/78	17/4/80	10/12/81	23/5/85	12/5/93	10/3/94	23/8/94
118	18/9/78	16/4/80	13/8/82	4/7/85	24/8/95	26/10/95	9/11/95
119	11/10/78	16/4/80	4/10/82	2/9/85	15/3/95	11/5/95	14/5/95
120	28/11/78	16/4/80	-	4/10/83	22/6/94	3/11/94	8/11/94
121	1/12/78	16/4/80	-	8/11/83†	6/4/95	1/6/95	5/6/95
122	23/11/78	19/11/80	-	1/11/83	10/3/94	2/6/94	10/6/94
123	8/12/78	16/4/80	14/8/81	6/7/84	25/3/94	22/6/94	27/6/94
124	22/12/78	18/4/80	-	21/10/83	11/5/95	6/7/95	10/7/95
125	28/12/78	16/4/80	-	18/11/83	9/6/94	13/10/94	15/10/94
126	11/1/79	16/4/80	-	12/9/83	23/5/95	27/7/95	2/8/95
127	15/2/79	16/4/80	18/6/83	21/4/86‡	13/1/94	5/5/94	10/5/94
128	19/12/78	16/4/80	19/10/82	17/4/85	14/9/94	8/12/94	17/12/94
129	14/2/79	18/4/80	-	25/8/83	8/12/94	15/2/95	19/2/95
130	19/2/79	16/4/80	27/8/82	29/4/85	6/7/95	7/9/95	24/9/95
131	3/5/79	18/4/80	27/5/83	3/10/85	5/9/94	20/12/94	4/1/95
132	29/5/79	16/4/80	-	5/8/83§	22/6/95	24/8/95	1/9/95
133	30/4/79	16/4/80	-	6/7/83§	2/6/94	22/9/94	24/9/94

† Last car to run in service in original livery 31/10/83
‡ Last car in Transclyde Livery - last day in service 10/4/86
§ Strathclyde Transport Logo Transfers fitted 17/8/83

Part B – **Hunslet TPL Trailer Cars**

No.	Date delivered	Date in service	Retro-fit Modifications (Dates)		
			to H-B	from H-B	in service
201	30/4/92	26/10/92	31/5/93	17/8/93	19/8/93
202	3/6/92	17/11/92	22/6/93	20/8/93	24/8/93
203	9/6/92	26/10/92	13/8/93	30/8/93	1/9/93?
204	13/8/92	11/11/92	30/8/93	14/9/93	15/9/93
205	21/7/92	26/10/92	7/9/93	29/9/93	2/10/93
206	15/7/92	26/10/92	23/9/93	4/10/93	6/10/93
207	10/8/92	27/10/92	20/8/93	7/9/93	9/9/93?
208	17/8/92	2/12/92	8/10/93	22/10/93	25/10/93

H-B = Hunslet-Barclay at Kilmarnock.

Part C – **Miscellaneous Vehicles**

No.	Description	Put to use	Origin
L2	Clayton 4-wheel battery locomotive	1978	New - Delivered 11/77 Clayton Serial 0965B
L3	Clayton 4-wheel battery locomotive	1978	New - Delivered 11/77 Clayton Serial 0965A
L4	Clayton 4-wheel battery locomotive - (Purchased 3/87, Refurbished by Clayton 9-11/88, Rebuilt by H-B 10/89 - 3/90)	12/88	Ex-Taylor Woodrow No. TE3A003 Clayton Order BO186
W16	Bogie Wagon Flat/Cable laying (Converted by PTE at Broomloan 1977/8)	6/78	Underframe ex-Car16
W57	Bogie Wagon with battery air compressor (Converted by PTE at Broomloan 1977/8, and compressor added c. 1981)	6/78*	Underframe ex-Car57
RW2	Bogie Rail-carrying Wagon with gantry (Converted by Barclays)	1983	Underframe ex-Car2
RW20	Bogie Rail-carrying Wagon with gantry (Converted by Barclays)	1983	Underframe ex-Car20
W5	4 - wheel flat wagon (Purchased 3/87 as derelict locomotive, converted by Hunslet-Barclay 7-12/91)	1992	Ex-Taylor Woodrow No. TE4A002 Clayton Order BO186

* As Cable Wagon

Part D – **Miscellaneous Vehicles Prior to Modernisation**

Loco (L1)	4-wheeled jackshaft drive battery locomotive supplied by British Electric Vehicles (Wingrove & Rodgers, Agents), 1927	Rebuilt c.1937 with chain drive, new cab etc. Fitted with Wedglock coupler at one end c.1979. To Glasgow Museum of Transport
'Wee Wagon'		To Glasgow Museum of Transport (never displayed)
Bogie Wagon No. 1	Hand Brake Only	Scrapped c.1977
Bogie Wagon No. 2	Hand Brake Only	Scrapped c.1977
Bogie Wagon No. 3	Hand Brake Only	Scrapped c.1977
Compressor Wagon	c.1965 – an old coach bogie – with 600V compressor	Scrapped c.1977
Welding Wagon	On old coach bogie	Scrapped c.1977

Appendix 7

Car Layouts

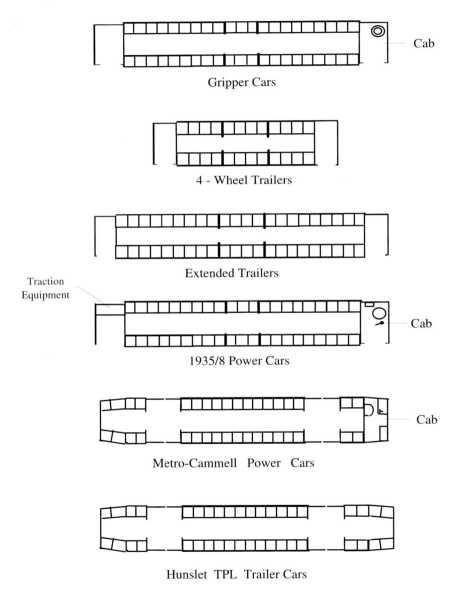

Gripper Cars

4 - Wheel Trailers

Extended Trailers

1935/8 Power Cars

Metro-Cammell   Power   Cars

Hunslet TPL Trailer Cars

Cab

Traction
Equipment

Cab

Cab

Appendix 8

The Route and the Stations

Govan – Merkland Street – Partick – 958 metres

From Govan station the tunnels head in a north-westerly direction under Govan Road and Water Row, descending at about 1 in 18 through sand and curving right to pass under the River Clyde after about a quarter of a mile. Beneath the river the tops of the tunnels are 56 feet below high water mark, and at the bottom of the slope is a sump and pump installation, known as the Clyde Man-hole, which keeps any ingress of water in check. At this point the Inner circle tunnel is slightly lower than the Outer, and is the lowest point on the system. On the north side of the river the route crosses under Castlebank Street, the Clydeside Expressway and Railtrack's elevated North Side Electrics line, the heading becoming north-north-east. Here the sub-soil is muddy, and near the top of the 1 in 20 gradient the tunnel structure, which has been entirely of cast-iron segments, changes briefly to partly brick as the tracks run through the site of the 1940 bomb explosion. The summit is marked by the empty echoing chamber of the former Merkland Street station, and a short descent (still in cast iron) leads into Partick station, the double flank platform chamber of which was built new as part of the 1974–80 modernisation. Pairs of escalators connect the concourse to the western end of the platforms. The station also incorporates a high level ScotRail station of the same name with its platforms on the embankment above the ground level joint booking hall. This is the longest section at 958 metres, and there was an intermediate signal in each tunnel from 1980 until October 1996.

Partick – Kelvinhall – 558 metres

From Partick the line passes beneath Partick Bus Station and Vine Street, at the same time bearing right towards Dumbarton Road, under which it runs for almost quarter of a mile before turning north-east at Dowanhill Street to enter Kelvinhall station (Partick Cross until 1977) which retains an island platform. The sub-soil has gone from mud through clay and rock to shale with coal waste, and the construction changes from cast iron segments to masonry.

Kelvinhall – Hillhead – 603 metres

Leaving Kelvinhall station on a left hand curve, the tunnels align themselves with Byres Road, which runs north-north-east, as far as Ashton Road, where the line bends to the right to enter Hillhead station, climbing all the way. Hillhead station has a flank platform for the Outer Circle and one face of an island platform serves the Inner Circle. The depth of the tops of the tunnels from street level has varied between 20 and 38 feet, and the ground encountered has been shale and sandstone.

Hillhead – Kelvinbridge – 901 metres

Exiting the station on a continuing right hand sweep, the line of Glasgow Street is soon reached and followed all the way to the River Kelvin, where a sharp left hand bend – the 'Kelvinbridge Kink' – and a more gentle right hand arc, through cast iron segments under the river and the adjacent alignment of the former Glasgow Central Railway, bring the tracks into Kelvinbridge station. Although the line has been fairly level all the way from Hillhead, the surface topography is such that the tunnels have been at one point 115 feet below ground level, the deepest on the system. On the other hand, the Kelvin is normally relatively shallow, and the top segments of the short section of cast iron tunnel were built little more than two feet below the river bed.

Kelvinbridge retains its island platform, which is wider than the others. This section also had an intermediate signal in each circle from 1980 until October 1996.

Alternative Routes between Govan and Kelvinbridge.

The Glasgow Museum of Transport has in its Subway collection a copy of the Subway Company's original (1887) proposals for the courses of 'Subway No.1', route from Govan Cross round by the north side of the Clyde to Buchanan Street at Dundas Lane, and 'Subway No.2', its counterpart from Govan Cross by the south loop to Dundas Lane.

From Govan Cross the 1887 line would have gone directly north-east under the Govan Ship-building Yard (later Harland & Wolff), the River Clyde and most of Ferry Road, passing beneath the North British Railway at Yorkhill station, and then curving slightly left to cut under the River Kelvin and then Dumbarton Road at Partick Cross. It too, would have followed the line of Byres Road, but continuing further to Viniecombe (sic) Street, where it would have turned sharply east to align itself with Great Western Road and, at Park Road, almost half a mile later, taken up the course of the present tunnels.

No doubt the more westerly crossing between Govan Cross and Partick Cross was thought to have greater traffic potential and give the Subway an advantage in fighting the competition of the alternative river crossings, the ferries. The second variation, from Hillhead via Botanic Gardens and Great Western Road to Kelvinbridge, could not be achieved because the Subway Company was pre-empted by the Glasgow Central Railway, which received Parliamentary powers for its Great Western Road tunnel, part of its Stobcross to Kirklee line, while the former was preparing its second Parliamentary Bill.

Kelvinbridge – St Georges Cross – 791 metres

From Kelvinbridge station the tunnels continue on their right hand arc until they are beneath Great Western Road. From this point the route of the Outer Circle should have continued straight to St Georges Cross, as does the Inner Circle from St Georges Cross in the opposite direction, but the foundations of St Mary's Cathedral spire are close to the tunnel alignment so the Outer Circle tunnel takes a kink to the right to give a wide berth to the obstructions. This is not obvious when travelling in the train, but from the platform at St Georges Cross an approaching train's headlights show the extent of the deviation required.

St Georges Cross – Cowcaddens – 708 metres

At St Georges Cross, Great Western Road becomes New City Road and the course of the railway remains straight and nearly level under the street on an east-south-east heading until abreast of the Normal School, where the 'Cowcaddens Curves', speed restricted right and left hand bends incorporating a sudden rise, ease the train into Cowcaddens station. The last section round the curves and into Cowcaddens is in cast iron and is speed restricted to 25 Kph: the entry to Cowcaddens station is the highest point reached by the Underground tracks, and is some 34˙5 metres higher than the low point under the Clyde between Govan and Partick. Intermediate signals were removed from this section in October 1996.

Cowcaddens – Buchanan Street – 798 metres

Extensive property redevelopment and street realignment in the Cowcaddens district have made the area almost unrecognisable to anyone who has not seen it since the 1970s. In those days the tunnels from Cowcaddens station followed the long curve of Cowcaddens Street to its junction with Port Dundas Road, and then swept right to head, as they do today, due south under Buchanan Street, in a few more yards passing under the Railtrack Queen Street Low Level tracks, themselves in tunnel, and arriving at Buchanan Street station. Cowcaddens Street has since become the straighter and longer Cowcaddens Road, and the line is now only briefly beneath it. Most of this section is through rock. The Royal Concert Hall straddles the tunnel at what is now the northern end of Buchanan Street, and four of the cross-passages were bricked up in 1989 as a precaution as the Hall was being built. The Inner Circle intermediate signal was removed in November 1993, but the Outer Circle one survived until October 1996.

This is the fastest section of the modernised railway, and the trains take full advantage of the falling gradient quickly to attain maximum governed speed, which is held all the way to the Buchanan Street approach. Buchanan Street has a similar layout to Hillhead.

Buchanan Street – St Enoch – 550 metres

Buchanan Street continues directly south for just over a quarter of a mile and terminates at Argyle Street, with St Enoch Square opening out beyond. Running east-west under Argyle Street is the cut-and-cover of Railtrack's Argyle Line on its way to and from Glasgow Central Low Level station.

From Buchanan Street station the Underground tunnels follow the line of Buchanan Street, and on approaching Argyle Street dive under the Argyle Line and rise steeply into St Enoch station. The roller-coaster nature of the track at this point is best seen from St Enoch Outer Circle platform as a train approaches.

The subway tunnels were the first to be built, the Parliamentary Act obliging the Subway Company to finish its works at this point within two years, so that the ground would have consolidated before construction of the Glasgow Central Railway, as the Argyle Line was originally known, began

From a point near St Georges Tron Church the tunnel is in cast iron to St Enoch, Bridge Street and part way to West Street. St Enoch station has two flank platforms, and single escalators at each end of each platform connect with the concourse.

St Enoch – Bridge Street – 676 metres

Leaving St Enoch, the tracks curve gently to the right under Dixon Street, descending on a 1 in 20 gradient to pass under the Clyde, after which a rise of similar severity beneath Carlton Place, Oxford Street and Coburg Street brings them on a sharp right hand bend into Bridge Street station. The ground on this stretch consists mainly of sand, and the tops of the tunnels are 41 feet below the river's high water mark. The low point is some 4 metres higher than the other Clyde crossing. Two separate drainage sumps are provided at the low point, one in each tunnel.

Bridge Street – West Street – 518 metres

After leaving Bridge Street and passing under Eglinton Street, the tunnels straighten and continue south-west beneath the accumulation of Railtrack lines two levels above which lead to and from Glasgow Central Station. At the end of the straight is a right-handed curve and the approach to West Street station. The last section into West Street is of circular brick arch construction.

An Alternative Route between St Enoch and West Street

Mention has already been made of the Subway Company's map in the Glasgow Museum of Transport. On it is shown a second suggested variation of route (probably from the 1887 Bill), obviously intended to offer a better interchange with the Caledonian Railway at *its* Bridge Street station, which was on a viaduct on the west side of Bridge Street between Clyde Place and Nelson Street.

From a point under Dixon Street at its junction with (Great) Clyde Street the line would have swung south-south-west under the Clyde to come beneath Bridge Street at Carlton Court, opposite the 'Caley' station. From there the tunnels would have burrowed along under Nelson Street, Commerce Street, Wallace Street and Cook Street to take up the present route at the threshold of West Street station.

West Street – Shields Road – 600 metres
Still curving right, the line leaves West Street and points itself west under Scotland Street, which it will follow as far as Kinning Park station, two stops further on. After about 300 yards, the tracks run through the site of the former 'cross-over', which was where the haulage cables of the 1896–1935 Subway left and re-entered the Power station.

The entry lay at right angles to the left hand wall of the Outer Circle tunnel, and two interruptions to the circular continuity of the tunnel mark the spot. On the left, a brick-lined inshot was formed in the spring of 1992 to replace the wooden staging and fencing which closed off entry after 1935, and on the right, the intermediate wall between the Outer and Inner tunnels still has at its base a gap about 20 feet long by 4 feet high, this being where the Inner Circle cable crossed over to enter the Power Station alongside its Outer counterpart. Unfortunately both these features are too low to be seen from the passenger saloons of the trains. A drainage sump provided in 1980 was removed during the 1992 works.

From here the tracks run straight to Shields Road station on a slightly rising gradient.

Shields Road – Kinning Park – 816 metres
From Shields Road the line drops on a 1 in 18 slope in cast iron and winds beneath the alignment of the former Caledonian Railway Harbour Branch, which led to the General Terminus goods yard at Paisley Road Toll, and the foundations of a viaduct carrying the M8 Motorway, and then rises at 1 in 16 – the steepest gradient on the system, before levelling out and reverting to masonry construction. The modern rolling stock is so tight to tunnel profile here that the track of the Outer Circle has been set into mass concrete without sleepers, and the cast iron section is permanently speed-restricted to 35 Kph on both tunnels. Once out of the dip, the tunnels run only 9 feet below street level directly to Kinning Park station, which is entered after a sharp right hand bend.

Kinning Park – Cessnock – 494 metres
Almost all the way from Kelvinbridge the tunnels have run beneath streets, but from Kinning Park the line strikes out north of west under tenemental housing until it arrives at Cessnock station, which is situated just north of Paisley Road west at Cessnock Street. This section is the shortest on the system.

Cessnock – Ibrox – 666 metres
Still on the same heading, the route continues to Copland Road, descending gradually to pass under the alignment of the former Princes Dock Joint Railway between White-field Road and Carmichael Street in cast iron, and then rising and bearing right to enter Ibrox station, which is similar in layout to Hillhead and Buchanan Street.

Ibrox – Govan – 918 metres
The curve through Ibrox station and the 130 metres thereafter set the course of the line to north-west, and from beneath Brighton Street the tracks run straight to Govan, passing through three of the main features of the railway *en route*, on this the second-longest inter-station section.

First, after about 500 metres, comes the South Turnout Chamber, with a trailing crossover and a junction diverging left from the Outer Circle to the South ramp, and so to the Depot yard, followed, about 100 metres further on, by the North Turnout Chamber, with a converging track from the North ramp and a facing crossover. Finally, there is the former Lifting Pit, now roofed over by the floor of the Stabling Shed and containing pumping equipment positioned between the Outer and Inner tracks. After another 140 metres, trains roll into Govan station (with two flank platforms, and a similar escalator arrangement to St Enoch).

Bibliography

The help of Mr Peter Bancroft of Nebulous Books in providing much of the information in this bibliography is acknowledged with thanks.

Books

The Glasgow District Subway, by A. Home Morton, Glasgow, 1897.

The Glasgow District Subway – Its Construction and Equipment, R. Gibson, Glasgow, 1905 – also reprinted by Light Rail Transport League (London Region), 1970.

The Glasgow District Subway, by T Watson, Glasgow, 1906.

Bradshaws Railway Manual, Shareholders' Guide and Directory, 1905–23

Glasgow Municipal Transport: an historical account of the inauguration and development of the Corporation Transport Services, by Lachlan Mackinnon, Glasgow Corporation Transport Department, 1934,

British Electric Trains, by H.W.A. Linecar, Ian Allan, c. 1949

Untergrundbahnen und ihre Einsatzgrenzen by R Berger, Berlin, 1951 – Comparison of economic aspects of underground railways in various cities, including London, Liverpool and Glasgow.

Famous Underground Railways of the World by A J F Wrottesley, F Muller, London 1956 (Second edition 1960)

Glasgow Tramway and Railway Rolling Stock: an illustrated guide to the vehicles operated by the Tramway and Underground Sections of Glasgow Corporation Transport Department, past and present, by J A N Emslie, Scottish Tramway Museum Society, 1958.

A Handbook of Glasgow Tramways, by D L Thomson, Scottish Tramway Museum Society, 1962

ABC of British Bus Fleets – Glasgow – by I Maclean, Ian Allan, 1963

The Glasgow Subway, by David L. Thomson and David E. Sinclair, Scottish Tramway Museum Society, October 1964.

Underground Railways of the World by O S Nock, A & C Black, 1973 (includes a chapter on Glasgow District Subway)

I Belong to Glasgow, by Gordon Casely and Bill Hamilton, Nexus Press, 1975.

Glasgow Subway Scenes, by Alastair Stirling and Stanley Leech, A. Stirling, 23 Westbourne Gardens, Glasgow, July 1977.

Glasgow Underground . . . the end of an era, by David H. Barzilay, Century Books, Belfast, September 1977.

Glasgow Subway 1896–1977 by Paul J Kelly, M J D Willsher and W H Bett, Light Railway Transport League, London, 1977, ISBN 0 933433 68 X

Glasgow's Great Exhibitions by Perilla and Juliet Kinchin, White Cockade, 1988, ISBN 0–9513124–0–5

The Glasgow Underground by Brian Kettle, Dornoch Press, Dornoch, July 1989 ISBN 9513358 6 3

A Regional History of the Railways of Great Britain, Volume 6 – Scotland – the Lowlands and the Borders by John Thomas (Second edition revised by Alan J. S. Paterson, 1984), published by David St John Thomas and distributed by David & Charles ISBN 0–946537–12–7.

Glasgow's Trams and Buses by Robert Grieves, XS Publications, Renfrew, 1994, ISBN 0–9506381–3–7.

The Glasgow Encyclopedia by Joe Fisher, Mainstream Publishing, Edinburgh, 1994, ISBN 1 85158 212 6.

Reports etc.

Board of Trade Railway Accident Reports dated 4th February 1903, 9th September 1907, July 4th 1912, April 1913, October 1914 and 22nd May 1917.

Department of Transport Railway Inspectorate Reports, 1975 and 1977.

Glasgow Corporation Minutes, 1922–73

Glasgow Corporation Tramways, Account of Revenue and Expenditure, No. 30 (1923/4) –1972/3

Glasgow Corporation Transport Department Annual Reports, 1948–73

A Report on the Future Development of Passenger Transport in Glasgow, by E. R. L. Fitzpayne, Glasgow, May 1948.

Passenger Transport in Glasgow and District, by British Transport Commission/Glasgow & District Transport Committee (Chairman Robert Inglis), Edinburgh, 1951

Glasgow Underground: a study in urban transport planning, by J S Bownes, Thesis for MSc, University of Strathclyde, c. 1974

Modernisation of Glasgow Underground – Application to the Secretary of state for Scotland for Infrastructure Grant, Greater Glasgow Passenger Transport Executive, December 1973.

Annual Reports, GGPTE and SPTE, 1973/4 to 1994/5.

Legislation

Glasgow Harbour Tunnel Act, 1889.
Glasgow District Subway Act, 1890.
Glasgow District Subway (Additional Powers) Act, 1894
Glasgow District Subway (Additional Capital) Act, 1899
Glasgow Subway Railway Order Confirmation Act, 1914
Glasgow Corporation Order Confirmation Act, 1923
Glasgow Corporation Order Confirmation Act, 1925
Glasgow Corporation Consolidation (Water, Transport and Markets) Order Confirmation Act, 1964
Greater Glasgow Passenger Transport Order Confirmation Act, 1975

Public Records
Public Record Office (Kew) Files:-
MT6 534/12, MT6 1961/8, MT6 1428/3, MT6 3248 and MT6 2343/6

Periodicals

Contract Journal and Specification Record, April 15, May 20 and 27, December 23, 1891, January 27, 1892.

Engineering, Vols LXII and LXIII – Serialised item in issues from November 1896 to March 1897.

The Railway World, 1896–1900

The Tramway and Railway World, 1901–23

The Railway Magazine, January 1899, January 1923, November 1938, January and April 1955, June 1968, 1977 (pages 193/194)

Railway Gazette – Electrifrication Supplement, 1935

Scottish Tramlines, No. 5 (September 1964) to No. 18 (December 1969)

Scottish Transport No. 19 (June 1970) to No. 50 (June 1995)

Trains Illustrated: 1959, page 255 (May) – note on 3-car train.

Modern Railways: 1966, page 563; 1974 pages 10, 47, 88 and 129; 1975 pages 139, 256, 351; 1976 page 153; 1977 pages 154, 157, 199 and 447; 1978 page 36; 1979 pages 58, 430 and 525; 1980 pages 246 and 390; 1981 pages 7 and 485; 1984 page 593 (November).

The Glasgow Herald, including January 22 and September 17, 1896; January 21, 1897; February 28, 1907; October 17, 1908; January 3, 8, 15, 17, 19, 24, 28 and 31, February 20, 24, 25, and April 21, 1920; March 18, 1921; June 8 and July 24, 1922.

North British Daily Mail, 11 March, 1893

Daily Record and Mail, including January 20, January 21 and February 19, 1920.

Daily Record, including June 29, 1953

Evening Citizen, including December 12, 1896

Evening Times, including March 7, March 16 and April 1, 1935

Journal of Transport History (New series), Volume 1 (1971–72) – Urban transport and the development of Glasgow's West End, 1830–1914 – article by M Simpson.

Railway World: 1958, pages 159 – 161 (June) – article by W A C Smith; 1976, pages 193/194 (May) – note on collision; 1977, page 57 and 183.

Modern Tramway: 1977, February to May issues inclusive

Electronics & Power: May 1982 – The reconstruction of the Glasgow Underground Railway – by I P Burdon and A G Middleton.

Societies and Institutions

Tickets of the Glasgow Underground by B P Pask, Transport Ticket Society, 1971

Transactions of the Institution of Engineers and Shipbuilders in Scotland:-
Vol xxxix, 1895–96 – Tunnelling in soft material with reference to Glasgow District Subway by Robert Simpson.
Paper by W. R. Bruce delivered on 3/12/35
Paper by A. G. Middleton delivered c. 1981

Proceedings of the Institution of Civil Engineers, Volume 114, issue 3, May 1996 – Centenary of the Glasgow Subway, 1886 – 1996 – by J S Shipway.

Chapter Notes

Chapter 1
1 Scottish Transport No. 33
2 A Regional History of the Railways of Great Britain, Volume 6 – SCOTLAND – the Lowlands and the Borders by John Thomas (Second edition revised by Alan J. S. Paterson, 1984), published by David St John Thomas and distributed by David & Charles, pp 17, 23, 24
3 Glasgow's Trams and Buses by Robert Grieves, XS Publications, Renfrew, 1994, p 3.
4 The Glasgow Encyclopedia by Joe Fisher, Mainstream Publishing, Edinburgh, 1994, page 295 et seq.
5 The Glasgow District Subway its Construction, Plant and Working by Andrew Home Morton, 1897
6 The Glasgow Harbour Tunnel Act, 1889, 52 & 53 Vict., Ch. clxvi.
7 Glasgow District Subway Act, 1890, 53 & 54 Vict.
8 Company property plans at Broomloan Depot (incomplete).
9 Some early accounts render this 'Copeland Road'.
10 Engineering, Volumes LXII and LXIII – series of articles in issues of November 6, 1896 to March 5, 1897.
11 Public Record Office File No. MT6/534/12
12 Anonymous account of building system, date 1905
13 Drawings in Public Record Office File MT6 1961/8
14 North British Daily Mail, March 11, 1893.
15 McAlpine Centenary Book.
16 Contract Journal and Specification Record, January 27, 1892
17 Oldbury Railway Carriage & Wagon Co. became part of Metro-Cammell, the builders of the cars supplied for the 1974–80 Modernisation.
18 The Glasgow Subway by David L. Thomson and David E. Sinclair, Scottish Tramway Museum Society, 1964.
19 Photographs in Home Morton Book (Ref 5 above) etc.
20 Conversation between Eddie Traynor, former Driver and Station Master and J. K. Wright on 27/11/95.
21 December 1896 Rule Book, undated amendment to Rule Book and April 1902 Rule Book – all in Public Record Office File MT6 1961/8
22 The Glasgow District Subway (Further Powers) Act, 1894, and The Glasgow District Subway (Additional Capital) Act 1899

Chapter 2
1 Public Record Office File MT 6 1961/8.
2 H. Arthur Yorke joined the Royal Engineers in 1866 at the age of 17, and was promoted to Lieutenant-Colonel in 1894. He joined the Railway Inspectorate in 1891, becoming Chief Inspecting Officer in 1900. He retired in 1913 and was knighted on his retirement. (From 'Railway Detectives' by Stanley Hall, Ian Allan, 1990.)
3 The B. o. T file suggests the letter was sent on 3rd December, but this does not relate to Sloane's reply also on the B. o. T. file. A letter from the Solicitors to Sloane dated 7/12/96 returning papers used for the London meeting refers to the B. o. T. letter of 2nd December, and this is taken to be correct (found in the St Enoch Station attic c. 1977)
4 The Glasgow Herald, September 14, 1896
5 Evening Citizen for Saturday 12th December 1896, p. 3.
6 'I Belong to Glasgow', by Gordon Casely and Bill Hamilton, Nexus Press, 1975.
7 Original 1896 Rule Book in Public Record Office File MT 6 1961/8.
8 The Glasgow Herald, January 21, 1897, page 6 (See also 22/1/96 page 6.)
9 The Glasgow District Subway, its Construction, Plant and Working by Andrew Home Morton, 1897
10 Tickets of the Glasgow Underground by B. P. Pask, Transport Ticket Society 1971.
11 Notes by General Manager on proposal by Cll'r Thomas A. Kerr that there should be a universal 1d fare on the subway, dated 17/4/25 – in Glasgow Corporation minutes, 1924–25, pages 1350–3
12 Originals of 'Daily Return of Bookings and Remittances' for (5H) 'Hoist' Station, and Cowcaddens, Tuesday 31st March 1908.

13 Original letter from R. P. Lamond and Turner of 163 West George Street to Company Secretary, passed to the Authors by Mr Tom Watt, former Manpower Officer, G. C. T. and G. G. P. T. E.

14 Mr Francis J. S. Hopwood was a career Civil Servant, who entered the Board of Trade in 1885, and in 1892 was appointed as official secretary to Mr Mundella, the President of the Board of Trade. In May 1893 he became Assistant Secretary to the Railway Department of the Board of Trade, and about May 1901 he became Permanent Secretary to the Board of Trade at the early age of 40. – The Railway News, June 1, 1901 – Public Record Office File ZPER 7/66.

15 1902 Rule Book in Public Record Office File MT 6 1961/8.

16 Railway World, issue of 8/9/98, pp 294–5

17 Tramway and Railway World, April 9, 1903, p. 357.

18 The Glasgow Subway by David L. Thomson and David E. Sinclair, S. T. M. S., 1964

19 Railway World, August 1897 issue.

20 Bradshaw's Railway Manual, Shareholders' Guide & Directory 1905 – 23

21 The Glasgow Herald, March 3, 1906

22 Railway World issue of 13/10/98, p. 349.

23 Tramway and Railway World, issue of 17/10/01

24 Tramway and Railway World, issue of October 1903, p. 372.

25 Notes by General Manager, Tramways Department dated 21st February 1922, Glasgow Corporation Minutes.

26 The Tramway and Railway World, issue of October 12, 1912, p. 317.

27 Railway World, December 1897, p. 369.

28 Reports by Inspector C. Moar to General Manager dated 16th and 18th January 1907.

29 The Glasgow Herald, October 17, 1908

30 Bound Volumes of Board of Trade Railway Accident Reports, National Railway Museum Library, York.

31 The Glasgow Herald, February 28, 1907.

32 John Wallace Pringle was commissioned in the Royal Engineers in 1883. He was appointed an Inspector of Railways in 1900, and was Chief Inspecting Officer from 1916 to 1929. He held the rank of Major in 1912, but had been promoted to Colonel by 1917. He was knighted in 1925 and died in 1938. (From 'Railway Detectives' by Stanley Hall, Ian Allan, 1990.)

33 Railway World issue of 5/10/99, page 414.

34 Documents in File found in St Enoch Station attic, c. 1977

35 The Tramway and Railway World, issue of October 12, 1911, p. 346.

36 Glasgow District Subway (Additional Capital) Act, 1899

Chapter 3

1 Public Record Office File MT 6 2343/6, former Board of Trade files R23 and R6295 of 1914.

2 Glasgow Subway Railway Order Confirmation Act, 1914, 4 & 5 GEO. 5., Ch lxx

3 Bradshaws Railway Manual, Shareholders' Guide and Directory, 1905 – 1923.

4 Glasgow Subway Railway Co. Car Sheds Employees Book No. 1 found at Broomloan.

5 Tickets of the Glasgow Underground by B. P. Pask, Transport Ticket Society 1971.

6 Tramway Department General Manager's Report Dated 17th April 1925. – Glasgow Corporation Minutes.

7 Notes by General Manager on proposal by Councillor Thomas A. Kerr that there should be a universal 1d fare on the Subway, dated 25th March 1925 – Corporation Minutes, 1924–25, pages 1350–3

8 Annual Shareholders' Meeting – The Glasgow Herald, February 28, 1919

9 The Glasgow Encyclopedia by Joe Fisher, Mainstream Publishing, Edinburgh, 1994, page 137.

10 Illustration of 1d Ferry Ticket in 'Tickets of the Glasgow Underground', by B. P. Pask, Transport Ticket Society, 1971

11 The Glasgow Herald, March 18, 1921.

12 The Glasgow Herald, Saturday, January 3, Thursday January 8, Thursday January 15, Saturday January 17, Monday January 19, Wednesday January 28, Saturday January 31, Friday February 20, Tuesday February 24, and Wednesday, February 25, 1920.

13 Daily Record and Mail, Wednesday January 21, and The Glasgow Herald, Saturday January 24, 1920.

14 Daily Record and Mail, Tuesday January 20, Wednesday January 21, and Thursday February 19, 1920.

15 The Glasgow Herald, Wednesday April 21, 1920.

16 Corporation Minutes, 1920–21, pages 899, and 901–904

17 The Glasgow Herald, Tuesday August 17 and Tuesday December 7, 1920.

18 Surviving notice, passages in 1921 Rule Book and Govan Press, Friday February 11, 1921

19 Actual copies of 1912 and 1921 Rule Books.

20 Timetable sheets pasted into cover of surviving 1921 Rule Book.

21 Notes on the Glasgow Subway Railway by General Manager, Tramways Department, dated 21st February 1922 – Brian Longworth collection.

22 Letter from Mr Ferrier, dated 12/94 recounting stories told by his father who was the 'smoker boy.'

23 Corporation Minutes, 1921–22, pages 743, 1099 and 1100
24 Article in Modern Tramway, March 1977 by Paul J. Kelly and M. J. D. Willsher, reprinted as Glasgow Subway 1896–1977 by LRTL
25 Tramway and Railway World, June 15, 1922
26 The Glasgow Herald, June 8, 1922, Tramway and Railway World, July 13, 1922 and The Railway Magazine, January 1923.
27 Glasgow Corporation Transport Account of Revenue and Expenditure No. 44
28 The Glasgow Subway by David L. Thomson and David E. Sinclair, Scottish Tramway Museum Society, October 1964, page 31.
29 Scottish Transport No. 33, December 1977 – Glasgow Subway in the 1920s by Brian T. Deans.
30 Corporation Minutes, 1921–22, pages 1942, 2187 and 2789.
31 Corporation Minutes, 1922–23, pages 604, 1052, 1261, 1276, 1530 and 1954.
32 Corporation Minutes, 1925–26, page 274.

Chapter 4

1 Corporation Minutes, 1922–23, page 2327
2 Report of General Manager to Special Sub-Committee on Wages of Subway Employees dated 22/10/23, Corporation Minutes, 1923–24, pages 324–328.
3 Corporation Minutes, 1923–4, pages 548, 918, 1524, 1777–8, 1811, 1896, 2165, 2213, 2309, 2311, 2317 and 2401.
4 Corporation Minutes, 1928–9, pages 326, 2091, 2126 and 2199
5 Synopsis of Report by the General Manager to the Sub-committee on General Purposes (referred to in 1930–31 Print No. 7, page 574, paragraph 2.) – Brian Longworth collection, and leaflet stuck into front cover of surviving 1921 Rule Book.
6 'Traffic' File found at Broomloan Depot
7 Service History Book 3 (added later), Brian Longworth collection.
8 Service History Book 3, Brian Longworth collection.
9 Corporation Tramways Account of Revenue and Expenditure No. 30, 1923–24.
10 Corporation Minutes 1924–25, pages 702, 1220, 1357–8, 1954 and 2496
11 General Manager's Report to Sub-Committee on General Purposes dated 19th November 1930 in Brian Longworth collection, but contrary to Glasgow Subway, 1896–1977, Light Railway Transport League. Part 4 Tickets and Fare Collection by W. H. Bett, FCII
12 G. C. T. Account of Revenue and Expenditure No. 39: change recommended by Transport Committee on 5/1/32, and agreed by Corporation on 21/1/32 (Corporation Minute Books)
13 The Glasgow Herald, Monday July 24, 1922.
14 Glasgow Subway 1896–1977, Light Railway Transport League, London
15 General Manager's Report to Sub-Committee on General Purposes dated 19th November 1930 in Brian Longworth collection.
16 Photograph in 'The Glasgow Subway' by Thomson and Sinclair
17 Corporation Minutes, 1924–25, page 2405 and 1925–26, page 921.
18 General Manager's Report to Sub-Committee on General Purposes dated 19th November 1930 – B. Longworth collection.
19 Corporation Minutes, 1929–30, pages 945, 1867/8 and 2441.
20 Corporation Minutes 1924–25, pages 384 and 600, and 1925–26, page 924.
21 Corporation Tramways Account of Revenue and Expenditure No. 32, 1925–26
22 Conversation with Mrs Wallace (ex-Turnstile Attendant) on 23/11/95
23 Corporation Minutes, 1925–26, page 2454
24 Corporation Minutes 1926–27, pages 171, 202, 206, 403, 608–9 and 653.
25 Report of Consulting Engineer and General Manager to the Sub-Committee on the Subway dated 21st December 1925 (included in Corporation Minutes)
26 1925 Glasgow Corporation Order Confirmation Act
27 Corporation Minutes, 1930–31, page 2199
28 Corporation Minutes, 1932–33, page 1882
29 Stores Goods Received Books – SPT Broomloan Collection
30 Letter from General Manager to Bailie Laing dated 25/8/26 found in file at Broomloan, and Corporation Minutes, Sub-committee on Works and Stores 11/8/26, Committee on Tramways, 18/8/26 and 1/9/26, and Corporation 26/8/26.
31 Corporation Minutes, 1931–32, page 1978, and 1932–33 page 150.
32 Technical Correspondence File found at Broomloan Depot
33 B. E. V. Drawing No. 1527 and surviving G. C. T./B. E. V. correspondence.
34 Corporation Minutes, 1935–36, pages 353, 2416 and 2511.

Chapter 5

1 Letter from G. F. Moller to General Manager, dated 28th November 1935 – SPT Broomloan collection.
2 Public Record Office File MT6 1428/3
3 The Tramway and Railway World, April 15, 1906, p. 302
4 Notes by General Manager, Tramways Department on the Glasgow Subway Railway, dated 21st February, 1922 – Brian Longworth collection.
5 Corporation Minutes, 1923–24, pages 1052 to 1067 and 2455 to 2460
6 Report by the General Manager to the Sub-committee on General Purposes on Glasgow District Subway Railway, dated 19th November 1930 – Brian Longworth collection.
7 Corporation Minutes, 1931–32, pages 332 and 2535
8 Synopsis of Report by the General Manager to the Sub-committee on General Purposes, dated 31st December 1931 – Brian Longworth collection.
9 Goods Received Books – SPT Broomloan collection.
10 Bogie Drawing – SPT Broomloan collection.
12 1933–35 Modernisation of Glasgow Subway by Brian T. Deans for I. E. E. History of Electrical Engineering Weekend 1981
13 Proceedings of Institution of Engineers and Shipbuilders in Scotland – paper by W. R. Bruce 3rd December 1935.
14 The Electrical Review, January 18th 1935
15 Corporation Minutes 1932–33, pages 1348, 2456 and 2838
16 Public Record Office File MT6/3248
17 A tripcock is a device which, if it strikes a raised trainstop situated at the trackside, opens an air valve, and applies the automatic air brake (see photographs on pp 60 and 74). The trainstop is driven down when the adjacent signal clears to a proceed aspect, and rises when the signal is at danger, or under fault conditions. The system prevents a driver accidentally passing a red signal without stopping, and is still widely used on London Underground lines, on the Drayton Park to Moorgate section of the Great Northern Electric service in London, and on the Merseyrail Electric lines.
18 Specifications found at Broomloan.
19 Corporation Minutes, 1933–34, pages 223, 522, 1045, 2653 and 2743.
20 The term 'chilled iron' referred to the casting method during manufacture: the material was iron, cast in moulds constructed wholly or partly of metal, and sometimes water cooled (as opposed to sand moulds), so that the surface of the casting was white, dense, and hard, while the interior remained grey.
21 Conversation between Mr Tom Cameron, retired electrical Foreman, and J. K. Wright about 1983.
22 Conversation between Mr Quinten Findlay, retired electrician, and J. K. Wright at a retirement function, about June 1974.
23 Conversation between Mr John Fraser, former Car Sheds Electrician and J. K. Wright in July 1994.
24 Corporation Minutes, 1937–38, page 1536–7
25 The Thermit process is more akin to foundry work than electric or gas welding, and involves creating a gap about 1 inch wide at the rail ends, creating a sand mould round the gap, positioning a crucible above the mould, placing a measured quantity of a patent granular material (known as the 'portion') into the crucible, igniting the portion, and at the appropriate moment tapping the crucible which allows molten metal to flow from the crucible into the sand mould. The process is completed by removing the remains of the sand mould, and grinding the rail head flush.
26 G. C. T. Signal installation drawing – SPT Broomloan collection.
27 Conversation between J. K. Wright and Mr Eddie Traynor, retired Driver and Station Master, 27/11/95
28 The Evening Times, Monday, April 1, 1935
29 The Evening Times, Saturday, March 16, 1935 . . .
30 Corporation Minutes, 1935–36, pages 501, 802, 1286 and 2649.
31 Corporation Minutes, 1935–36, page 1160; 1936–37 page 374; 1938–39, pages 1028, 1265, 2116 and 2823
32 Corporation Minutes, 1935–36, pages 1160 and 1638, and 1936–37, pages 1800–01.
33 Corporation Minutes, 1936–37, pages 868, 2751–2 and 2929.
34 Corporation Minutes, 1938–39, pages 1464, 2659, 2823, 2943, 2945 and 3030.
35 Corporation Minutes, 1937–38, pages 637–8, 2205–6, 2699–2700; and 2897–2900 and weekly ticket sales returns – SPT Broomloan collection.
36 Surviving copy of notice – SPT Broomloan collection.
37 1938–39 Account Number List – SPT Broomloan collection.
38 Glasgow's Great Exhibitions by Perilla and Juliet Kinchin, p. 166, White Cockade, 1988, ISBN 0–9513124–0–5
39 Service History Book 3 – Brian Longworth collection.
40 Glasgow Corporation Transport Accounts of Revenue and Expenditure Nos. 38 to 46, for years 1/6/31–31/5/32 to 1/6/39–31/5/40 respectively.
41 G. C. T. Account of Revenue and Expenditure No. 44

Chapter 6

1 This Time of Crisis (p51) by Andrew Jeffrey, Mainstream Publishing, 1993, ISBN 1 85158 582 6
2 G. C. T. Report on Repair of Bomb damage to Underground Tunnels at Merkland Street, dated 14th October 1941.
3 Glasgow Corporation Minutes, 1940–41, page 336
4 Service History Book Nos. 3 and 4 – Brian Longworth collection.
5 An actual notice in SPT Broomloan collection.
6 Census results of passengers entering the system 6.15 to 9.0 am, Sunday 4th September 1949 – Brian Longworth collection.
7 The Glasgow Subway by David L. Thomson and David E. Sinclair.
8 Census results of passengers entering the system from 11 pm, Friday 28th and Saturday 29th October 1949 and memo from Mr Kellock, Traffic Superintendent to General Manager, dated 3/12/49 – Brian Longworth collection.
9 G. C. T. Annual Report, 1951/2
10 Scottish Tramlines No. 7, March 1965.
11 G. C. T. Annual Report, 1964–5
12 Glasgow Corporation Minutes, 1941–42, page 1774.
13 Public Record Office file MT6/3248
14 Replies dated 13/12/49 and 18/8/61 by General Manager to public letters – Brian Longworth collection.
15 Duty Officers' Log Book No. 48 – Brian Longworth collection and Meetings with Shop Stewards Book – SPT Broomloan collection.
16 Southern Division Weekly Report for W/E 11/4/64 – Brian Longworth collection
17 Southern Division Weekly Report for W/E 20/6/64 – Brian Longworth collection
18 Scottish Tramlines No. 6, December 1964
19 G. C. T. Annual Report, 1953–4
20 Signals Section Log Book – SPT Broomloan collection.
21 Daily Record, Monday, June 29, 1953.
22 "I belong to Glasgow" by Gordon Caseley and Bill Hamilton.
23 Duty Officers' Log Book No. 47 – 4/6/61 – 19/10/61 – Brian Longworth collection.
24 'Components on Test' cards – SPT Broomloan collection.
25 The term 'Route Number' is used as a means of identifying trains – apart from the Inner and Outer Circle numbers being in separate series, it has no significance as to where the trains are going – there is not much choice! As far as possible the timetables are arranged so that trains follow each other in numerical sequence, however.
26 Duty Officers' Log Book Nos. 48, 49 and 50 and 'Car Defects in Service' cards.
27 Car Record Cards – SPT Broomloan collection.
28 Photograph in G. C. T. Annual Report
29 G. C. T. Annual Report for 1962–3
30 Letter to Pickfords Heavy Haulage dated 24/2/59 – Brian Longworth collection.
31 G. C. T. Annual Reports, 1958–63
32 The Glasgow Subway by David L. Thomson and David E. Sinclair and G. C. T. Annual Report of 1949
33 G. C. T. Annual Report for 1963–64
34 G. C. T. Annual Report for 1965–6
35 Letter from The District Valuer (Glasgow No. 2 District) to Town Clerk dated 20th June 1951, and letter from General Manager to Town Clerk dated 29th June 1951 – Brian Longworth collection.
36 Scottish Tramlines No. 10, December 1965
37 G. C. T. Annual Report for 1953/4
38 Glasgow Corporation Consolidation (Water, Transport and Markets) Order Confirmation Act, 1964
39 Southern Division Weekly Report for W/E 14/3/59 – Brian Longworth collection
40 Accident Book – SPT Broomloan collection
41 Meetings with Shop Stewards Book – SPT Broomloan collection
42 Southern Division Weekly Report for W/E 2/7/60 – Brian Longworth collection
43 Report by Chief Inspector J. Granger, Southern Division, to General Manager, dated 21/2/49 – Brian Longworth collection.
44 Southern Division Weekly Report for W/E 8/8/59 – Brian Longworth collection
45 Letter from General Manager to Town Clerk dated 3/6/50 – Brian Longworth collection.
46 Letter from Alexander Reid to General Manager dated 14/9/50 – Brian Longworth collection.
47 Letter from R. D. Ewen, Tramways Engineer, to General Manager dated 2/10/50 – Brian Longworth collection.
48 Southern Division Weekly Reports – Brian Longworth collection
49 Letter from General Manager to Pressed Steel Limited, dated 18/1/61 – Brian Longworth collection.
50 G. C. T. Drawing No. 38-A–63 (undated) – SPT Broomloan collection.
51 Scottish Tramlines No. 9, September 1965.

Chapter 7

1   G. C. T. Annual Report, 1972–73
2   G. C. T. Annual Report, 1970–71
3   Scottish Tramlines No. 10, December 1965
4   Scottish Tramlines Nos. 14, March 1967, and 15, December 1967.
5   Scottish Tramlines No. 7, March 1965.
6   Scottish Transport No. 21, November 1971.
7   Scottish Tramlines No. 15, December 1967
8   Scottish Tramlines No. 16, Summer 1968.
9   Car Mileage returns – SPT Broomloan collection.
10 Scottish Tramlines No. 17, February 1969.
11 Scottish Transport No. 29, May 1977.
12 Scottish Tramlines No. 8, June 1965.
13 Scottish Tramlines No. 12, June 1966.
14 Axle Note Book, Traffic Delay Sheets – SPT Broomloan collection.
15 Traffic Delay Forms – SPT Broomloan collection.
16 Underground Line Call Book – SPT Broomloan collection.
17 Internal Accident Enquiry Report SPT files.
18 Scottish Transport No. 28, October 1976.
19 Scottish Transport No. 24, December 1973.
20 Car Sheds Diary – SPT Broomloan collection.
21 Scottish Transport No. 25, August 1974.
22 Railway Employment Inspector's Report – SPT files.
23 Scottish Transport No. 27, December 1975.
24 I belong to Glasgow by Gordon Caseley and Bill Hamilton, Nexus Press, Glasgow, December 1975.
25 'New Wine in Old Bottles' – Address to the Electric Railway Society by J. K. Wright, 1980.

Chapter 8

1   Modernisation of Glasgow Underground, Application to the Secretary of State for Scotland for Infrastructure Grant, Greater Glasgow Passenger Transport Executive, December 1973
2   'New Wine in old Bottles' – address to Electric Railway Society by J. K. Wright, 1980
3   'Passenger Conveyor' is the generic title for machines possibly better known as 'Trav-o-lators', but the latter is strictly reserved for the products of the Otis Company, and the Glasgow Underground machines were manufactured and installed by O&K escalators, whose trade name for them is 'Autowalk'.
4   Scottish Transport No. 37, September 1982
5   Scottish Transport No. 41, December 1985
6   Scottish Transport No. 47, December 1991
7   The 'Shell' is a First World War Naval 15 in. shell set up in the middle of the concourse at Central Station as a charity collecting box. It is a well-known and prominent feature, and became a recognised meeting place. It was moved to a corner of the concourse near the Caledonian Railway War Memorial in the 1980s.
8   Scottish Transport No. 42, December 1986
9   Scottish Transport No. 43, December 1987
10 Scottish Transport No. 48, 1993
11 Scottish Transport No. 38, June 1983
12 Information from John Scott, SPT Purchasing Officer.
13 Underground Railway Weekly Circular.
14 The Glasgow Underground, Notes Hand-out by J. K. Wright, originally produced May 1983, with subsequent up-dates.
15 Clayton Maintenance Manual for their Order No. BO 0965.
16 The National Coal Board was a significant customer of Claytons and, since the PTE had not specified anything else, they followed NCB practice for underground locomotives, and painted them yellow.
17 File 43.5.4 at Broomloan Depot.

Chapter 9

1   'New wine in old bottles' – Address to the Electric Railway Society by J. K. Wright, 1980
2   For further details see Electric Railway Society Journal No. 161 – September-October 1982.
3   Scottish Transport No. 46, December 1990
4   Scottish Transport No. 44, December 1988
5   Scottish Transport No. 41, December 1985
6   Scottish Transport No. 50, 1995
7   Scottish Transport No. 49, 1994

8   Scottish Transport No. 42, December 1986
9   Info supplied by Mr R Cairley – Engineer Mechanical – SPT – 15/03/96
10   File 19.5 at Broomloan
11   Scottish Transport No. 43, December 1987
12   Scottish Transport No. 48, 1993
13   Scottish Transport No. 47, December 1991
14   Scottish Transport No. 40, December 1984
15   Scottish Transport No. 36, March 1982
16   Scottish Transport No. 45, December 1989
17   Scottish Transport No. 37, December 1982
18   Rail corrugation is a wear phenomenon in which a longitudinal wave is worn on to the head of the
     rail – in the case of the Glasgow Underground of about 80 mm wavelength, and when the amplitude
     exceeds about 0.05 mm the noise increases – the condition has been called 'roaring rails'. It is
     particularly prone to develop on railways and tramways where vehicles of similar type (especially with
     regard to suspension characteristics) predominantly use the track concerned, and run at the same speed
     at a particular location, and encounter (initially) a minor imperfection.
19   Underground Railway Weekly Circular.
20   Scottish Transport No.38, June 1983
21   On the basis of April 1980=100, the Retail Price Index for July 1996 stood at 230.4 – calculated from
     figures in 1996 Annual Statistical Report and September 1996 figures – Central Statistical Office.

Chapter 10

1   Corporation Minutes, 1936–37, Print No.7, page 635 and 1937–38, Print No.5, page 369.
2   Modern Tramway and Light Rapid Transit, April 1977.
3   The Glasgow Subway, by David L. Thomson and David E. Sinclair, Scottish Tramway Museum Society,
     October 1964.
4   A Report on the Future Development of Passenger Transport in Glasgow, by E. R. L. Fitzpayne, May
     1948.
5   The Feasibility of Extending the Glasgow Underground Railway – Report by Sir William Halcrow &
     Partners, 30th April 1954 – Brian Longworth collection.
6   Strathclyde Transport Development Study Report, 1988–90

Acknowledgements

We wish to acknowledge the help and assistance given by the following: D Boyd of ABB Transportation
Ltd (now ADtranz), Derby and P Kewney of Hunslet-Barclay Ltd, Kilmarnock for access to photograph cars,
and for the use of other photographs; R Grieves, Paisley, G Watson, Chesterfield, Brian Hardy, Ruislip, D
McPherson, Glasgow and J Wilson, Cumbernauld, for use of photographs from their personal collections;
The Herald and Evening Times, Glasgow, and Alistair Smith of Glasgow Museum of Transport for the use
of photographs; M Nicolson for arranging access to photograph illustrations from magazines, and other
staff at the Mitchell Library and former Strathclyde Archive, Glasgow, and Public Record Office, Kew, for
finding reference material, staff at the National Railway Museum, York, for photocopying Board of Trade
accident reports; Miss E Organ, City of Liverpool Record Office; C F Reynolds, Caradon Gent Ltd, Leicester;
Cliff Hanley, Glasgow for permission to use the subway song; C Dempsey of Workington for the cartoon
on page 215; P Adams, Ralston for finalising the signalling layout diagrams; Brian Longworth, Glasgow,
for supplying documents and his own research data; Peter Bancroft of Nebulous Books, Alton, for research
at the PRO, Kew, for advice and for supplying the basis of the Bibliography; members of the public who
have responded to requests for assistance, including Miss Russell, Giffnock, Mrs Wilkie, Coulsden, and Mr
Ferrier, Glasgow; former employees, including Tom Watt, Walter Habbick, now of Ilford, Mrs M Wallace,
Bishopbriggs, Messrs McGhee, Eddie Traynor, both of Glasgow; and staff of Strathclyde Passenger Transport
at Broomloan Depot and Consort House too numerous to mention individually for giving factual
information, answering obscure questions, reading and commenting on drafts, making helpful suggestions,
assisting with the taking and reproduction of photographs, and typing captions etc. Finally, our thanks to
Jane Wright for research at the Mitchell Library, Annabel Wright for reading drafts, and our families for
their forbearance during the two years or so it has taken to prepare this book.